CHRISTIAN CHOICES IN HEALTHCARE

CHRISTIAN CHOICES IN HEALTHCARE

Edited by M. Dominic Beer

CMF/IVP

INTER-VARSITY PRESS
38 De Montfort Street, Leicester LE1 7GP, England

First published 1995
Reprinted 1998

British Library Cataloguing-in-Publication Data
A catalogue record for this book is available from the British Library.

ISBN 0-85111-144-0

Set in Palatino

Typeset in Great Britain by Avocet Typeset, Brill, Aylesbury, Bucks

Printed in Glasgow, Scotland by Caledonian International

Inter-Varsity Press is the book-publishing division of the Universities and Colleges Christian Fellowship (formerly the Inter-Varsity Fellowship), a student movement linking Christian Unions in universities and colleges throughout the United Kingdom and the Republic of Ireland, and a member movement of the International Fellowship of Evangelical Students. For information about local and national activities write to UCCF, 38 De Montfort Street, Leicester LE1 7GP.

CONTENTS

PREFACE

The aim of *Christian Choices in Healthcare* is to encourage Christlikeness both in the character and in the medical practice of Christian professionals. It is primarily orientated towards doctors and medical students, but some parts will be useful to nurses and others involved in caring for patients. By the same token, the articles are inevitably written in a British context, but I hope healthcare professionals from elsewhere will also find helpful material here.

The inspiration for this book was, in fact, a request from Korea asking permission to translate *Medicine and the Christian Mind*.[1] After much thought, the editor of that book turned down the request because some of its authors had changed their views, and it was thought that a new book should be produced for the 1990s. Therefore *Christian Choices in Healthcare* has been written by a new group of Christian men and women who have expertise in their various fields. Some of the articles have been specially commissioned, some have appeared elsewhere, and others have been adapted before inclusion here.

I recognize that some of the topics covered are controversial issues among Christians. We should not, however, be afraid of addressing these subjects. In line with the aims of the Christian Medical Fellowship, we should try to discover the truth. Thus, both sides of a difficult issue need to be made known, whether explicitly or implicitly. It should be remembered that contributors who are members of the CMF will have signed their adherence to the truth and relevance of the Bible. As we know, the Bible gives clear messages on principles, but does not give unequivocal answers to every problem.

I hope this book will help provide guidance, wisdom and enjoyment for all who dip into, read or consult it.

I would like to express my special thanks to Drs Andrew Fergusson and Peter Saunders and the staff of CMF for their time, wisdom and expertise; without them this book would not have been possible. Thanks are due also to my wife Naomi for all her enouragement and patience during the editing of this book.

M. Dominic Beer

Part 1

CHRISTIAN VOCATION IN HEALTHCARE

1 THE DOCTOR'S CHARACTER AND LIFESTYLE

AN OPEN LETTER FROM A PROFESSOR TO A MEDICAL STUDENT

Alan G. Johnson

At your interview you probably said something vague about wanting to help people or to be a member of a 'caring profession', to use the modern jargon. The comment 'well motivated' may have been pencilled in against your name. You may have meant it, but others said it because *they* thought the interviewing panel would be pleased.

Now you have started studying medicine. It can be hard work with little glamour. You see your fellow students from other faculties with far more spare time, and you begin to ask yourself again, 'What is the point of it all?' It is a question that must be asked now, and at regular intervals throughout the course. You have no need, at this stage, to decide whether you want to be a neurosurgeon or a haematologist, a consultant physician or a general practitioner – that can wait. But you should know why you are doing medicine. In other words, you must begin to think through what you hope to get out of life and what you hope to give to the professional career you are just starting.

The following are some of the motives, expressed or subconscious, for taking up medicine.

- to help people;
- to have the satisfaction of curing patients;
- to have status in the community;
- to have a secure job;
- to make enough money to provide a good standard of living for the family;
- to have the fascination of finding out the causes of disease;
- to serve God by serving others (for those with a strong Christian faith).

11

Most students probably have a mixture of motives in different proportions, but it is important to have the right order of priorities.

Those who have seen anything of life, for example, will not need Paul to remind them that 'the love of money is the root of all kinds of evil'. If money-making becomes a dominant aim, patients will become a means to that end. If status-seeking becomes all-pervading, not only may some patients suffer, but you will become disillusioned as the status of doctors in our society diminishes. It is wrong to think that status is achieved by trampling on colleagues and by dominating patients. To some, the following description of Theodor Billroth (1821–94), one of the great pioneers of surgery, is the epitome of medical status:

> Positively God-like in demeanour, he not only wore a long Prince Albert coat suitable to such a position, but always performed his work with the utmost formality. Promptly at nine o'clock the wide doors of the clinic swung open and Billroth with his staff of twenty assistants made a grand entrance.

By contrast, the concept of serving our fellows has been incorporated in the very name of the British National Health *Service*. On a worldwide scale, the Declaration of Geneva states that 'the health of my patient will be my first concern'. Even if you are lying in bed on a cold winter's night or have just settled down to watch your favourite television programme, when your patient really needs you, you must get up and go to him, whether or not he is going to pay you.

In Britain, we have become so used to the concept that we should help those who cannot help themselves, that we must ask where it came from. It is not a natural human quality, and is certainly not derived from some evolutionary hypothesis about the survival of the fittest. Training plays a part, but, to sustain such an approach, we need a climate of opinion and motivation that comes from beyond human beings themselves. If we take the trouble to find out what a 'God-like demeanour' is really like, how God acts in the human situation, we find to our surprise that he takes the role of a servant and teaches that true greatness lies in service (Mk. 10:42–45).

Stamina

One of the great problems with the modern medical course is that it is long, and very demanding of time and energy. The medical student is cooped up in a practical class, while a colleague from another faculty is lazily lying on the grass with a set book open beside her! Stamina is at a premium, and the medical student can be forgiven for thinking sometimes that 'life is one long process of getting tired'. Nearly everyone, at some time in the course, wonders whether it is all worthwhile, and it is at these times that a clear sense of vocation is important.

It is increasingly difficult just to drift through medicine, or to emulate the hero of *Doctor in the House*, who purposely failed exams because a rich relative kept him supplied with money as long as he was a student. Often, problems with the course are simply a matter of insufficient sleep – of trying to burn the candle at both ends. Transient depression is not at all uncommon, and it is important to talk over your doubts with someone as soon as possible – parents, tutor, counselling service or student health doctor. The times when problems most commonly occur are soon after the start when the initial excitement has worn off, when starting on the wards and, perhaps, when doing psychiatry for the first time.

Ups and downs there will be, but there should be a growing conviction that, whatever branch you will choose later, you are on the right line.

Science: servant or hard taskmaster?

Some medical schools have an orthodox curriculum with separate clinical and pre-clinical sections, while others have varying degrees of integration. Whichever way the course is structured, there are an alarming number of scientific facts to be learned, and it is common to hear a student say 'I wanted to be a *doctor*, but not to be back at school learning all this science off by heart.' To put it in perspective, one or two years of learning facts is a small proportion of the forty-five years you will hope to spend practising clinical medicine. But at the time it seems an age.

One of the mistakes we have made is to think of anatomy, physiology and biochemistry *merely* as means to an end. Of course, accurate factual knowledge is important, in contrast with some arts subjects, where discussion and opinion are the order of the day. It actually *matters* whether the spleen is on the right or the left – it is not just an academic point. But, having said that, we often forget the fascination of studying the structure and function of the human body for its own sake. We have no sense of God's creation. Our thinking has been so dominated by a theory of purposeless forces working on chance mutations that we fail to see the beauty and plan behind the mechanisms. When we are discussing the incredible chemical reactions that happen in every cell, or looking at the ultrastructure of the mitochondria, we are not inventing them, but we are in Kepler's phrase 'thinking God's thoughts after him'.

On the other hand, science itself can become an obstruction to the right care of patients. It can become an end in itself – our 'god' – or a mere game of discovery in which the patients are the pawns. Scientific learning has dangers and problems in many directions, and a right attitude at the beginning is invaluable.

In the presence of death

In those medical schools where anatomy is taught by dissection, students are brought face to face with death (albeit in a pickled form!) at the beginning of their careers. To many, this is a disturbing experience which causes them to ask questions about the relationship of the soul to a stiff, wizened body. Some react by becoming flippant and casual about death and dead bodies, while others question whether there is any justification for showing respect to a half-dissected assortment of preserved tissues.

In the clinical course, the impact of death takes on a new form with the emotional involvement of relatives and the feelings of defeat on the part of the medical team. One is tempted to wonder whether any efforts at cure are worthwhile when death always wins in the end. There is no doubt that all of us must have a philosophy and motivation for studying medicine that incorporate a view of death. It cannot just be ignored in the hope that it will go away. There are those who believe that death is the end of everything and that there is nothing beyond this world. To them it is logical to allow people to enjoy this life as much as possible in any way they please.

To those who believe in an afterlife, and particularly a life which is far more wonderful than this one, where there will be 'no more death or mourning or crying or pain' (Rev. 21:4), death is *not* the worst thing that can come to a person. But, as with science, there must be a balanced view, and enthusiasm for the afterlife must not lead to a fatalistic refusal to interfere with the disease process, or to the practice of hurrying the patient into a better world by a discreet overdose of morphine! In any case, you could be wrong about the destination, and be hurrying a person into hell.

Let us return to the dissecting room and ask why we should respect the body. The only reason I can deduce for a body being worthy of respect, even after death, is that it once housed that amazing and complex spiritual being, the human personality, and it was through this body that the spirit expressed itself. There is a quaint old epitaph to a clockmaker which gives the right perspective: 'Here lies the outer casing of Robert Smith, clockmaker, who died in the certain hope that he would be thoroughly overhauled, given a new case and set going to work perfectly in the world to come.'

Early problems with patient care

First contact with patients is often traumatic. Some find it difficult to pluck up courage to talk to them, and some feel embarrassed that patients are 'used' for teaching when it does not contribute to their recovery. Others find the apparent vagueness and lack of structure of clinical medicine a problem after the relative precision of the basic sciences. In fact, the scientific process involved in diagnosis (that is, making an hypothesis, and then testing the deductions from that hypothesis) is just the same as in other branches of science; but the clinician often has to act on a probability considerably less than 99.9%.

It is far simpler in the long run to introduce yourself to the patient by your name and say at the outset that you are a medical student (or 'doctor in training' if you think that conveys a better image). Even if you are prematurely bald, it is difficult to keep up for long the pretence that you are really the professor! The more you can take part in the practical aspects of patient care the better, because then you are part of the team rather than a mere passive observer. Although as a student you are not in a position to answer many of the questions that patients may ask, you often have the privilege of a close relationship with them. They will tell you things that they will not tell the consultant – 'He is too busy', or 'I didn't want to bother him with small details.' Above all, be natural with patients and don't rely so much on *techniques* of history-taking and examination that the relationship becomes stilted and artificial.

One of the really important principles in patient care is to put yourself in the patient's place or, in its original form, as spoken by Jesus Christ, 'do to others as you would have them do to you' (Lk. 6:31). Therefore, take every opportunity to find out what it is like to be a patient. If you happen to be warded during your student days with glandular fever, appendicitis or a broken leg, look upon it as an opportunity, not as a disaster to your student career.

Telling patients the truth

It will not be long before you have to face this problem. Fortunately, attitudes are changing and we are now more open about diagnoses than we were twenty-five years ago. If you are wise, you will never lie to a patient. Truthfulness has an important impact on the handling of disease by both the patient and his relatives, whereas lying, as a short-term expedient, can have very harmful long-term repercussions. After all, it is the patient's illness and his body, not yours. What you have to decide is how much of the truth to tell, in what way and when. You have a few years to think about this, to observe, to learn and to form your own principles before you yourself are in the hot seat. At present you should pass the question on to your seniors who have to carry the clinical responsibility.

Over-involvement with patients' problems

It is sometimes said that you have to become 'hardened to suffering' in order to survive the medical course. This is not true. It is *possible* to remain sensitive without being sentimental, and to combine sympathy with clear clinical decisions. These contrasting characteristics were uniquely combined in Jesus Christ. It is well worth reading the description by two laymen and a doctor of the way he treated a promiscuous woman (Jn. 4:7–30), an epileptic boy (Mk. 9:14–29) and a woman with menorrhagia (Lk. 8:43–48).

It is normal of course, for medical students to think they have most of the diseases that their patients have. If you have ever read *Three Men in a Boat*, you will remember that Jerome K. Jerome's hero had read a medical encyclopedia in the British Museum and came away convinced that he had every condition except housemaid's knee! On the other hand, just being 'in the profession' does not make us immune to diseases that afflict everyone else. If you are genuinely anxious, it is far better to see someone – a student health doctor or general practitioner, rather than the houseman on your firm.

'Why has this happened to me?'

In this world, we should never expect to find an intellectually satisfying answer to the problem of pain and suffering; it is all bound up with what is wrong with our world (see Chapter 18). I hope you never become so familiar with *suffering* that you fail to react to it and ask questions. There are, however, several principles that can help us react positively and practically in the ward.

1. Much suffering results directly from wrong or irresponsible acts, not necessarily by the patient himself; for example, injuries from drunken driving, venereal disease, battered babies, cirrhosis of the liver, carcinoma of the lung, bomb-blast injuries, and industrial diseases. Much is preventable if mankind really wanted to prevent it.

2. On the other hand, many illnesses, for example most kinds of cancer, cannot be traced directly to something the patient, or anyone else, has done or not done. It is important not to imply to the patient that her illness is her fault.

3. Suffering can be turned to good both for the patient and for others. There are many inspiring biographies, such as those of Helen Keller and Joni Eareckson Tada, and great works of music and art which bear witness to such achievement.

4. God understands and has experienced human suffering. Allowing him into the patient's suffering can make all the difference. Indeed, an illness may be the first event that makes a person think about matters of eternal importance. 'God whispers to us in our pleasures, speaks in our conscience, but shouts in our pains' (C. S. Lewis).

5. Beyond death there is the promise, on certain conditions, of a life free from sorrow, pain and crying. So we should help our patients to ask, 'What can I learn from, and achieve through, this experience?' rather than to exclaim in bitterness, 'Why has God allowed this to happen to me?'

The future

It is one thing to have a general conviction that medicine is your scene, but quite another to have to decide soon after qualifying what specialty to aim at. If you are really enjoying medicine – and that is good – you may find that you enjoy each part of the course more than the one before. That makes choices difficult. Even if your medical school has a formal system of careers guidance, you must not expect to be told what to do. You need to learn to make a realistic appraisal of your gifts and abilities, and especially to recognize that temperament is an important factor. An orthopaedic surgeon is a very different person from a psychiatrist, and a neurosurgeon from a general practitioner. If you are not of an obsessional character, you will find the minutiae of some aspects of medicine merely frustrating.

Perhaps the best way to sort out your aims at the beginning of the medical path is to look fifty years ahead. What would you like written about you in your obituary? How would you like to be remembered – as the surgeon with the biggest private practice in London or the doctor who helped to rehabilitate refugees in South East Asia? Would you prefer a yacht or a second house to the gratitude of the widow in the village or the immigrant family in the inner city? Will you settle for the recollection of generations of students taught with enthusiasm and insight, or is international recognition what matters? Is a quiet life with a reasonable income and time off the extent of your ambition, or is perhaps the Creator's verdict, 'Well done, good and faithful servant', better than anything else?

Finally, never forget what a privilege it is to be entrusted with the life of a fellow human being, and never forget your own fallibility.

MAINTAINING PRIORITIES AS A CHRISTIAN MEDICAL STUDENT

John Wyatt

The calling to serve Christ in the medical profession is a high privilege. But effective Christian service in the midst of the pressures of modern medicine requires a clear sense of direction. We will not be effective Christians if we let life wash over us passively. We all need to set priorities in our busy lives to make sure that we are concentrating on the most important things. Your time at medical school will be relatively short; make sure you make the most of it.

Pressures to resist

All of us are subject to negative pressures in trying to serve Christ in medicine. Each of us is particularly vulnerable in certain areas, and these may be different for different people. I would like to highlight four types of pressure which reduce our effectiveness as Christian medics.

Idolatry

One of the repeated themes in the Bible is the risk of idolatry, which is to accord any man-made object the value and worship which should be given only to God himself. Medicine itself can easily become an idol for the ambitious medic. Subtly and imperceptibly, our careers and professional skills become the supremely important factor in decision-making. We can become very good at rationalizing our attitudes and thinking up 'spiritual' reasons for our ambitions, but in reality God himself has been displaced in our lives.

It is one of the terrible ironies of the Christian life that something like medicine, which is good and worthwhile in itself, can become an evil influence in our lives when it becomes an idol. And medical idolatry often starts at medical school. Medicine is important, but it must never take the supreme place. One test to apply to ourselves is to ask this question: 'If God called me to give up medicine to follow another calling, how would I react?'

Cynicism

Many medics start their careers with idealistic and over-romant-icized notions of curing the sick, combating suffering and triumphing over disease. You only have to listen to the average conversation of jaded housemen in the hospital canteen to realize that this kind of idealism usually does not last long! World-weary cynicism seems a very fashionable attitude in medics. The cynic sees medicine not as a supreme privilege but just a way to earn a living. Try to earn the maximum amount for the minimum expend-iture of effort; look after number one; cultivate a cynical and malicious sense of humour.

Because cynicism is so all-pervasive in medicine, it is easy to become infected. But it is a virus that is very destructive to Christian motivation. Cynicism and pessimism are weapons of the evil one, and they are utterly out of place in the Christian believer. Being called to serve God in medicine really is a supreme privilege, though it is often an unromantic, costly, hard slog. Let us thank God for this privilege and ask forgiveness for the taint of cynicism in our hearts.

Spiritual schizophrenia

I am using the concept of schizophrenia not in the technical psychiatric sense, but in the lay sense, meaning a split personality. Spiritual schizophrenia is a common disease of modern twentieth-century Christians, and it is quite common among Christian medics. Spiritual schizophrenics live in two worlds, the religious and the secular. They have two separate modes of existence – two ways of thinking, speaking and acting – and there is no real link between the two. When spiritual schizophrenics are in church, they are in religious mode. They think religious thoughts. They use religious words about God and the Holy Spirit and prayer and faith. But when they are on the ward round, or in the hospital canteen, they click instantaneously into secular mode. They talk medical talk. They blend into the environment as easily as a chameleon. Their two modes of existence have no real contact.

The trouble with spiritual schizophrenia is that it is funda-mentally unsatisfactory. Living one's life in watertight compart-ments leads to confusion, unfruitfulness and ultimately breakdown. It is not how we are intended to live. We are meant to be integrated Christians, with every aspect of our life integrated in common submission to the lordship of Christ. Our behaviour, attitudes and beliefs need to be the same on the Monday-morning ward round as they are in the Sunday-evening worship service.

Medical arrogance

Arrogance is the besetting sin of the medical profession, and unfortunately Christian medics are by no means immune. The trouble with arrogance is that it is like BO. You do not necessarily realize you have got a problem; only other people do! Just ask one or two nurses about how they are treated on their ward; they will tell you about medical arrogance. Medical pride starts early. You can often detect it in the first-year medical student, who already fancies himself as a cut above 'ordinary' students. It is stimulated by our tendency to gather into professional cliques, which can so easily become mutual admiration societies.

Pride is not just a professional problem; it is a spiritual problem. Jesus had some hard things to say about the professional pride of the Pharisees. What would he say about our professional attitudes? Secret pride is one of the main reasons our spiritual lives are so often barren and unfruitful.

So here are four areas where medics are especially vulnerable – idolatry, cynicism, schizophrenia and arrogance. In which areas are we especially vulnerable? What can we do to resist negative pressures more effectively?

A model to follow

John 20 records a dramatic confrontation between the risen Jesus and his frightened disciples. It contains one of the great commissioning statements of the New Testament. Jesus said, 'Peace be with you! As the Father has sent me, I am sending you' (Jn. 20:21). It is a well-known verse but it has profound implications. First, the Father sent Jesus into the world, and now Jesus is sending us. But the verse tells us something of even greater significance. *In the same way* that the Father sent the Son into the world, he is now sending us.

How did God choose to communicate with a fallen, lost and helpless world? It was not by mounting a mass publicity campaign, by writing supernatural messages in the stars, or by sending angels to the four corners of the world to proclaim the truth. He chose to communicate with the world by becoming flesh, by incarnating himself in an obscure part of the globe, in an obscure period of world history, as an unknown carpenter's son. The incarnation is God's chosen method for communication, and Jesus said, 'In the

same way that the Father sent the Son, I am sending you.'
   In what ways did the Father send the Son?

Sent to serve

Christ did not come as the glorious conquering king, as his disciples expected. Instead he came as a servant, as described in Philippians 2:5–7: 'Christ Jesus ... being in very nature God, did not consider equality with God something to be grasped, but made himself nothing, taking the very nature of a servant.' Christ had the right to everything but made himself nothing, and in the same way he sent out his followers as servants. The trademark of the servant in first-century Palestine was a towel wound round the waist. And a rather smelly and dirty towel it often was, as one of its purposes was the washing and drying of other people's feet. This is the brand image that Jesus gave his disciples, the sign of their calling (cf. Jn. 13:14–17). Doctors do not like to think of themselves as servants. They prefer to be seen as high-status, highly qualified professionals. They expect to be treated with respect and deference, and to wield authority and influence. But if we want to be genuine followers of Jesus Christ our attitude must be radically different. The mark of the authentic Christian is not the crown of authority but the towel of the servant. Is this the trademark, the brand image, of our lifestyle?

Sent to seek

Jesus was engaged in a rescue mission, as he explained to Zacchaeus in Luke 19:10: 'The Son of Man came to seek and to save what was lost.' He came to reach out to those who were prisoners, trapped and enslaved in evil, hopeless and lost without any knowledge of God and his love. He followed this aim with great single-mindedness and refused to be deviated in any way from his overriding purpose. And he has sent us in exactly the same way. We too are surrounded by those who are trapped, blind and lost. Do we care enough for those around us to go out of our way to reach them for Jesus? Are we praying and looking out for opportunities to share the spiritual riches with which we have been entrusted?

Sent to care

Eleven times in the gospels comes the phrase 'Jesus was moved by compassion.' The verb in Greek means 'to be deeply moved in the entrails'; which is where the Greeks thought the seat of emotion was! (Interestingly, the Greek word is *splanchnizomai*, related to our word 'splanchnic'.) Jesus was not cold, detached or cynical about people's need. He cared deeply, he empathized, he was emotionally involved. He embodied God's love – not just an emotional response but practical caring, healing and meeting physical and spiritual need. So we too need to care, to be emotionally involved.

But again this does not fit very well with our professional image. Doctors like to be seen as cool, clinical, detached, objective. It is part of the professional mystique. But I do not believe it is the Christian way. I think we need to care for people who are suffering with tears in our eyes, metaphorically or literally, because that is the way that Jesus would respond in the same situation. That kind of caring is costly. It hurts to open our hearts to the suffering that is all around us. It is easier to be cool and clinically detached. But the way of Jesus is always a costly way.

Jesus was sent to serve, to seek and to care, and each of these three goals led to the cross. If we want to be authentic followers of Jesus in medicine then we must expect to pay a price too. An ancient proverb says, 'He who would be a Christ must expect a cross.'

Suppose Jesus had not been born as a carpenter in first-century Palestine. Suppose God had broken into history in human form as a medical student in Britain in the 1990s. How would he have behaved? What would have been his response to the people with whom he came into contact? That is the challenge of being an authentic Christian disciple. We are called, in a sense, to be Jesus to those with whom we come into contact. We are called to demonstrate the reality of God by the quality of our lives and the authenticity of our caring. It is a high calling, and humanly speaking it is completely impossible, laughably unrealistic. But the amazing thing is that the Holy Spirit, the very Spirit of the Lord Jesus himself, is available to dwell in our hearts, to live out the life of Jesus in our lives. So it is no longer a completely unrealistic possibility; it is sober reality.

Putting priorities into practice

Priorities are not just a matter of theory. They need to be brought down to earth in practical action. I would like to challenge you to put your Christian priorities into practice. Many people have found it helpful to write down on a sheet of paper specific goals and priorities, as a private record. There are three practical steps we need to take thoughtfully and prayerfully.

Analyse the current situation

In Romans 12:3, Paul commands us to 'think of yourself with sober judgment'. In other words, he instructs us to analyse ourselves, not so that we become preoccupied with morbid introspection but so that we can serve Christ more effectively.

What are my current strengths and weaknesses? In what areas am I most vulnerable to pressure? What gifts has God given me that I need to develop further? Where are my life and behaviour least those like of Christ? This analysis should lead on to the next stage.

Set practical goals

In Philippians 3:13–14 Paul gives an illustration of priorities in practice. 'One thing I do: Forgetting what is behind and straining towards what is ahead, I press on towards the goal to win the prize for which God has called me heavenwards in Christ Jesus.' We need to set specific goals that are practical and achievable. Vague goals like 'to be more spiritual' are of little value. We need to be specific. What are my practical goals for the period ahead?

Set a time to review progress

We need to set a time when we review the progress made and see how near we have come to achieving our specified goals. This might be in one month's time, next term, the next academic year. This process of review should lead on to fresh goal-setting, and so the process continues.

It is often helpful if we can find a close friend or spiritual counsellor with whom we can share our goals and priorities. It helps to nail us down to practical action.

May the power of the Holy Spirit fill our hearts and lives so that we can put our priorities into practice and live out the life of the Lord Jesus in the medical world of the 1990s into which he has called us.

THE HOUSEMAN: HAGGARD BUT HAPPY?

Paul Cosford

Writing this has made me look back over my year as a houseman and realize that it was not nearly as bad as I had expected. In fact it was mostly an exciting and satisfying time, looking after a large variety of people, and seeing many of them get better from quite serious illnesses. God was allowing me to be involved, for the first time, in healing people by using the skills I had spent so much time learning at medical school.

There were also, however, times of great pressure. I could be rushed off my feet with no time to talk to my patients or to take meal breaks. 'A diabetic ketoacidosis. Right. Rehydrate, get the insulin pump going, two-hourly U & E's overnight. Get him up to the ward. Next patient. Only four more waiting. Ugh. Another sleepless night. Why do they have to be ill tonight?' At times this was a common train of thought. The work could seem endless, and I had little time to study God's Word, spend time with my wife or go to church or home-group. The frustration could be immense.

Most Christian doctors, I suspect, will remember their house-jobs as a mixture of these two extremes – essentially enjoyable and satisfying, but at times under great pressure with little time for anything other than medicine, and seemingly little thanks from anyone for all the hard work.

Under these pressures many Christian medics fall away from the Lord. Although none of us is immune to them, however, there are ways of coping with these difficulties, and in this section I would like to share some that I have learnt.

Pressure of time and tiredness

One of the greatest pressures on housemen is that of a heavy on-call rota and the tiredness it creates. This in turn can mean that our daily quiet times are either missed completely or of poor quality (for instance, we fall asleep while praying). Working on Sundays causes us to miss church services. Midweek on-call may also mean that we miss our homegroup or fellowship group. Thus both our personal time with God and fellowship with other Christians are seriously impaired, leaving us much more vulnerable to backsliding as

Christians. If we are married it can also create pressure in this area, with little time to spend with one's wife and family.

This aspect of time is probably the greatest pressure on our Christian faith as housemen. It can never be completely removed, but there are ways of reducing it significantly.

The job itself

A '1 in 3' is obviously the worst from this point of view. A '1 in 4' can be difficult but is generally manageable, and a '1 in 5' not too bad at all. In other words, be careful before applying for a '1 in 3'. Be aware of what you are letting yourself in for, and be sure that the job has clear advantages over those with a less onerous rota.

Quiet times

A daily routine becomes a thing of the past when working a busy on-call rota. When not on the night before, however, it is possible to have a morning quiet time as usual. I found that even when on call I was rarely bleeped between 8am and 9am and was often able to have a good QT then, depending on how much sleep I had had. Besides QTs, it is also very helpful to cultivate the habit of praying during the day – for instance, when holding the retractor in the operating theatre, or during the five minutes in the loo when you can't answer your bleep anyway. To 'pray continually', as Paul urges in 1 Thessalonians 5:17, can be of practical help in maintaining a close walk with God.

Fellowship

Christian fellowship is crucial to survival as a houseman. Other Christian doctors in the hospital can be an excellent source, but in my own view it is also essential to become involved in a local church and in a fellowship group within it. This may be difficult in an unfamiliar area, but is not impossible. Personally, my wife and I found good fellowship from both these sources during both house-jobs, despite their being in new areas. Explain that you cannot always be there, but remember – it's better to go and fall asleep than not to go at all. More than once I was prayed for by our fellowship group while fast asleep and oblivious to it!

Pressure while at work

Pressure while actually on the job comes from a number of sources. Though usually manageable, the workload can become unbearable, especially on a busy on-call day. Consultants are usually realistic in what you can achieve, but occasionally expect the impossible. Nursing staff can seem very demanding, and are often unaware of obligations you have away from their ward. In addition, if you are at all a caring doctor you want to give your patients the best possible care in terms of time, thoroughness and provision of adequate information about their illness. Sometimes I found a 'learned helplessness' developing, whereby I knew that however hard I worked I could neither succeed in my aims for the job, nor fulfil everyone else's expectations of me.

This kind of pressure can, at worst, lead to a disillusioned feeling towards God, our faith and our work. At these times it is very important to have Christian friends around us and supporting us, whether they are other Christian doctors or from a local church. Christian fellowship is crucial.

In terms of maintaining a Christian lifestyle I found it particularly helpful to be known as a Christian while at work. This encouraged me to want to maintain Christian standards, as it is very easy to slip into conformity with everyone else's attitudes if those around you are unaware of your Christian faith. A simple fish badge or something similar can be useful in this respect.

Over relationships with other staff I found Romans 12:18 helpful: 'If it is possible, as far as it depends on you, live at peace with everyone.' With regard to consultants, we should respect them and submit to their authority, even though they may at times be pedantic and difficult. Remember that they carry ultimate responsibility for anything that goes wrong, and may be under much pressure themselves.

Colossians 3:23–24 says 'Whatever you do, work at it with all your heart, as working for the Lord, not for men, since you know that you will receive an inheritance from the Lord as a reward. It is the Lord Jesus Christ you are serving.' We may not always get thanks or praise from our boss, or from anyone else for that matter, but it is actually Jesus whom we are serving, and from whom we receive our ultimate reward.

A good relationship with nursing and other staff (especially phlebotomists and ECG technicians) is invaluable, and can considerably ease the burden of work. Ward sisters and charge nurses can be an endless source of help and advice if treated in the right way. We need to be humble, and not afraid to ask their opinion too at times. Remember they may have been doing their job for twenty years longer than you have! Thanking staff when they are helpful, and giving positive affirmation in appreciating the importance of their role, are not just common courtesies, but will pay dividends when we need assistance later on. A ward sister on your side is probably of more value than anything else in helping you to look after your patients well.

One of the most satisfying aspects of being a houseman is the contact with your patients. There is frustratingly little time, however, to spend discussing with them their illness, its possible consequences and their subsequent worries. Bearing in mind the lack of time available, it is helpful to identify the occasions when people particularly need time from their doctor. To my mind the most important are on admission, post-operatively, and with the more seriously ill or terminal patients.

On admission one is usually rushed, especially if on emergency take. It often takes only five minutes' careful explanation, however, to give a good idea of the nature of a patient's illness and/or details of his subsequent operation, and this can greatly reduce the fear which may arise from not knowing what may happen to him. Post-operatively, patients need an explanation of how the operation went, and this will often be given by the consultant or registrar. You may, however, find yourself left as the bearer of bad news. If this is the case, time is essential, even if it means coming back at the end of the day. Everyone develops his or her own way of breaking the news. The essentials are to be honest, but sensitive to how much the individual can take at a time. If possible, have a nurse with you to lend the patient moral support, and also so that the ward staff know what has been said, and can then be sensitive in their dealings with the patient later.

With seriously ill or terminal patients, again time and sensitivity are required. Although time is rarely available in sufficient quantity, I found that it is possible to make use of what *is* available at least to begin to help patients and their families to face the situation. On occasions I was able to talk about death and dying, and the simple question, 'Do you have a faith that helps you?' led to some of the all-too-few opportunities to share my faith.

Loneliness

A houseman's life can be very lonely. This is especially true if you are single and working in a previously unknown part of the country. Most of your life seems to be spent working, or sleeping off the subsequent tiredness. When there is free time, there may be no-one around to spend it with. Such loneliness can have a very detrimental effect on our Christian lives, and is another good reason for stressing the importance of finding good Christian fellowship.

It can also lead to entering relationships that you would not otherwise have considered, and which may lead to further problems. Although there are no hard and fast rules in this area, I do think that one should be very wary of entering serious relationships for the wrong motives, something that would be very tempting during house-jobs. Certainly, as always, one should resist the temptation to go out with non-Christians. As 2 Corinthians 16:14 says: 'Do not be yoked together with unbelievers.' House-jobs are not the stage at which to try to convert a non-Christian boyfriend or girlfriend, while maintaining Christian standards in the relationship at the same time.

The usual pressures of life

All the major life events that can happen to anyone can also happen to you as a houseman. My experience of this was through bereavement, which can obviously come at any point to any of us. During house-jobs such strains are added to the major life events of changing jobs frequently, and often moving to live in a new area, on top of the other pressures already discussed. Again, at times like this, it is particularly important to be involved in a good local church which can offer on-the-spot support and advice. It is also crucial to take time off work as necessary. Whatever anyone may say, you are not irreplaceable, and it is essential to take sufficient compassionate leave and supplement it with sick leave as needs be. Remember, it is the administrators' job to arrange cover, not yours!

Conclusions

Although this section has of necessity centred on the more difficult aspects of being a houseman, I would conclude by reiterating that I found my house-jobs on the whole both satisfying and enjoyable. At times the work caused great pressure, but in my experience God works through that pressure to refine and purify us, leading to a more mature and practical faith in a living God who cares deeply about us and the patients we seek to serve. To use Jesus' analogy in John 15, it can be a time of pruning and trimming, but the purpose of this is solely that we may bear more fruit for him.

THE STRESSED DOCTOR IN A STRESSFUL SOCIETY

Michael Jones

The reality

Stress factors in modern high-pace western society are legion. With an increase in marital disharmony and breakdown, many enter adult life with painful childhood experiences which render them more vulnerable to high levels of stress. Increasing numbers of children are scarred by physical and sexual abuse. Doctors practise medicine in an environment of soaring public expectation, matched by steep upward trends in defence-society subscriptions, and they struggle to keep abreast of medical advances. Advances in technology have brought more information within tantalizing reach, but we do not have nearly enough time to absorb all we think we need to know. More recently, for some doctors, AIDS has added to frustration in the form of a cohort of deeply needy young people with declining health, some of whom have sown the wind and reaped the whirlwind.

One serious personal experience of stress went very close to the point of breakdown. While working in East Africa, my wife became seriously ill with a gradual and unrecognized onset over several years. While there were many positive and rewarding aspects to service overseas, chronic under-staffing, overcrowded out-patient clinics and wards, attempts at bribery by patients, constant risk of nocturnal theft, problematic working relationships and a shortage of domestic essentials compounded deteriorating health within the family.

Christmas 1980 was marked by two major events. A very close friend and surgical colleague, who was under my care, died of fulminant hepatitis. He was forty-two and left a wife and five children. The chaplain of the local church was on leave in the UK and I had the responsibility of helping to conduct his funeral.

The second major event was the tentative diagnosis of Cushing's syndrome, cause as yet undefined, in my wife. She was repatriated to the UK in a state of quite severe labile depression for further investigation and treatment. There is no question that I was burnt out in the aftermath. I felt as one imagines a boxer feels emerging punch-drunk from a fight in which he has been defeated. Surgery was wonderfully successful for my wife and we were able to rebuild our relationship and family life. Someone has commented, 'A small wave is all that is needed to drown someone already up to his neck in water.'

Evidence that stress is harmful

'The estranged worker, besieged from above and below mixes internal rage and incessant frustration into a fatal brew.'[1] It is common sense to assume that excessive stress is harmful, and that assumption is now supported by a good deal of excellent evidence.[2] Furthermore, stress-reducing measures may improve life expectancy.[3]

What the Bible has to say about stress

The apostle Paul was no stranger to stress, which he felt as a great pressure (2 Cor. 1:8). 2 Corinthians reveals that this was due not only to opposition and persecution but also to his concern for his fellow Christians.

> Besides everything else, I face daily the pressure of my concern for all the churches. Who is weak, and I do not feel weak? Who is led into sin, and I do not inwardly burn?
>
> (2 Cor. 11:28–29)

Both James and Peter emphasize the positive value of stress in their letters (Jas. 1:2; 1 Pet. 5:7). The experience of stress or trial is used to bring about maturity and a deeper, fire-refined faith. Joy and grief are mixed up together in stress, and Scripture does not underplay the negatives. Middle-class utopianism, which now seems to affect much Christian thinking, suggests that stress should always be kept under control. The physical and mental stress upon Christ was, however, supreme and intense both at Gethsemane and on the cross, and we are called to share in the sufferings of Christ. Suffering is by definition stressful, and if we believe that we can and will avoid stress ourselves, we live in a dangerous delusion about the true nature of the Christian's walk.

Mark Gabrielczyk, a senior anaesthetic registrar, vividly describes how the premature birth and neonatal death of twin daughters was the means of growth and greater wholeness.

> After a decade in hospital practice I considered myself insens-
> ible to the tragedies that I encountered everyday on the wards

31

and intensive care units of my hospital. The intensity of my feelings came as a complete surprise, yet paradoxically my profound grief reassures me, for my dead daughters have returned my humanity. They have restored to me the ability to feel genuine sorrow and more importantly their death showed me the fatuousness of trying to deny my own emotions in professional as well as personal life. I believe this will make me a better doctor.[4]

David Watson, however, described the destructive potential of stress in the onset of bronchial asthma that was to dog his ministry for the rest of his life.

During the month before our wedding I was involved in some Christian activity and an incident occurred which although slight in itself seemed to oppose all the new-found joy and freedom in worship that had become so important to me. I felt a deep grief within my spirit and sensed that this was only a pale reflection of the much more serious grief of the Spirit of God. Whether or not I was right about this I suddenly felt in a spiritual strait-jacket. At that moment I experienced something like a steel band tightening round my chest and I began coughing. [5]

The stages of stress

Stress has been defined as pressure or tension when much energy is needed, and a reaction of the mind and body to change. But the experience of stress is highly individual. The following scheme has been adapted from the *Christian Listeners'* course material.[6]

Stage 1

Extra energy is produced for a short time to enable extra achievement. Though demanding, this experience of stress is positive and individuals can return to normal through relaxation. Where prolonged, however, stage 2 will develop.

Stage 2

Dr Marjory Foyle[7] has used the analogy of the fading of lights due to the drop in voltage in electricity supplies so often experienced in developing countries. Extra energy is provided at the cost of physical and mental well-being. There is lower output for hours worked, but a compulsion to continue. Normal, less attractive characteristics are accentuated. Short-term memory deteriorates, concentration flags and there may be mood alteration. Physical symptoms may develop and immune responsiveness may decline.

Return to normal (and stage 1) may be helped by increased physical activity, provided it is introduced and built up gradually. Relaxation is insufficient on its own.

Stage 3: Burnout

'Burnout' – a popular but imprecise term – was coined in 1974 by Freudenberger to describe a syndrome he believed was especially common among healthcare workers.[8] Extra effort, produced at a high physical and emotional price, fails to maintain productivity. The components are as follows:

● *Emotional exhaustion* – tiredness, somatic symptoms, irritability, accident-proneness, depression, excessive alcohol consumption, violent temper outbursts, exaggerated emotional responses to small stresses.
● *Depersonalization* – treating patients and other people as if they were objects.
● *Low productivity* accompanied by feelings of low achievement, contributed to loss of concentration and short-term memory, and loss of decision-making ability.

This third stage of stress therefore seriously threatens health, relationships and wholeness. Physical manifestations (e.g. tension headaches, dyspeptic symptoms or bronchial asthma), or other psychological manifestations (depression, emotional lability, disorders of eating) may occur. Rest and reduced exposure to the operative stress factors are vital for recovery.

Particular problems of stress and the doctor

Idleness is not a significant problem within our profession, which suffers rather from an epidemic of busyness. But do doctors benefit from their medical knowledge? Finnish and UK doctors[9] have lower death rates from most major health risks except for suicide, pointing to mental strain as the major occupational hazard for doctors. Why are so many doctors unhappy despite well-rewarded, interesting work? Glin Bennet FRCS, FRCPsych, in a book entitled *The Wound and the Doctor*, reviewed in the *Lancet*,[10] argues that there is a disorder endemic in the profession, of which the pathognomonic symptom is professional busyness. Professional busyness may be imposed or sought.

Imposed busyness

This is a significant problem in the pre-registration resident year and early years of training. Entrenched attitudes within the medical establishment maintain the house-officer year as a form of intense and severe initiation rite.

A. J. M. Quayle asked whether this is really necessary,[11] and commented that 'despite God the Creator's pre-eminent example, the medical profession appears to have chosen to ignore the fourth commandment!' J. Firth-Cozens[12] followed a cohort of junior house officers from medical school through their house year using a general health questionnaire. The result showed that 50% were emotionally disturbed, 28% revealed evidence of depression and nearly one fifth reported occasional or repeated bouts of heavy drinking while 7% used 'recreational' drugs. More empathetic and self-critical house officers seemed at particular risk. 'Such attitudes' understates the author, 'seem important in members of a caring profession.' The system therefore tends to hit hardest those of a more gentle nature who are able to relate well to patients. 28% showing signs of depression is an unacceptably high proportion when this reflects symptoms of lack of concentration, memory problems and difficulty in decision-making.

Does the way we structure the resident year then qualify as a form of institutionalized sin? The best interests of patients are never served by stretching medical or nursing staff beyond their limits, and if we are to heed the apostolic warning to avoid conforming to the world's patterns and to be transformed by the renewing of our minds (Rom. 12:2), we have an obligation to improve the structure of medical workload whether for the pre-registration year or elsewhere in medical practice.

Sought busyness

The larger problem for many of us is that we like to *be* busy and to *appear* to be busy. Glin Bennet[13] asserts that busyness provides emotional rewards, satisfying a doctor's immediate unconscious needs, and assisting him or her to avoid the anxiety inherent in clinical practice and genuine emotional intimacy with patients and colleagues. Doctors with greater clinical involvement, he states, not only have more problems in adult life, but will also have had less-happy childhoods. 'The more highly developed the persona and thus the more powerful and effective the outer self, the weaker, in all probability, will be the inner self.' Paradoxically, therefore, busyness prevents us from coming to terms with the perceived greater stresses of real relationships, but to our personal detriment, since it is only as we deepen relationships that we discover our real humanity.

Gordon MacDonald contrasts the called person and the driven person:

> Christ separated people on their tendency to be driven or their willingness to be called. He dealt with their motives, the basis of their spiritual energy and the sorts of gratification in which they were interested. He called those who were drawn to him and avoided those who were driven and wanted to use him.[14]

The mark of a driven person is stress. Driven people often make great contributions. Driven people are most often gratified only by accomplishment and are preoccupied with its symbols. MacDonald draws out the point made by Bennet, that because accomplishment results in good feelings, and the praise of others, the driven person will look for ways to accumulate more and more achievements. J. D. McCue makes the same point:

> The diligent self-sacrificing physician who surrenders personal life to patients wins respect from colleagues ... even physicians with reasonable habits often praise colleagues who abandon their personal lives to their profession.[15]

A second factor is fear of failure and of success:

> Physicians who put all their energy into medicine ensure that their efforts are above criticism – their failures must be attributed to misfortune. Being always on call avoids the risk that patients will criticise them for being unavailable when needed.[16]

Charles Colson commented recently as he coped with operable and, one hopes, curable gastric cancer: 'In the hospital I began to consider that in trying to do all those worthy things that everybody wanted me to do, I have become subject to a tyrannical schedule rather than to God's priorities.'[17]

Just as serious, Gordon MacDonald comes to the following conclusion about church life in the USA which I have no doubt applies to growing successful churches in the UK.

> Our churches unfortunately abound with these driven people as well. Many churches are fountains gone dry. Rather than being springs of life-giving energy that cause people to grow and delight in God's way they become sources of stress. The driven man's private world is disordered. His cage may be lavishly golden. But it's a trap; inside there is nothing that lasts.[18]

A way out of inappropriate stress

As we look at Scripture, we may rightly comment that Jesus' world and ours are very different. We may point out that Jesus knew nothing of jet-lag, jangling telephones, filled mailboxes, international consultations and Sunday school picnics,[19] and that the pace of life in Jesus' time was automatically governed by practical obstacles guaranteeing a more serene schedule, but which we have largely overcome in western society. Jesus, however, had a deep sense of personal mission and was under constant pressure, but *also* seemed to have had *an inner governor* that effectively checked any urge to do more than was wise and prudent.[20] Others in God's service have also had this inner governor. John Wesley once remarked: 'Though I am always in haste, I am never in a hurry, because I never undertake more work than I can go through with calmness of spirit.'[21]

A Christian leader who has been preaching 350 times a year recently testified to making a deal with God which greatly concerned me in this regard: 'I said I would go and serve him if he would be a husband to my wife and a father to my children. If at any time I saw them facing neglect, the deal was off.'

In today's world we badly need that inner governor. I am deeply concerned that, as Christian doctors, we allow God to work among us; to stimulate insight and the profound personal change that some of us need and thus to move *from a constant worldly activism to a pattern of life controlled by the Holy Spirit,* with biblical patterns of work and recreation that will enable us to cope in a healthier way with the stresses that are inevitable. We need to hear and respond to the word of God through Paul that we should not conform to the pattern of this world but be transformed by the renewing of our mind.

Our needs

I have selected three things among many others that seem important and which we need to do if we are to avoid inappropriate stress.

Listen to what God is saying about our busyness

When busyness takes over, stillness gets swept aside, and where there is no stillness in our lives, we will be deaf to what God is saying. We need stillness if we are to know that God is God and to live under his lordship. We need stillness if we are to offer our busyness to him and find out what he has to say about it. It is in stillness that we will rediscover, or perhaps discover for the first time, what it is to be called and to hear his voice saying, 'Come, follow me' (Mk. 1:17). Following Christ and 'leaving our nets' may mean leaving that unnecessary extra research project or extra church commitment which, if we are honest, may have more to do with a vain bolstering of self-esteem than with God's call.

Deepen our relationships

The way to find a true sense of worth is through deepened relationships, and, above all, depth in our relationship with God. The cure for the inner inadequacy that seeks constant busyness is closeness to the Lord Jesus Christ, and the discovery that, sinners though we are, he loves and cherishes us. In the context of that relationship we can open up the empty spaces that are present to some measure in all of us, to be filled by God.

Salvation (*yĕša'* in the Old Testament) encompasses not only the vital aspects of forgiveness for past wrong and receiving a right moral standing with God through Christ, but also coming out into a broad place of liberty and freedom, in which we are delivered from factors that constrain and confine.[22] The basis of this spacious freedom is alluded to by Christ himself, who invited us to pray with intimacy to God the Father (Lk. 11:2), and by Paul: 'You received the Spirit of sonship. And by him we cry, "*Abba*, Father." The Spirit himself testifies with our spirit that we are God's children' (Rom. 8:15–16). What an enormous depth and breadth there is in that relationship! We can develop a relationship which we do not deserve, made possible by the work of Christ on the cross, in which we can receive acceptance, succour and significance as adopted children of a loving heavenly Father. From that relationship, truly called by him, we can then move into God-ordained achievement. God longs to fill our empty spaces if only we will let him do so. 'How great is the love the Father has lavished on us, that we should be called children of God!' (1 Jn. 3:1).

Set priorities

We need to set right priorities for time, remembering that if we are driven people, our automatic defence will be to say that we have to do all these things, when the reality is that we want to do these things for the sake of personal gratification and the need to satisfy the empty areas of our lives. In *Ordering Your Private World*, Gordon MacDonald has written two helpful chapters on this, entitled 'Has anyone seen my time? I've misplaced it!' and 'Recapturing my time.' The unpalatable fact is that we find the time to do the things we want to do.

Resetting priorities is often desperately difficult in practice, because it is part of the problem of getting to grips with our old sinful nature. The corrective process required is not merely a change of gear and driving more slowly, but the determination to drive by a different route under the lordship of Christ. Failure to view life-pattern and priorities in the light of scriptural teaching and common sense may cost us dearly in our health and relationships, both with our fellow human beings and with God.

God may be calling us to do all we currently shoulder. Or he may be asking us to share some of those responsibilities with others, or to delegate. Alternatively he may be asking us to withdraw completely from some activity. Whatever he is saying to us, we need not fear. Shedding our excessive busyness will not diminish our stature in God's eyes. It may furnish a vital opportunity for us to grow in our relationship with the Lord Jesus Christ and with others, to discover our real humanity, and to experience a greater breadth and depth of our salvation than we had ever believed possible and which was purchased for us at such infinite cost.

2 MEDICAL CAREERS

Michael Webb-Peploe

The purpose of a medical career

In any profession that offers such a wide scope for differing talents, such a wealth of opportunity in both the humanities and the sciences, it is easy to lose sight of ultimate aims, and become distracted by the details of daily demands and decisions. We can do no better than start with the motto of Dr Edward Livingstone Trudeau: 'To cure sometimes, to relieve often, to comfort always.' In the light of this aim, arguments about whether medicine is art or science, trade or calling, pale into insignificance.

The scope of a medical career

Never before has medicine offered such a wide variety of career openings. From the morbid anatomist (who spends no time talking to patients) to the psychiatrist (who spends all his time talking to patients); from the anaesthetist to the zoologist; the scope is enormous. There are openings for a whole world of different personalities, inclinations, aptitudes. This very fact poses its own problems. For the medical community to survive, let alone live up to Trudeau's motto, it must have a certain moral cohesion embodied in its conventions. G. R. Dunstan said:

> Conventions are possible because men are capable of moral insight, of agreeing in the recognition of moral insight, and of committing themselves to maintain it; they rest on a presupposition of *fidelity to a common interest and purpose*. Conventions are necessary because men fail conspicuously to follow their moral insights and are capable of ruthlessly exploiting one another in the pursuit of self-interest; they rest on a presupposition of infidelity to the common purpose.[1]

The ever-widening scope of medicine is placing a growing strain on professional conventions. Too often the 'common interest and purpose' (the welfare of the patient) is forgotten amid the clamour of rival bids for power and money.

The changing role of the doctor
In medicine

Modern hospital medicine can be viewed as essentially the art of applied technology. The greatest advances in this technology have not been made by the medical profession, but rather by the pure scientists who have mastered their speciality: from heart pacemakers to Teflon bypass grafts, from antibiotics to body scans – the list is long and impressive. The physician's role has been to apply this technology to the patient in the most appropriate way. He has had the difficult, and often impossible, task of preserving humanity in an ever more sophisticated environment. Comfort and care have had to be balanced with electrodes and oxygen masks.[2]

The hospital doctor no longer practises in isolation. In the total care of the patient, the cardiologist (for example) forms part of a team composed of administrators, bacteriologists, biochemists, cleaners, clerks, caterers, computer specialists, dietitians, electronics experts, haematologists, histochemists, morbid anatomists, nurses, physiotherapists, porters, radiologists, radiographers, secretaries, social workers, statisticians, and technicians in a variety of disciplines. No longer can the doctor expect to be the leader of the team by virtue of being a doctor. True authority (as Ivan Illich has remarked) is 'a grant of confidence'; as such it is not a right, but must be earned and continue to be earned. Only as the doctor is seen to use the skills of each member of the team for the good of the patient (and not to enhance his own reputation, or save himself work, or line his own pocket) will he earn the confidence of the team, of the patient, and ultimately of society. It is the responsibility of the clinician to impose on the whole team 'fidelity to a common interest and purpose' – that of serving the patient. This demands ruthless self-discipline, great integrity, and powers of leadership of a very high order. Too often such qualities have been lacking.[3]

Similarly, in primary medical care, the general practitioner forms part of a team made up of district nurses, health visitors, social workers, secretaries and receptionists, and has the responsibility of welding this team into an effective unit. Complexity so often spells the inhuman, the impersonal. The team approach can become mechanical, inflexible, automatic. Only if it is obvious that the doctor is concerned with each patient as a person (and not merely as an example of X's syndrome) can the team be humane, flexible, compassionate.

In society

As modern industrial society changes from being dominated by tradition and religion to become a rational and secular state, so there is a progressive weakening of religion, of traditional values, of social hierarchies, and of extended family ties.[4] Their place has been largely taken by a crudely materialistic outlook.

In any society whose religion is material well-being, medical science becomes a god, and the medical profession that god's priesthood. It may well be that this popular attitude to medicine will prove only temporary, and confined to the thirty years after the Second World War. Already the public is beginning to realize that its idol has feet of clay. The places of nutritional disorders and infectious diseases as causes of morbidity and mortality have been taken by diseases that are in part genetic, by degenerative disorders in an ageing population, and by self-induced disease: lung cancer, motor-car violence, overdose with alcohol and drugs, and coronary artery disease.

> More and more time and effort is now being diverted to the 'incurable' diseases, since the 'curable' patients are by definition less of a burden to us. As time has passed, however, the ratio of the incurable to the curable has increased greatly and the resulting reputation of medicine has fallen on hard times.[5]

The pendulum is swinging from too great a public confidence (verging on superstition) in medicine to too cynical an attitude towards the motives, methods, and achievements of the healthcare professions. Both extremes are encouraged by ignorance of the facts. The role of the doctor as an educator of the public in health matters has been neglected. This education should be aimed at equipping the lay public:

● to prevent the preventable, i.e. sound rules for personal health care – the right food; the right exercise; the right rest and recreation; how to deal with problems of misuse of drugs, sweets, tobacco, alcohol; the need for prudence in driving; the importance of friendships in the maintenance of mental health;
● to treat the trivial themselves; many diseases, such as the

common cold, are self-limiting – small nuts which do not require a modern medical sledgehammer;
● to recognize the early signs of the serious, e.g. cancer, and to know that effective treatment in the early stages will often produce a 'cure';
● to accept, adapt to, and live with degenerative disease, old age, and infirmity (growing old gracefully);
● to promote mutual help rather than dependence on social workers and doctors;
● to accept the reality of death, to prepare for it, to help the bereaved.

> The concept of family doctors replacing the clergy as problem solvers and soothers is false and unrealistic since they should be catalysts to each other. Furthermore, by taking this role on themselves the family doctors of today have only themselves to blame for their apparent inability to advance their standard of actual medical care, which is what they are trained and paid to do.[6]

What is required is 'a counselling service for people to solve their problems by discussion rather than medication'.[7] As one patient (also attending the psychiatrists) said to me recently: 'I do not want ECT; all I want is someone to talk to.'

These are some of the challenges presented by the changing role of medicine in society. But there is a yet more fundamental challenge.

Professions: disabling or enabling?

Far from seeing the medical profession as disinterested, altruistic, and enriching, Ivan Illich and his colleagues[8] claim that it is 'dominant' and 'disabling'. The doctor gains his dominance by discovering need, defining it, prescribing for it, and he alone is competent to say when need is met, i.e. when the patient can be discharged from his 'care'. Too often, according to Illich, the patient is maintained in a 'disabled' and 'dependent' condition for the benefit of the professional 'carer'. The right of a professional to self-assessment and self-government is under attack. Bureaucratic enquiry and an ombudsman with powers to question clinical decisions are the suggested alternatives.

'Undoubtedly we now spend money in the Health Service for its employees' sake but with remarkably little concern for the patients, their children, or society as a whole.'[9] It is true that physicians are among the most highly selected, most highly educated and most highly privileged members of our society. It is disappointing to see the privileges dissipated, and to watch as responsibility for the rights of others is ignored. It is disappointing to hear demands for higher fees in certain sections of medicine when incomes may be twenty times the median income for the country, or five to ten times the income of colleagues. From whom can we expect moral leadership to come if it is not from ourselves?[10] We have to acknowledge that there is truth in these accusations. Are we prepared to lead and co-operate in ways of assessing and improving the quality of medical care, care that has as its aim the restoration of the individual patient to an independent life of acceptable quality in as short a time as possible?

Commitments and implications of a medical career

'The essence of good clinical practice is continuous responsibility, said a wise old GP. The individual patient has suffered and will continue to suffer if trade union attitudes to off-duty, overtime, working to rule and the like gain further ground. Modern medicine is in danger of pricing itself out of the market, and the large hospital has been called 'the most rapidly failing enterprise of our time'.[11] Just as Christ, the Great Physician, gave up all claim to the rights and privileges that were his as Son of God in order to enter this needy world to serve, to save, to comfort, to suffer, and to die, so we must be prepared to do the same (Phil. 2:5–8).

Christ's example, his teaching, and above all his Holy Spirit, must dictate and determine the way we practise medicine. We are Christians who happen to be doctors, not doctors who, in what little spare time they have, are Christians. Of course gross miscarriages of social justice, gross overburdening with work leading to impaired efficiency, and lack of time for rest, recreation and family life, must be put right. But how much of the present agitation for more pay for less work is motivated by greed, and how much by a genuine desire for a fair day's wage in return for a fair day's work?

> Mutual expectation is at the heart of professional ethics . . .
> Fidelity in this context means meeting the expectations
> appropriate to one's role. Personal integrity may often require
> a man to go beyond them; and always it is necessary to guard
> against formalism, against meeting the bare formal demands

> while ignoring or impairing the live human ethical reality of
> the demand behind it. The expectations are not static: they are
> raised in response to pressure from the ethical sensitivity of
> individuals or groups; they are lowered by insensitivity and
> sloth.[12]

The expectations that the public attach to the doctor's role are
changing rapidly and are thus often imperfectly met. The doctor's
expectations in terms of facilities, hours of work, remuneration, and
status in society are also imperfectly met. There is often a disparity
between the standards the public (rightly) expects of the medical
profession, and the standards it sets itself.

The doctor is expected to be honest, hard-working, self-sacrificial
in terms of his or her time, always available on demand, and
scrupulous in maintaining the highest standards of care and
conduct come what may. By contrast, large sections of the public
ruin their health and their finances by indulging themselves in
alcohol, tobacco, sweets or gambling, and are unwilling to accept
even sensible restraints (such as seat belts). It may be considered
legitimate for miners and power workers to withdraw their labour
(always in the depths of winter), but unthinkable for doctors to
strike. We must be prepared to accept this double standard, and not
allow it to infect us with the anger or weary cynicism of so many of
our colleagues, attitudes that lead so easily to 'insensitivity and
sloth', to 'formalism . . . meeting the bare formal demands while
ignoring . . . the live human ethical reality of the demand behind it'.

Useful criteria in choosing a speciality

Individual preference

During student and pre-registration periods, sample as wide a
selection of specialities as possible, and see if any has a particular
appeal. Do not be in too great a hurry to specialize. The specialist
with no general training wears blinkers and can make disastrous
mistakes.

Individual aptitudes

List as honestly as possible your aptitudes and failings. Ability to
relate well to patients, clinical ability, manual dexterity, factual
memory, visual memory, powers of reasoning, mathematical ability,
administrative ability, stamina, whether you are able and willing to
work long hours, your attitude to emergency calls, whether the

human or the scientific content of your work attracts most; these are some of the factors to be taken into account. If you relate well to people and are anxious to build a long-lasting relationship with them, you should consider general practice. If you are 'fingers negative' and always came bottom in anatomy, surgery is not for you. If you have a poor visual memory (as I have), do not enter dermatology.

Check your own assessment of your aptitudes:

● by asking an honest friend;
● by finding out how well or badly you have done in exams; your weakest subject is probably not the speciality you should aim for.

Find out

Talk to people in the speciality you are considering (people at all grades) to discover the problems they have encountered in training for the speciality.

Variety and content

Choose a speciality with enough variety and content to keep you interested for your working life. This means choosing a speciality that has your genuine interest, and not because you think it is the fastest route to the top. Any doctor who loses interest in his work (and many tragically do so) becomes a menace to both his patients and his colleagues.

Planning a career

The Royal Colleges have now laid down guidelines for training in the various specialities (and this includes the vocational training scheme for general practitioners). In most specialities at least two years of general training are required after full registration (during this period it is expected that the appropriate higher qualification – MRCP, FRCS – will be acquired). Following this, three or four years' specialist training (in most cases at senior registrar level for hospital specialities) is envisaged. Details of these recommendations should be available in your dean's office, and are well worth studying in preparation for training in any speciality. The Colleges are in the process of inspecting all senior house officer, registrar, and senior registrar posts in the country to decide if they can be recognized as suitable training posts. Once the scheme is fully implemented, it will be disadvantageous to do jobs that are not so recognized.

Where should we work?

As a general principle it is wise to start with posts that are well supervised, in which it is possible to acquire by teaching and example sound habits of history-taking and physical examination. The aim of the pre-registration year is so to condition your 'clinical reflexes' that thereafter, no matter how tired or ill or short of sleep you are, you can still take a good history (missing no relevant fact), and perform a thorough physical examination (missing no physical sign). More mistakes are still made in medicine through neglect of these two fundamental arts than for any other reason. Once these sound habits have been engrained, you will be ready for a busy, less supervised, post where you will see a wealth of clinical material and learn which corners you can legitimately cut when the pressure is on. Talk to people who have done the jobs you contemplate applying for. Do not be unduly worried if you do not obtain a pre-registration house-officer post in your own teaching hospital. The days when this spelt death to a career in hospital medicine are over, and many district general hospitals give you better training.

How does God guide?

● Through the use of our common sense sanctified by his Holy Spirit (Jn. 16:13);
● through the advice of wise friends whose prayer and support we have enlisted – this ought to be one of the functions of the church (Acts 13:2–3);
● through strong inner conviction (the 'voice behind you' of Is. 30:21). Note that this verse implies that we should be pressing on along the road ahead, and that when the time comes for us to turn either to left or to right we shall be shown. It does not imply spineless inactivity or introspective misery while awaiting some miraculous vision from heaven;
● through the seal of inner peace and joy once the decision has been made (Acts 20:22–24);
● through force of circumstance. Knock on all the doors, and some (often only one) will open (Mt. 7:7–8).

The pattern of guidance is usually clearly seen only in retrospect. We have to trust our heavenly Father both for the faltering step and the confident stride. We have to remain sensitive to the promptings of his eye (Ps. 32:8–9) or we shall require the painful corrective of the bit and bridle. We have to keep our spiritual eyes open for the 'hand signals' of God (Ps. 123:2). We have to 'fix our eyes on Jesus' (Heb. 12:1–2). If we are to 'eat the best from the land', we must be 'willing and obedient' (Is. 1:19).

Amid the pressures and demands of 'life on the house', this is easier said than done. But be warned that it does not get any easier as you climb the ladder. Each rung brings its own particular problems and temptations. Just as it is important to condition your clinical reflexes correctly early in your medical career, so it is vital to establish sound spiritual habits if the 'spiritual reflexes' are not to become sluggish. Neglect of time spent in the presence of God (either alone or in the company of other Christians) lies at the root of many a spiritual shipwreck in early professional life.

> With eyes wide open to the mercies of God, I beg you, my brothers, as an act of intelligent worship, to give him your bodies, as a living sacrifice, consecrated to him and acceptable to him. Don't let the world around you squeeze you into its own mould, but let God remould your minds from within, so that you may prove in practice that the plan of God for you is good, meets all his demands, and moves towards the goal of true maturity.
>
> (Rom. 12:1–2, JBP)

3 COMMUNICATION

TALKING WITH PATIENTS

Gordon Scorer

When patient and doctor meet, there is an interchange of words. One individual is in personal need; the other has the means to help. If the need is trivial, the encounter is short and words are then few, and few is enough. On the other hand, the meeting may be the beginning of long friendship set in a professional context in which conversations are long and deep. Words are the cement and strength of each encounter. Be they grave or gay, the meaning is always important, because illness is always important.

A helpful attitude

If reports from patients are true, it seems that the doctor sometimes fails in his or her efforts to convey information, or consolation, or even interest. Thoughtless words can so easily be damaging – 'words as hard as cannon balls'. Considered words, precisely tailored to anticipate the anxious fear, can help and heal. Paul advised Christians how they should talk with people. The same advice is well suited to the doctor's consulting room: 'Let your conversation be always full of grace, seasoned with salt, so that you may know how to answer everyone' (Col. 4:6).

What is conversation that is full of grace? Surely it means that the speaker is using words not merely from a sense of duty but out of respect for, and interest in, the listener. Gracious words warm the heart as well as inform the mind; they are acceptable and appreciated.

Such speech should not stand alone; it needs to be 'seasoned with salt'. Salt has two purposes. It brings out the flavour of the food and, in the long term, it acts as a preservative. Perhaps, in medical practice, our conversation needs to be spiced (not overloaded) with humour and homeliness, so that our patient can the more easily grasp our meaning. Important too is the need for our counsel to be incorruptible and such as will make it easier for the patient to want the right things in life.

It is, of course, in the Christian context – and presumably in the defence of his faith – that Paul ends his advice with the phrase, 'so that you may know how to answer everyone'; or better, as in the NEB, 'study how best to talk with each person you meet'. Conversation in the consulting room needs to be natural and relaxed, but we can afford to sit back from time to time and see if we are making our interviews as effective and helpful as they ought to be. It is a salutary experience when a patient comes back and repeats to us what we told him a year ago or ten years ago. It is surprising sometimes to learn of the impression we gave or of the nonsense we apparently talked.

Economy of words

A physician speaks with authority. He or she must do so, having had many years of training to give the basic knowledge of how the body works in health and in disease. The patient is not only in need, but is more or less ignorant of what is going on with her. She comes to the doctor because the doctor is an expert, and she expects an authoritative answer. This means in the first place that we need to be sure of our facts before we make a pronouncement, and, secondly, that we need to be careful in the choice of words we use. A doctor's word is final in the clinical context, unless the patient chooses to question it and seek a second opinion. If we are not certain of diagnosis and treatment, we need to say so. If time alone will solve a problem, we need to say so. If a second opinion is needed it is better to swallow our pride (if we are allowing it room in our hearts) and to mention the need for further help before the patient does.

The imparting of gratuitous medical information is better avoided. It is wiser to wait till the patient gives a lead and asks. Many are satisfied with simple two-syllable explanations in two sentences; a few want to know more. It is not that we majestically preserve our professional secrets, but rather that we speak to the intelligence of the patient and give him what he needs in order to make his own way forward to full recovery. A learned judge said that he did not think it necessary to warn a patient of *all* the possible complications of an operation. He regarded a doctor who did this as going beyond her duty.

Tips from clinical experience

Here are a few points about talking to patients. Most of them are glimpses of the obvious, but they can so easily be overlooked.

Look the patient in the eye

Not a studied gaze to embarrass, of course, but at least a reassuring welcome as he comes nervously to sit down opposite you; a frequent glance as you speak, and then a momentary strong look when you stand to say goodbye. At least the patient then leaves you knowing he has met a human being and not a robot behind a counter. Incidentally, you can learn so much about a patient from his eyes, quite apart from the clinical information they give. Character is more quickly revealed here than elsewhere. Mouth and hands and gait also speak volumes – but that is another story.

Get alongside the patient when you talk

It is an old trick of the interviewer to put his patient in a strong light and himself stand or sit where the light is behind him and his face cannot so easily be seen. This is gamesmanship and not always right in clinical medicine. In talking to a patient it is often prudent to get down to the same level as she is, to sit by a bedside or to go down on your haunches in talking to a child. It puts them at their ease. Better still, move around occasionally.

Speak slowly

It is surprising how often we speak too fast for patients – particularly the old – to understand. Simple sentences in simple words, repeated in the same interview are often needed. There is no need to shout – that is rightly considered rude – but it is surprising how many old people are a little deaf, and politeness forbids some of them from asking you to repeat yourself. Clear and simple speech needs to be cultivated and it is a great asset to be able to describe complicated procedures in one-syllable Anglo-Saxon.

Be human

Perhaps the lightest and simplest touch of humanity is to pick up something of interest in a patient's story and digress for a moment. 'A holiday? Where did you go?' 'The family? How many children have you? How are they doing?' 'Your work? Tell me a little about it, I'm interested.'

This reveals medical competence as well as humanity, for a patient is far more likely to expose her own problems if she knows that her physician is a ready and gracious listener. What a sad indictment it is when we hear someone say, 'I can't talk to my doctor.'

Curb impatience

Temper your busyness and learn to listen. If a patient is anxious, she needs to be allowed to talk, she needs to be drawn out and encouraged to express her fears. If a patient is angry, he needs to get if off his chest; let him talk: you will win a friend. If a patient is a chatterbox, beware; she may be wasting your time. Some patients need to be interrupted politely but firmly: 'But wait a minute, let's get to the point. What is it that is really troubling you?' Or, 'Look, if we get that pain of yours cured, will you then be perfectly fit?'

On the whole we need to listen more than we do, and at least to offer opportunity for them to talk. 'Was there anything else that you wanted to mention?'

Beware of clichés

As doctors, most of us are far too prone to lapse into clichés. They are the mark of slipshod thinking. Here are some common ones. 'Don't worry.' (Probably the patient had never thought of worrying until you mentioned the word.) 'Take it easy.' (What does that mean?) 'You'll be all right.' (Does that mean, 'We hope you will survive this drastic treatment', or 'We know you will make a complete recovery'? There is a world of difference.) 'Don't eat too much.' (Feeding habits need to be precisely investigated before such advice is of any value.)

'When words are many, sin is not absent, but he who holds his tongue is wise' (Pr. 10:19). Too many words and too much exhortation confuse. A few well-chosen words addressed to the main point at issue go much further than half-baked medical jargon buttered over with clichés.

Always keep a step ahead

Anticipate your patient's next probable anxiety and her likely course ahead. It is a wonderful comfort to a patient if she is told what to expect during her course of treatment. A neurologist examined a patient after he had become paralysed as a result of a haemorrhage into the spinal cord. After careful assessment, the neurologist outlined a programme showing how recovery of function would occur, how long it would take and what would be the likely residual disability. The patient was then well armed to face his prolonged convalescence with courage and confidence. It is a wise doctor who thinks ahead for his patients.

Keep to the truth

Lies, especially white ones, breed like mice. On the other hand, it is not right for the doctor to be driven by an over-sensitive conscience and destroy a patient's hope by saying too much. If it is a matter of a bad prognosis or a probable fatal outcome, it is better to wait until the patient gives a lead. And in any case it is always right to let the patient know that however difficult or ineffective the treatment may be, you will always be available to help and to do something. Incidentally, of course, if you say you will do something for the patient, don't forget to do it and do not break your word. Almost always in terminal illness, the best treatment we can give our patient is a regular dose of our interested selves.

Christian witness

Should the Christian speak of his Lord and Saviour? Yes, certainly, as occasion offers (see the next section). It is better to be brief unless the patient specifically asks for a discussion. A word of personal testimony does not offend. A single challenging verse or thought about Christ in the context of the patient's need is more valuable than a theological debate. Firm friendship with the hospital chaplain or a local Christian minister means you can work together for those in need. He can often do much more than you, after you have given the introduction. But it needs to be said again and again that the doctor's task is first and last, and all along, to be a good doctor – not an evangelist.

Beware of arrogance

Pomposity and hypocrisy are the errors of a cultured élite. It is all too easy to adopt the pose of infallibility and inwardly preen ourselves when success and popularity come our way. Others detect the dread signs in us before we notice them ourselves, for our speech betrays us. It is a betrayal of our calling as Christians and as doctors. It is an attitude of mind that needs to be avoided at all costs. After all, what have we, as doctors or as Christians, that we have not received from others? To them be the honour.

SHARING OUR FAITH WITH PATIENTS

David Short

Looking back over my career as a hospital doctor, one of my greatest regrets is my lack of skill in sharing my faith with patients. So this section is not written by an expert. It is rather a statement of some of the lessons I learned over a period of forty-five years as a student, junior doctor and consultant physician.

Let me say at once that in some ways my best days for sharing my faith were as a student and junior doctor. My great consolation is that I never grew to accept my poor performance. I was always concerned about it, and prayed for wisdom and grace to do better.

Is sharing one's faith important?

I am convinced that it is. If we are disciples of Christ, plain obedience demands it. Jesus said to his disciples: 'You are the light of the world . . . let your light shine . . .'(Mt. 5:14, 16). Loving concern for our fellow men and women requires it, and God's honour in the world demands it. Each of these arguments is enlarged on in John Stott's valuable book *Our Guilty Silence*.[1]

Is it the student doctor's responsibility?

It is every disciple's responsibility. Moreover, those working with patients have a unique opportunity, because patients are very open to those who are part of their healing team. Furthermore, it is my experience that, as a rule, patients relate best to the least powerful members of the team. On a visit to New York, some years ago, I stayed with a doctor whose son was a medical student. The student told how he had clerked a patient and followed him through his various investigations. Then the big day came when the 'prof' visited the ward with his retinue of staff and students. The results of the tests were produced. The 'prof' considered them carefully, and advised surgery. To the amazement of all present and the consternation of the student, the patient replied, 'Before I agree to your recommendation, I want to discuss it with my doctor.'

'Who is your doctor?' the 'prof' asked.

The patient pointed to a lowly figure on the edge of the crowd.

'There he is.' It was the student!

What is involved in being a witness for Christ?

In essence, a witness is someone who tells what he knows, from first-hand experience. A Christian witness is someone who tells what he knows personally about Jesus Christ. This, of course, raises the question whether we do in fact have a first-hand personal experience of Jesus Christ in our lives. If we have not, there is no point in reading further.

If we do, it is important that we should know the elements of the gospel, and how to present them. Peter May has dealt very fully and helpfully with this aspect.[2] But it is vital to recognize that knowledge of what to say and ability to say it are absolutely useless, and even counter-productive, if our lives detract from our message. Too often, I have heard the comment: 'If he is a Christian, then I don't want anything to do with Christianity.' We must attract people to Christ, and not repel them.

The witness of the life

A friend of mine found himself in hospital as a patient. In the next bed was an Indian in great distress. Most of the nurses ignored him, but there was one for whom nothing was too much trouble. Her attitude toward him and her soothing words were a joy to see. My friend told me, 'I marked her out as a Christian, and sure enough she was.'

We should follow Lord Lister's advice: 'Put yourself in the patient's place.' We should never refer to a patient as 'a case of . . .', but as 'a patient with . . .' The Christian student must be conscientious at his work.

Intellectually, Christians are just average; but we should be the most caring and reliable member of any team. One of the Christian lecturers when I was a junior put it well when he said that 'Christian opportunity depends on medical efficiency'. Courtesy is important, and our dress should be tidy and appropriate to the patient's expectation for a student doctor.

Are kindness and efficiency enough?

I do not think so. If a bus was going in the direction in which you wanted to go, but gave no indication of its destination, you would hesitate to board it. (If it displayed the destination you wanted, but was going in the opposite direction, you certainly would not!) It has been well said that 'lip without life is idle gossip; but life without lip is an uninterpreted parable'. Then should Christians speak to everyone indiscriminately about the Saviour? I think not. Jesus appears on occasion to have left people to whom he could have ministered in order to help others (Mk. 1:37–38). We are all made differently, and have different gifts. We need to be ready, willing, prayerful, sensitive to the voice of the Holy Spirit – and natural.

Literature can be helpful

There are cards and booklets specially designed for patients, and attractively presented. There is a wide selection, and it is important to make oneself familiar with what is available. Offered by a student who has already shown care and efficiency, these can be very effective. In addition to their message, they often prompt an enquiry from the patient: 'Are you a Christian? Tell me about it.'

Religious services are often valuable

If there is already a service for patients, consider supporting it. Even if the chaplain is not an evangelical, he or she will publicly read the Word of God, and show something of the love of God. In time, you may earn the opportunity to take some part. If there is no service for patients in your hospital, ask God if he wants you to be instrumental in starting one. If you do get involved, be wise. I know of one regular hospital service which was stopped years ago because of unwise preaching, and has never been allowed to recommence.

What to avoid

Avoid appearing moralistic. Patients with lung cancer, cirrhosis of the liver, AIDS or an unwanted pregnancy may have been foolish. But we are all foolish in different ways; yet God loves us in spite of it. Avoid frightening dying patients, especially when they have not been told the diagnosis and prognosis. (It is never the student's role to impart serious information.) Avoid giving the impression that you are interested only in people's souls.

Why do we find sharing our faith so difficult?

In some cases, it is because we are not really convinced that the gospel is the truth and the only way of salvation. Sometimes, it is because we do not really accept that unbelievers are lost. Often our problem is knowing what to say and how far to go. We dread being thought a prig.

Our resources

For most of us, sharing our faith is not easy. But we have the supreme resource of the help of the indwelling Holy Spirit, and prayer. It is only in the last few years that I have come to realize that it is literally true that, as the apostle Paul put it, 'I can do everything through him who gives me strength' (Phil. 4:13). We need to start every day with Jesus, reading a part of his Word, and committing our day to him. And then we must seek to live in communion with him. Witness should flow naturally out of that.

LANGUAGE MATTERS

Andrew Fergusson

Everyone in healthcare will, one hopes, have received some training in communicating with patients and with colleagues, and in particular in the importance of language – the words we use. Christians are further exhorted in the Bible to be especially careful with words. James 3:1–12 is a clear warning. Proverbs puts it more poetically: 'A word aptly spoken is like apples of gold in settings of silver' (Pr. 25:11). Paul puts it plainly in Colossians 4:6: 'Let your conversation always be full of grace, seasoned with salt.'

What we say can have either a negative or a positive effect. Christians in healthcare need to be sure that what they say is never doing harm; rather, that it is doing good.

What we say affects both ourselves and those who hear. This adds to our responsibility. Often we fail to realize the powerful effect of words on our attitudes, and on the attitudes of others. Attitudes govern behaviour, and so the very way in which we practise medicine can be influenced for better or for worse by the words we use. (It may be worth remembering at this point that the word 'doctor' literally means 'teacher' and that James warns us: 'Not many of you should presume to be teachers, my brothers, because you know that we who teach will be judged more strictly' (Jas. 3:1)!) Language matters, not least because it creates attitudes which govern actions.

This is particularly important in the case of attitudes to disability, and a few examples will show how subtle changes can convert a negative message into a positive one.

What is the difference, for example, between describing someone as 'partially hearing' as opposed to 'partially deaf'? Or 'partially sighted' as opposed to 'partially blind'? One concept underscores the negative; the other emphasizes a Christian concern to 'strengthen the things that remain'. Which best helps your patient? Which best helps you?

It is to be hoped that we will have been taught to refer not to 'the appendix in bed 4' but to 'Mr Smith in Bed 4 who's recovering from an appendicectomy'. But for some reason most of us find it much harder to avoid this trap when referring to chronic situations. In our culture, 'handicapped' is now less acceptable as a description than 'disabled', and most of 'the disabled' would prefer to be thought of as 'people with disabilities'. Obviously, this approach can lead to some absurdly cumbersome constructions which are actually counter-productive, but it does no harm to emphasize that our patients are people. Is it possible, moreover, to get away from the word 'patient' as much as possible? While 'AIDS patient' is infinitely preferable to 'AIDS victim', 'a person with AIDS' is better still.

Most doctors fail to realize how negatively they view people with disabilities. Rather than saying that 'John Smith has been confined to a wheelchair since . . .', it may actually be more correct as well as more constructive to say, 'John Smith has been liberated by a wheelchair since . . .'

Most able-bodied people fail to realize how well most people with disabilities adjust and adapt, discovering different interests to pursue and in fact leading lives which may much more closely measure up to the 'life in all its fullness' which Jesus offers than the lives of many of the so-called 'healthy'. May we as Christians watch our words and the effects they have on us, on our patients and our colleagues. 'Apples of gold in settings of silver' should be the fruit of our lips.

Suggested words to avoid	*Comment or suggestion*
afflicted with	most people with disabilities don't view themselves like this
burden	person who needs additional care
cabbage	person in a coma, in a persistent vegetative state
cripple, crippled	person with a disability
crumble	person with multiple problems
cerebral palsied	person with cerebal palsy
defective/deformed	there are dehumanizing value judgments here; say 'has spina bifida' or 'born without legs', *etc.*
dwarf	person of short stature
freak	describe physical details – *e.g.* 'a person born without arms'
handicapped	person with a disability
hopeless	'We canot cure this, but we can care by . . .'
idiot/imbecile	although these are medical terms, 'person who has an intellectual disability,' *etc.* is better
incurable	'We cannot cure this, but we can care by . . .'
invalid	person who has a disability
midget	person of short stature
monster	describe physical details
moron/retarded	person who has an intellectual disability
suffers from	most people with disabilities don't view themselves like this
vegetable	person in a coma, person in a persistent vegetative state
victim	person with . . .

This list is by no means exhaustive and is meant mainly to give examples. You can probably come up with a better alternative for each unhelpful expression.

RELATIONSHIPS WITH OTHER PROFESSIONALS

Carl Whitehouse

No doctor is an island unto himself or herself. We all have to work with teams of other people if we are to provide the best care for our patient. Even the concept of the single-handed general practitioner is now a misnomer (and probably always was), for such a doctor will employ clerical and nursing staff and will have to work with other professional carers in the community, from district nurses to local clergy.

But what picture do we have of such a team? Traditionally, the hospital has spawned two images. One is the picture of the consultant and retinue commanding the attention of everyone else as they march through their wards seeing the patients in their beds. The other is the picture of the all-powerful ward sister, known by the name of her ward (Sister Gynae) rather than by her personal surname (Sister Smith), the dragon of whom house officers and junior nurses stand in awe. Neither of these images portrays the real situation in the 1990s, but their influence is still strong in the attitudes shown by different members of the team to each other. Similarly, in the community, general practitioners may consider that they should control the team, for the patients are registered with them and they are responsible. Nursing managers and social-work team leaders on the other hand do not see why they and their staff should be at the beck and call of other professionals. Such attitudes leave the situation ripe for inter-professional conflict. It is to the credit of all the professions concerned that most of the time we do work together amicably for the sake of the individual patients.

Our colleagues

If we think of the number of other professionals we meet in our daily work as doctors, we soon realize that we are part of a very large team of carers. Whether in hospital or community, we will be working with nurses, physiotherapists, occupational therapists, psychologists, dietitians, speech therapists, orthoptists, audiologists, social workers, welfare rights workers, managers, secretaries, records clerks, clergy and so on. Many of these groups will be subdivided: for instance in nursing we will have various specialist nurses such as midwives and psychiatric nurses, stoma care nurses and diabetic nurses. In the community you will find health visitors, in the hospitals theatre nurses, and there are many others. You will find generic social workers and social workers with special interests, and chaplains of various denominations as well as clergy of different faiths. This great and increasing complexity of the team in itself explains some of the difficulties we can encounter in working together. In small team units it is possible for all the members to know each other well – their strengths and weaknesses, their foibles and fancies. This in itself promotes good communications and encourages the working of the team. In the larger units with increased specialization then it can be much harder for such a working relationship to develop.

Why relationships go wrong

The size of teams may be one factor, but it is probably not the most important reason for difficulties in relationships between professionals today. The attitudes that different groups have is equally important. June Huntington[1] researched the relationships between social workers and general practitioners in Australia over a decade ago, and found that many difficulties could be traced to the differences in occupational status. Medicine is an old occupation, dominated (still) by males who are usually somewhat older and of middle-class origins with a higher income. Social workers, on the other hand, are from a much younger profession, and tend to be younger in age, female and often from different class origins, with lower income. The same differences would be seen with many of the paramedical professions, though clearly not with the clergy. This is a fertile bed for the development of pride. A sad corollary of such pride in our own professional status is a lack of respect for the achievement, status and work of others. Listen to many groups of doctors when they come to discuss social-work input, and you will hear comments about their inefficiency or inaccessibility, coupled with little realization of the complex and difficult tasks that they often have to perform with minimal resources.

Another major factor that leads to lack of respect and poor communication is ignorance of the work of other professions. It is unfortunate that so little of our education is carried out in multi-disciplinary forums, even at a postgraduate level. One result of this is that we lack awareness of the skills and training that our colleagues possess, and so make inappropriate use of these skills. We may request them to do things that do not use their skills to the best advantage, and fail to ask for their help when patients would benefit. One outcome is the common complaint that people are being used as 'handmaidens' or 'dumping grounds'.

Building relationships

In these circumstances Christian doctors will be helped if they go back to the basic principles of Christian relationships. Pride cannot grow and destroy our respect for our colleagues if we remember Peter's call to 'clothe yourselves with humility towards one another, because, "God opposes the proud but gives grace to the humble"' (1 Pet. 5:5). Between Christians, there should be relationships where there is 'neither Jew nor Greek, slave nor free, male nor female, for you are all one in Christ Jesus' (Gal. 3:28). We will want to carry that attitude out into all our contacts, not only in Christ's church but in the world at large, where there should in a sense be neither doctor nor nurse, social worker nor chaplain, but all carers for the sick and distressed.

Putting it into practice

To put these attitudes into practice requires four approaches.

The first is the need to accept one another, to accept the different backgrounds, skills, methods and even professional languages used. The health professions talk of patients; social workers speak of clients and the clergy may still speak of souls. In broad terms there may be differing emphases on caring, treating, restoring function, facilitating social functioning, or coping with emotional and spiritual needs. We need to ask which professional group is best placed both to determine and to manage the real needs of the person who is seeking help.

The second approach which follows from this is to learn from one another. As Christians we will be used to learning from the ordained ministry, but we may still marginalize them when it comes to 'treating the sick'. The Royal College of General Practitioners and the Churches' Council for Health and Healing have produced a joint report on *Whole Person Medicine* that encourages closer cooperation. But the reality is that few successful doctor-clergy groups have been set up, and in only a few group practices do clergy feel part of the team. Equally, in hospitals we often fail to include the chaplains in the caring-team meetings. This is a situation where Christian doctors could facilitate inter-professional communication to the benefit of patients. We also need to learn from nurses, therapists and social workers. It is likely to be the nurses and therapists who can give students and young doctors the best advice on moving patients, dressings and many other aspects of care. It is likely to be social workers who can open up to us the many problems that may exist when a patient is about to be discharged from hospital, or who can show us the various resources available within the community.

The third way of developing our collaborative relationship is by caring *with* one another. This may best be achieved by allowing the patient, wherever possible, to be the key member of the team, listening to his views on who can best help him at a particular moment. One of the dangers to which we are subject is the conspiracy of professionals 'against' the patient, often made worse by the knowledge that professionals share and that the patient does not. If we listen to patients, and negotiate with them, then they will often tell us which key-worker they find most helpful, and we will be less liable to fall into approaches based on professional hierarchies.

Finally, we will improve our professional relationships by caring for one another. At various times, different members of staff will be busier than others. How can we relieve the burden on our colleagues? There are many simple tasks which any member of the caring team may be able to do. Are we quick to act in such situations, maybe saving time and trouble for others? We also need to watch out for distress among our colleagues.

All team members can be distressed by a very sick patient. The chaplain, for instance, may have been brought in to comfort the family of a dying child, but may be overcome by the sight of a neglected, marasmic child. Nurses can crack when someone they have cared for over several weeks finally dies. Awareness of the needs of our colleagues shows that we value their contribution and above all respect them as people.

CONFIDENTIALITY

Carl Whitehouse

The problem of confidentiality is at least as old as Hippocrates, for in the code attributed to him we read, 'Whatever I see or hear, professionally or privately, which ought not to be divulged, I will keep secret and tell to no-one.' This aspect of the relationship between doctor and patient has always been considered important. We need to ask why, and whether, the Christian view of humanity affects our thinking and actions.

The purpose of confidentiality

Patients seeking help pour out all kinds of sensitive and secret information to doctors. They do so because they believe that doctors need this information to do their job, and they expect that doctors will make use of what is relevant, but keep it to themselves. Things that people do not easily share, even with those to whom they are closest, are shared with doctors (and other health workers) so that the doctor can do some good, or avoid some harm. These things are not shared in order to satisfy some intellectual curiosity or, even worse, some voyeuristic desire of the doctor. Patients will not trust the doctor with this precious information unless they are sure that it is not going to be divulged to others, except as part of this contract of receiving care and help. Ian Kennedy has put it succinctly: 'Implicit in the doctor-patient relationship is the promise that information imparted to the doctor *qua* doctor will not be divulged, otherwise the patient will not confide and the doctor will be unable to do his or her job.'[1]

Information confided by the patient is, of course, only one part of the doctor's knowledge of him or her. There are also details which the doctor collects in the process of the job, the results of examinations or tests or the findings of an operation; and there are the analyses, and the diagnoses that the doctor reaches. Yet that information also, in a sense, belongs to the patient, and, because it might harm the patient if it is spread abroad, the doctor has no right to share it without the patient's agreement. Occasionally, the state of a patient (such as coma) may prevent such agreement, and then it might be shared if that will ultimately benefit the patient. But such exceptions as these need careful consideration. Any other exceptions require even more stringent precautions.

Confidentiality is about not sharing information, and if we intend to make exceptions we must ask ourselves why we think we need to share the information at all, which parts we need to share, and with whom.

Keeping a tight rein on our tongues

One danger that we all face is the tendency to gossip. Christians are frequently warned to watch their speech, as in James' statement that 'if anyone considers himself religious and yet does not keep a tight rein on his tongue, he deceives himself and his religion is worthless' (Jas. 1:26), and Paul's anxiety about gossiping and slander among the Corinthians (2 Cor. 12:20). There is a tendency for doctors to gossip about the 'interesting case', even if that is sometimes called a case-discussion; and there is a tremendous risk that such gossiping in a nursing office, doctors' mess or practice reception area can breach confidentiality and thereby damage patients. One aspect of conversation that is 'full of grace, seasoned with salt' (Col. 4:6) is to show respect for our patients as fellow beings created in God's image; that means we must not make use of them to show how clever or good we are. However, true concern for the patient means that sometimes we have to make exceptions to the rule that we do not talk about them.

With whom might we need to share?

Relatives

Whatever information we have about patients, we have to consider who else might require that information both in the present illness and in the future, and whether we are right to share it with them.

Others may be involved in the care of the patient. Foremost among these are relatives, and here lies the source of many problems. The anxious wife or son rings up to discover how a patient has fared in an operation and at the same time wants to know what was found; or a carer hovers when one does a home visit. It used to be much more common to tell a relative of the situation even when it was not felt wise to inform the patient, but increasingly it is accepted that patients should decide whether their family is included.

Problems arise when the patient, who may for instance be a child, mentally disturbed, or elderly and confused, does not fully understand what is happening. If decisions have to be made about care, it may be necessary to share details with an understanding and responsible adult. But exactly when can we allow this need to overrule confidentiality?

This problem underlay the case Victoria Gillick brought about the giving of contraceptive advice to children under sixteen. Recent circulars in the light of the Children Act (1989) have tried to clarify this by stating that children under sixteen may also be able to give or refuse consent depending on their capacity to understand the nature of the treatment; it is for the doctor to decide this. Doctors may vary in their views on whether a child is mature enough to take these decisions, and whether he needs protection, but if we accept that a child can understand the implications and make his own decision then we have no right to breach the confidentiality of that child without his consent.

Christian doctors will be particularly concerned to balance their love and desire to protect with their own actions. That respect means that whatever the patient's age, whether teenager or elderly, we should not divulge confidential information to family members unless it is absolutely necessary for the benefit of the patient, and that may be a hard decision to make.

Professionals

The second group of people who may need to share information comprises other professional carers. Traditionally, doctors have felt they should be able to talk with other doctors who are involved in the care of the patient. A referral system without the right to share information could be very difficult. But are patients always aware that this information is being passed on, and are they involved in the decision about details to share? One way to overcome this is to dictate letters about patients in their presence, and ask their agreement with what has been said.

Increasingly, other healthcare professionals are involved in a team approach to care. Again, patients may not realize that information is going to be shared with nurses or with social workers. In hospitals it is often implicitly accepted that patients agree to this, but in both primary care and hospital we may need to negotiate further with patients how much of the information they have confided is for sharing.

A third group of professionals who have access to confidential details is the administrative staff, especially secretaries and record clerks, who could hardly perform their tasks without access to the records. Again, patient agreement is much more implicitly accepted than negotiated.

Other people

Patients have confidence that doctors will not share information with employers or insurance companies without their express agreement, and that has now been codified in law. But there are some exceptions where doctors claim that there is an overriding duty which makes them breach confidentiality. One clear example is when they are subject to a court order, although there are many times when doctors would like to be able to claim absolute medical privilege. Individual judgment, however, is required in the case of discussions with the police in the investigation of serious crime, and in involvement with other agencies in cases of suspected abuse.

Other uses of confidential information

There are many times when doctors will use information from patients in audit or research. They may also have to use such information for management purposes, in planning budgets, organizing screening programmes or making claims to contracting authorities. Others will want to use information in teaching. In all these cases it should be possible to ensure that the information used is anonymous, but at times this can be difficult. Again, doctors should act on behalf of their patients' interests, protecting their privacy and the details they have provided.

Records

When we record information for future use, other problems arise. Most doctors consider that keeping records is important to remind oneself, or future doctors, of salient points in a medical history, investigation or treatment. This is a main purpose of the written record and the computer. The problem is that such hard data are more accessible to others than the information in our own heads. Information that a patient freely provides on one occasion, in order to get help for a troublesome symptom, may not be relevant again and may cause distress if it is rediscovered years later. This can apply to stigmatizing conditions or to antisocial or 'immoral' acts. Christians, with their strong belief in the possibility of forgiveness, would not want people to be pursued for a lifetime with the memories of a single mistake in their youth, unless there were very good reasons to believe it had long-term effects on their health status. This raises the question of negotiating what information is recorded, regularly checking its relevance and considering the question of pruning records (which has in the past been considered almost sacrilegious). Doctors need have no concerns with records which have been effectively negotiated with patients when we consider the Data Protection Act (1984) and Access to Health Records Act (1990), which allow patients to see their records. Some doctors may find the loss of the use of the record as an *aide memoire* containing fleeting thoughts and impressions difficult, but again we need to see the information as something that the patient has committed to us for his own good.

All records carry the risks of unauthorized access, and considerable thought needs to be given to ensuring this does not happen. Computers, if provided with a good password system, and scrambling of confidential information, may well prove in the long run to be less accessible and more amenable to protecting the patient's information, especially as doctors' handwriting improves in legibility!

Confidentiality is protecting the precious and private information that patients commit to their professional advisers. The two basic approaches are to keep the mouth shut, and to ensure that what is shared, or recorded so that sharing is a possibility, is agreed with the patient (or the responsible, understanding adult carer) wherever possible. There will still be many minefields to negotiate, but these two principles will overcome most problems.

4 THE CHRISTIAN DOCTOR IN A HEALTH SERVICE

THE MEANING OF CARE

Michael Webb-Peploe

The confusion between care and cure

In the minds of far too many doctors, medicine is seen as solely curative. This idea, projected by the media (which even now are more interested in dramatic curative 'breakthroughs' than in the daily grind and self-discipline of preventive medicine and a healthy lifestyle), has cast the doctor (in the eyes of the public) as the 'garage mechanic of society' to whom you take a broken-down physical or mental vehicle for repair, overhaul, and servicing.

The widespread availability of antibiotics and the rise in standards of living and hygiene, have dramatically changed the pattern of medical practice. Infectious diseases and malnutrition (both relatively easy to 'cure') have been replaced as causes of morbidity and mortality by diseases that are at least in part genetic in origin, and by degenerative disorders in an ageing population (many difficult or impossible to 'cure').[1] The incidence of cancer continues to rise. This is to some extent the natural result of increased life expectancy, but in some cases (e.g. bronchus and cervix) self-indulgent habits (smoking and early promiscuous sex) play an important aetiological role. There is also an increase in self-induced disease, whether from driving dangerously, from drug or alcohol abuse, or from extramarital or homosexual affairs. Correct diagnosis followed by curative therapy is no longer enough. Many of the current causes of morbidity and mortality can only be palliated, and optimal treatment will demand co-operation from a patient who is fully informed about his condition by his doctor, and prepared to make a radical alteration in his way of living.

The confusion between care and cure leads to the following consequences:

● doctors who, when they are unable to effect a cure, say that there is nothing more that they can do for the patient;

● patients who, when orthodox medicine fails to deliver the expected rapid cure, and faced with doctors who concentrate on cure to the exclusion of care, turn to alternative medicine (whether in the form of homoeopathy, acupuncture, 'faith healing' of all kinds, or the occult).

Care is not merely cure. It extends far beyond rectifying pathology, and embraces the equipping of patients with the necessary knowledge and motivation to protect and make the most of their mental, physical and spiritual faculties so as to live life to the full, and to avoid dangerous and damaging relapses.

'Has no-one condemned you?' No-one, sir,' she said.

'Then neither do I condemn you,' Jesus declared. 'Go now and leave your life of sin' (Jn. 8:10–11).

Cure is not care; it is sometimes part of care (but not in all cases). With the rise in genetically determined, degenerative, and self-induced disease, cure becomes more and more difficult and costly.

What is care?

To care is to feel concern for a person

With the ever-increasing technical content of the medical curriculum, there is a danger that we are training medical technicians rather than physicians. There is the danger of losing the patient because we concentrate on all the apparatus. 'The physician has the difficult, and often impossible, task of preserving humanity in an ever more sophisticated environment. Comfort and care have to be balanced with electrodes and oxygen masks?'[2] This applies just as much to the computerized group practice as it does to the intensive therapy unit. We risk looking just at the lesions, interested only in what is technically possible, while neglecting to look at the patient to see what is humanely permissible.

The machine age has arrived in medicine as it has in industry.

> The most important effect of machine production on the imaginative picture of the world is an immense increase in the sense of human power . . . There thus arises among those who direct affairs or are in touch with those who do so a new belief in power, first the power of man in his conflicts with nature, and then the power of rulers as against the human beings whose beliefs and aspirations they seek to control by scientific

propaganda, especially education. The result is a diminution of fixity: no change seems impossible. Nature is raw material, so is that part of the human race which does not effectively participate in government. There are certain old conceptions which represent men's belief in the limits of human power; of these the two chief are God and Truth ... Such conceptions tend to melt away even if not explicitly negated, they lose importance and are retained only superficially.[3]

These words are applicable to medicine, as they are to society in general. Seeing patients as 'population units' or 'trials subjects'; failure to consult or involve them in decisions regarding their treatment or management; the use of patients as syringe, catheter or scalpel fodder; audit that concentrates solely on financial cost to the exclusion of physical and emotional cost in the patient; the pernicious tendency to reward managers for money saved with no account taken of quality of care given; and the widespread fraud that has emerged in medical scientific research in recent years - these are some of the dangers to be guarded against in the machine age in medicine.

With the increasing technical content in modern medicine has come the need for specialization. With a high degree of specialization, much of the technical content of the job is repetitive, and, no matter what the skill involved, it can become boring with the passage of time. Unless the doctor is interested in the patient as a person (rather than as an example of X's syndrome), he or she will degenerate into a bored technician, doing a job for the money it brings in or for the status if confers, rather than practising a caring profession. I have met more than a few colleagues who have lost interest in medicine and who concentrate their thoughts and energies on other matters.

If medical students are selected purely on their academic qualifications, and if their medical training concentrates solely on the technical to the exclusion of the human content of medicine (and this danger is, I feel, a real one), then we shall see a new generation of doctors who are interested only in terms and conditions of service, in on-call rotas, and in techniques rather than in people, and whose career choices will be dictated not by what they can give, but what they can gain.

To care is to provide for the needs of someone

The needs have first to be identified. This will require a cooperative effort by both patient and doctor, with ruthless honesty and self-analysis by the doctor if Ivan Illich's accusation (that the medical profession, far from being disinterested, altruistic, and enriching is rather 'dominant and disabling') is to be refuted.[4]

Honesty is the only foundation on which a valid doctor-patient relationship can be erected: honesty about what can and cannot be done; honesty about what options are available and their likely outcome; honesty about the doctor's own professional competence and that of his colleagues; honesty about the contribution that the patient and his family will be expected to make to his own care (contributions in terms of time, effort, suffering, and sometimes finance).

Having identified the needs, they then have to be met. Here doctors are the patient's servants, willing to spend time, thought, imaginative effort and emotional energy as well as professional skill to improve our patient's condition (physical, mental and spiritual). We will continue to do our best for the patient even if the patient refuses our advice, or the prognosis is hopeless, or medically he or she is facing defeat. The truly Christian doctor has the benefit of the indwelling Spirit of the greatest servant of all time and eternity. 'Whoever wants to become great among you must be your servant, and whoever wants to be first must be slave of all. For even the Son of man did not come to be served, but to serve, and to give his life as ransom for many' (Mk. 10:43–45). Meeting our patients' needs in these ways is costly in terms of time and effort, and may well prove to be increasingly costly in personal financial terms also if the new White Paper on the National Health Service is implemented.[5] It is impossible to measure the 'suffering servant' component in healthcare in 'cost-effective' or 'outcome' units. We cannot expect management accountants ('bean-counters') and our non-Christian colleagues to be sympathetic to the view that this sort of service should be the norm. To them the cross of Christ is 'foolishness', Hamilton King's exhortation is utter nonsense:

> Measure thy life by loss instead of gain;
> Not by the wine drunk, but the wine poured forth;
> For love's strength standeth in love's sacrifice;
> And whoso suffers most hath most to give.[6]

To care is to hold a person in high regard, esteem and affection

It is in this aspect of care that the Christian has a unique insight and motivation. Thomas Sydenham expressed it thus: 'Let him [the physician] remember that it is not any base or despicable creature of which he has undertaken the care. For the only begotten Son of God, by becoming man, recognized the value of the human race, and ennobled by his own dignity the nature he assumed.'[7] In the incarnation, God, by stooping to become human, affirmed once for all the value that he places on humanity, created in his image. On the cross, nailed there in our place, God finally expresses the lengths to which he is prepared to go, the unimaginable price he is prepared to pay to restore fallen humanity to the full glory for which he created it. Every patient, no matter how deformed the body, deranged the mind, or diminished the personality, carries this double hallmark of divine value. 'Are not two sparrows sold for a penny? Yet not one of them will fall to the ground apart from the will of your Father. And even the very hairs of your head are all numbered. So don't be afraid; you are worth more than many sparrows' (Mt. 10:29–31). This meaning of care is not an emotion, nor is it sentiment. It is the deliberate attitude of a mind and will submitted to a God who so loved that he gave his only Son to save a perishing world. Love for the unlovely, love for those who cannot or will not love in return, thus becomes possible.

G. R. Dunstan, in a chapter on abortion in his book *The Artifice of Ethics*,[8] contrasts two sets of values. On the one hand, there are the values of care and compassion for the handicapped - values painfully acquired and handed on from generation to generation, which owe a great deal to a Christian heritage that many are trying to deny and erode, and which bring great personal and communal rewards (the reward of gaining the trust and affection of a Down's syndrome child, for example, and of helping that child achieve his full though diminished potential; and the inner, civilizing rewards of giving rather than getting, and of service rather than selfishness). On the other hand, there are the values of waste disposal, of seeking by genetic engineering to create 'the perfect specimen' (an ideal that is impossible of realization), and of throwing away the many failures.

One final thought: the cross was not the end. At his resurrection and ascension Jesus incorporated humanity into the Godhead, and, seated at the right hand of God, he ever lives to make intercession for us. We have all encountered patients who are 'name-droppers'. Next week they are lunching with Maggie. Jim has just rung up to find out how they are getting on. They are informing us that 'they have friends in high places, so we had better treat them right or they will tell on us'. In Christ, each and every one of our patients has a friend in high places – one, moreover, who 'knew all men. He did not need man's testimony about man, for he knew what was in a man' (Jn. 2:24–25). 'The King will reply, "I tell you the truth: whatever you did once for one of the least of these brothers of mine you did for me"' (Mt. 25:40).

I can do no better than to end with Edward Livingstone Trudeau's great motto: 'To cure sometimes, to relieve often, to comfort always.'[9] This is care indeed.

RESOURCES, DECISION-MAKING AND AUDIT IN HOSPITAL PRACTICE

Anthony Jefferis

In the popular debate about healthcare, mention is often made of the ethical dilemmas that certain courses of action precipitate. These dilemmas are evident in all areas of medicine, not least in hospital medicine. Clearly each speciality has its own ethical problems, but there are some which are common to the whole of hospital medicine.

Many of the simple, everyday choices we make have an ethical dimension. Just as buying food to eat – a simple, necessary and everyday task – has ethical implications (where the food was grown, how the food was grown and who grew the food), so too do some of the simple, necessary and everyday tasks in hospital practice. In the busy and committed life of a hospital doctor it will not always be possible to evaluate the ethical implications of every choice, but doctors should be aware that there are moral implications and value judgments in almost all their decisions.

The doctor's ability to make decisions is being questioned by politicians, lawyers, consumer groups, other medical workers and patients. His or her decisions are increasingly influenced by outside interests. No longer are the choices the doctor makes confined to what he or she thinks is in the patient's best interest. It is not sufficient to consider only the patient's needs and the doctor's knowledge and skills. These outside influences are not altogether new, but they should be recognized by doctors, as should the effect they have on the choices doctors make on behalf of their patients.

Factors which influence our decision-making could be considered under three headings: resource allocation, authority in medical decision-making, and medical audit. All three have a bearing on medical decision-making, forcing the one-to-one doctor-patient relationship into a wider arena. They each throw up ethical dilemmas which affect all in the hospital service.

Resource allocation

All those working in the hospital service have been made to recognize that there is not an ever-expanding pot of gold to pay for every innovation in healthcare. Choices have to be made, not infrequently between two or three 'good' courses of action. These choices are made at every level and all the time in hospitals; managers, consultants and junior doctors make them.

The conflicts generated by resource allocation are clearly demonstrated in the use of hospital beds. Junior doctors are affected daily by the system of bed allocation in hospitals. Each consultant firm is allocated a number of beds to which to admit patients. Each 'bed' is staffed and supported by nursing and ancillary staff. Though the bed is notionally under a particular consultant, he may not have exclusive right to admit any patient he wants to it. He may be prevented from doing so by an emergency admission belonging to another consultant. The day-to-day arrangements and decisions about admitting to any bed are usually taken by the junior medical staff.

This can lead to the following ethical dilemma. The booked admission is an elderly lady for a hip replacement. She has been waiting four years, has had her bed cancelled once before and has organized her daughter to take care of her senile husband while she is in hospital. The emergency admission is an eighteen-year-old boy, from a good home, who following an argument with his girlfriend took an overdose. Clearly, in the best of all worlds there would be no conflict – booked admissions and emergencies would be allocated different beds. But it is an oft-repeated tale in our hospitals that a patient booked for admission has it cancelled because the bed has been used by another patient.

What should the junior doctors do? The implications of cancelling the elderly lady's hip operation involve the patient herself, her family and the medical and nursing staff on the ward and in the operating theatre. Not admitting the young man who took an overdose might cause him to take more, or to become very ill as a result of taking the tablets. No resolution of the problem will satisfy all parties.

Nor is the daily conflict in the use of resources confined to the junior doctor. The consultant is constantly having to make decisions which have implications for others. One of the most challenging is the use of time, from simple punctuality to the organization of outpatients, ward rounds and operating time. It was made clear to me when I was a not particulårly punctual junior doctor that the implication of my keeping six people waiting five minutes was that I had wasted thirty 'man' minutes. Using up other people's time is also evident in out-patients, where patients are frequently expected to spend half the working day in order to see the doctor for a few minutes. Patients not infrequently have to wait many months to have a specialist opinion or elective operation. Clearly, none of this is desirable, but one of the reasons these log-jams occur is that resources are limited. There are only a certain number of doctors in any one speciality and they have only certain times when they are allowed to see patients in out-patients and to operate.

How can we resolve these problems without spending more money and expanding the resources available? Certain remedies such as personal punctuality and organizing out-patient waiting times so that they suit the patient, are comparatively easy to institute. Again, there will be relative disappointment. Either patients have to wait a long time before being seen so that they can have a relaxed and unhurried consultation with the specialist, or they will be seen quickly and given a rushed consultation. The argument in favour of the former is that it gives the patient dignity when seen, and those who have become better since the referral can miss their appointment, whereas the case for the latter is that this approach enables the specialist to see all the patients soon. Unrecognized serious complaints can be identified early.

This debate on the use of limited resources stretches into many other areas in hospital medicine: what equipment to buy, which speciality to favour and whether to concentrate resources in one hi-tech hospital rather than in several community hospitals. How should they be resolved? Is there a blueprint for running a successful service where everyone is satisfied? Do we have to accept that there will always be a conflict between the interested parties – patient, healthcare worker and paymaster?

Authority in medical decision-making

Medical decision-making, classically, relies on the doctor's making the diagnosis and then prescribing the appropriate treatment for the disease. If several options exist, the choice of treatment is made by the doctor, who is exercising his or her clinical freedom. The doctor's right to make this decision has been challenged in recent years by several groups, all claiming to represent patients' interests.

The Government and its representatives in the health authorities continually influence the authority of the doctor. Their assessment of the priorities directly affects the freedom of doctors to treat their patients. This might be in resource allocation, where establishing priorities in one area might diminish resources in another. For example, if community care is deemed worthy of better funding, there will obviously be a reduction in funding for another aspect of healthcare, such as acute hospital medicine. This has the consequence of limiting the freedom of action of affected clinicians, as the price for increasing resources elsewhere.

Limits to the authority of doctors have also been set in defining what they may prescribe. Hospital formularies contain lists of prescribable drugs, and many hospitals restrict the length of time for which any drug may be prescribed. This is not an argument against limited lists, which are on the whole a sensible innovation, but an attempt to illustrate how the doctor's authority and clinical freedom are restricted.

Challenges to the right of doctors to decide are also coming from nurses and paramedical staff. Nurses frequently see their role as protecting the patients from the doctor. They certainly feel they should have a major role in defining the care of the long-term sick and dying. Physiotherapists and speech therapists are trained to make diagnostic assessments of patients and to treat them appropriately. Their diagnosis may differ from the doctor's, and their professional training inclines them to back their own judgment. Pharmacists too may question a doctor's prescription, or laboratory workers the appropriateness and urgency of a particular test. There are times when the doctor has made a mistake, and challenging his authority is the correct course to take; but increasingly the challenge is in the area of matters of opinion, whose opinion should prevail, and why.

The hospital doctor's ability to make authoritative decisions is also challenged by other medical staff. The patient's general practitioner has technically referred his patient to the hospital for advice and appropriate treatment, and the patient is still his patient. Therefore, contrary to common practice, those in hospital medicine should not say 'my patient'. Treatment should proceed only with the consent of the general practitioner. In practice hospital staff and GP colleagues develop working relationships where each understands the other's position. Other members of a firm may want to influence the management decisions of their fellows. Though, technically, final authority rests with the consultant, many of the important day-to-day decisions are made by the junior staff. A conflict can arise when a different approach is favoured by different members of the team; for example, what to tell a patient with a life-threatening disorder. Does it help the patient to have two conflicting views?

Medical decisions are also made in the light of a possible legal challenge. Tests are done on the patient because the patient might be dissatisfied with the treatment and decide to sue the doctor. This defensive medicine is widely practised in the United States, and is increasingly common here. The management of a particular patient is not governed by what the doctor decides would be best in this case, but by what he fears might happen if things go wrong. It is the lawyer, in his potential cross-examination of the doctor, who has decided what will happen to the patient.

Finally, patients increasingly want to question the doctor's decision. They are no longer satisfied with 'Doctor knows best'. They usually want to influence a decision on their management. They may want to seek a second opinion. Increasingly, the specialist is called upon to inform and advise, leaving the final decision-making in the hands of the patient and his relatives.

Medical audit

The National Health Service Act (1990) says that all doctors must be involved in medical audit. The medical Royal Colleges stress the importance of holding regular critical appraisals of the work being undertaken in any department. This is called medical audit. The appraisal is normally made by other medical staff, but increasingly management are making judgments on medical departments by analysing or auditing their performance.

Audit conducted by management tends to rely on physical measures of performance; until recently bed occupancy, discharges and deaths were the only universally held measures of performance. These are crude measures of clinical activity, but they formed the only statistical basis for increasing or decreasing a department's resources. They are open to manipulation, and doctors could alter their clinical practice to give a more favourable impression of their activity merely by adjusting the time at which they discharge their patients.

In our cost-conscious and resource-limited age, new measures for assessing performance have been introduced; for example, in establishing normal durations for admission or improving the throughput of staffed beds. These are measurable indices, and it is quite easy to compare hospitals' performance on managing patients with the same condition. However, deciding that one hospital is more efficient than another, purely because the throughput is better, may miss an important point. The hospital with the less efficient throughput might be more humane or technically safer. (Safety in medicine is difficult to quantify; one tragedy is too many, whether it is one in a hundred or one in a million.)

When audit is conducted by the doctor's peers, physical

measures are again easier to quantify. Thus for curable disease, the route taken to cure can be examined, as well as the cure rate and rate of relapse. For incurable or only occasionally curable disease the audit is much more difficult. Should occasional cure justify extensive and mutilating treatment for the majority who will die from their disease? Should improved survival or improved quality of survival be the goal? If it is the latter, how are we to judge the quality of survival? Is it to be measured by the patient or by the doctor? The difficulties are illustrated in a recent study of head and neck cancer patients and their doctors, where it was demonstrated that patients and doctors had different ideas of which symptoms were the most troublesome. Who then should assess the patient's quality of life? As the measurement is difficult, should it be ignored?

So far, the discussion has revolved around questions and not solutions. There is a need for guidelines. As Christians we look for authoritative guidance in the Bible, in the teaching of the church and the prompting of the Holy Spirit, with the latter two being tested against the former.

What does the Bible say about our ethical behaviour and how should we interpret this in the helter-skelter world of hospital medicine? The biblical guidance can be divided into the explicit and the implicit. The former is unchanging and includes the direct commands of Jesus and the Ten Commandments. So we should love God, and our neighbour as ourselves (Mt. 22:34–39), we should love one another as Jesus loved us (Jn. 13:34–35), have no other gods before God, not worship idols, not misuse the name of God, keep the Sabbath holy, honour our father and mother, not murder, not commit adultery, not steal, not give false testimony and not covet (Ex. 20:3–17). Though the biblical commands are addressed to us, by implication we must attempt to create the climate where others also are able to follow these specific commands.

Implicit guidance comes from passages where the historical context is different from our own, but there appear to be parallels in our day. For example, in relation to the state control of medicine, Jesus encourages submission to the civil power as part of our acknowledgment of God (Mt. 22:15–22), as does Paul in encouraging his readers to submit themselves to 'the governing authorities' (Rom. 13:1). Thus the hospital doctor should accept the directives issued by the Government, especially when disagreement with them is a matter of opinion and the directive does not contravene explicit biblical commands.

Guidance about establishing priorities among the various

problems which face the hospital doctor comes from Jesus' own example. Again and again in his healing ministry he responded to individual pleas for help; likewise the Christian doctor should respond to the particular patient who is calling him for help. An illustration of Jesus' ability to rank priorities because of his (implicit) assurance that God is continuously in control comes in the account of the healing of Jairus' daughter and the woman with the haemorrhage. Jesus is talking to the crowd and is asked to attend one emergency, Jairus' dying daughter. On the way, a more immediate problem confronts him, the woman with the haemorrhage. He is able to satisfy all the needs because he is God incarnate (Mk. 5:21–43). This story tells us that many of the problems we face, including the use of time and the utilization of resources, were known to Jesus.

Guidance about service might also be derived from the advice that Paul gives to masters and slaves (Eph. 6:5–9). Doctors are sometimes 'slaves' to their employing authority and to their patients, and sometimes 'masters' to other colleagues and again (in a different sense) to their patients. They should 'serve wholeheartedly, as if [they] were serving the Lord, not men', remembering that 'he is both their Master and yours is in heaven, and there is no favouritism with him'.

Disagreement about the proper course to follow in a particular situation is common in ethical debate. As Christians we should be agreed about the clear cut commands, but recognize that we might differ in areas of interpretation.

5 WOMEN IN MEDICINE: A CHRISTIAN PERSPECTIVE

Susan Clarke

Over 50% of students entering medical school are now women and half of all qualifying doctors are women. Despite this fact, they still encounter many problems and issues in their medical careers not experienced by their male colleagues. This chapter will endeavour to explore these issues and problems from a Christian perspective and will hope to challenge the current attitudes of Christian doctors today, both male and female.

The value of women in medicine

When considering the areas of difficulty which arise for women doctors, it is perhaps appropriate first to consider what special qualities women bring to medicine. As Christians we recognize and rejoice in the differences that exist between men and women and see them as being complementary. Qualities of gentleness and compassion, while not solely feminine characteristics are maybe more frequently evident in women.

Perhaps less often recognized is the holistic attitude to life women hold through their dual roles of homemaker and paid or unpaid worker. This is exemplified in the working mother who juggles the responsibilities of being a wife, a loving raiser of children, and an individual in her own right. This spread of responsibility will affect the way in which women doctors interact with both their patients and their colleagues. The ability to see a patient as not just a disease but an individual with family responsibilities and work pressures must improve the quality of the patient-doctor interaction and facilitate the healing process.

The same recognition of the whole person in medical colleagues will bring a sensitivity in dealings with other members of staff. Sadly, although communication skills and social studies are now becoming an integral part of the undergraduate course, for many years doctors tended to view their patients in a paternalistic and autocratic way, paying inadequate attention to the social pressures and anxieties that contribute to the expression of disease in an individual. The model of Christ in the gospels is of one who saw behind the presenting complaint to the underlying problem. As Christians we must endeavour to do the same in our handling of patients and of colleagues.

While these qualities are obviously not the sole prerogative of women, their special background training as carers in society equips them more effectively in this area. The mother who juggles homemaking with child-rearing copes with pressures and tensions, not by ignoring one to concentrate on the other, but by holding both in balance. Women receive a training which sadly many men have failed to experience by handing over all home responsibilities to their wives and concentrating on work and career.

An immediate question that arises is: 'But surely as Christians we must be seen to be giving our best to our careers?' The answer must be, 'Yes, but not at the expense of our other responsibilities.' Our responsibilities as members of a family, whether it be our own families of wives, husbands, children and parents, or our church family given to us by God, must be considered as of equal importance when allocating our time and our energies.

In a recent survey of Christian women doctors,[1] it was striking that many women appeared to have compromised their career aspirations because of their commitment to their husbands, children or church. Obviously, comparable data on male Christian doctors are not currently available, but it is likely that most men would not be prepared to compromise their careers in the current medical climate. Exceptions to this generalization exist, but are generally regarded as unusual and frequently bizarre. A call by God to be a full-time homemaker is just as valid as a call to be a full-time physician. As Christians we are called to live life in all its fullness, and to witness to the new dimension of living into which Christ has called us. This surely includes the recognition that all aspects of our life are important and God-given. A holistic approach to life is not a recent New Age discovery, but is our Christian calling. It is a sad reflection on our Christian witness that we were not, as Christian doctors, the first to promote this approach.

Medicine – a career for women?

Having explored the good qualities that women can bring to medicine, it is necessary to question whether Christian women should in fact be considering medicine as a career, given the conflict and problems that many women experience in medicine. It is essential that all women considering medicine as a career should examine their motives, and recognize the implications for their future lives.

The motives of 'helping people' or 'improving society' are not adequate. As Christians we are called to a prayerful consideration of God's plan for our lives. This will involve prayer, waiting on God and talking with other Christians. Part of seeking God's guidance is an honest appraisal of ourselves as individuals. As Christian women, will we be able to accept the call to singleness if God asks it of us? Will we be able to resist the call of the world to follow our careers at all costs, to the detriment of our own families and our walk with God? Will we be able to make the painful decision to set aside our career, either temporarily while children are young, or permanently if God shows us that this is his will? The optimistic idealism of youth sometimes prevents us from truly facing up to these questions and answering them honestly, but it is essential that as women we recognize that God may ask us to do what the world sees as foolish to bring him glory.

The need honestly and earnestly to seek God's will for our lives applies not just to women but to men also. Many Christian women medical students, however, confess that they had not considered singleness as an option to which God may be calling them, or the fact that their career should be followed with constant prayer and waiting on God at each point of decision-making. An obedient walk with God will minimize the pressures of conflict and tensions of time management that beset those who have attempted to struggle with an unsuitable career and a family.

The training years

At a time when equal numbers of women and men are admitted to medical school, it would be good to write that discrimination against women, both undergraduate and postgraduate, no longer exists. Sadly, this is not the case. The statistics confirm that while women students often do better than their male counterparts in their early years, the numbers of women achieving consultant posts and principal general practitioner posts are still less than could be expected, given the academic quality of many of the women entering medical school. The Royal College of Surgeons has addressed this issue.[2]

As Christians, we must ask the question: do the God-given differences in role and character between men and women necessarily mean that women will under-achieve in their medical careers? It is important to understand what the Bible says about the

84

role of women. We are reminded that women were created to be helpers to men in their marriage relationship (Gn. 2:18). The created biological difference confirms the role of women in childbearing. But the Bible also clearly states the equality of men and women in God's eyes (Gal. 3:28). How should we then interpret these apparent contradictions of Scripture? Surely we must believe that intellectually and spiritually men and women stand equal, that is, they are capable of equal achievements academically and are of equal importance to God spiritually. There is therefore no scriptural reason why women should not endeavour to do their best in their careers, provided they are certain this is what God is asking them to do.

As relatively few women are married in their undergraduate years, it can be assumed that performance and achievement levels should be equal between the sexes at that stage. The problem arises after qualification, when many women's careers change course. A recent survey of Christian women doctors confirms that a significant number of women are in part-time, non-career posts such as associate specialists and clinical assistants, and the number of women in these posts far outweighs the number of men. The important fact to determine is whether women have chosen these posts because they feel called by God to pursue a less academic or competitive career and it seems a satisfying option for them, or whether medical attitudes have encouraged women subconsciously to assume that a part-time career role is more appropriate for a woman. Unfortunately the data do not exist to compare the numbers of Christian women with the numbers of non-Christian women in part-time medical employment, in an attempt to determine whether a call to part-time practice is from God or is due to subtle influences during postgraduate training.

The answer must surely lie with the individual and the need to be walking in obedience to God's call for her life, whether this be to a full-time career, a part-time career or a withdrawal from medical practice completely. While the advice of colleagues and senior doctors is extremely valuable during the decision-making process, it is of prime importance that all Christians seek to know the will of God for their lives and are obedient to his will as it is revealed.

It can be expected that over the next few years the 'old guard' of senior consultants, who genuinely believe that no woman could hold a position of seniority, will retire from the medical scene, and leave in their place consultants who should be open to consider the merits of all job applicants regardless of gender. The question remains, however: should women opt for less pressurized careers that have part-time opportunities and will produce less conflict in subsequent years for those who marry and have children? Should women also go for careers where their feminine qualities are more appropriate, such as general practice, paediatrics, or psychiatry? The answer as in all decisions about one's career, must again be, that prayer and an openness to hear God are vital.

Career, husband and children?

Leading directly out of the previous discussion must be the question: is it right for Christian women who have children to continue in their medical career? For those women who are called to marriage and motherhood, the biological fact of pregnancy cannot be ignored. A Christian couple who feel called to have children must seek God's guidance about the timing for starting a family. The advantages of delaying pregnancy until postgraduate examination has been achieved should be offset against the increased risks for the elderly primip and the undoubted exhaustion that accompanies childbearing, which becomes more profound with age.

In all these decisions the Christian woman acts under the loving headship of her husband (Eph. 5:21–25). Time spent prayerfully considering issues of career and family at the beginning of a Christian couple's married life must be encouraged, so that priorities within the marriage are settled and an understanding of both partners' roles within the marriage relationship is reached. It is always difficult if, some time after marriage, it becomes apparent that there are major differences of expectation in a major area such as child-raising.

The privilege of singleness

When discussing the issues of career and family with Christian women medical students, it is an interesting observation that most students assume that they will marry. Career decisions are often based on this assumption, and it may be supposed that non-Christian women make similar assumptions. It is therefore important to realize that the proportion of Christian women doctors who are single is much higher than the proportion of single women in the population as a whole.

A significant number of Christian women doctors will remain single throughout their lives. It is important, then, to ask: is this a fault of medical training, or does God have a specific purpose for single women in medicine, the church and society? These questions must be handled sensitively, as many single women come to terms with singleness with great difficulty. Sadly, many see their role in society and church as second rate compared with their colleagues who are married Christian women doctors, although academically their achievement may well be superior. It is important to consider the issues of singleness from two perspectives. The first is the world's perspective. All junior doctors are limited by the pressures of their jobs in the amount of time they have available to meet possible partners. The long hours worked by junior doctors and the accompanying tiredness result in many being unable to fulfil a normal social existence, with even regular attendance at church being difficult. The opportunities to meet a possible partner are extremely limited, and this may explain why a significant number of Christian women doctors are married to Christian male doctors. A second possible reason in the world's eyes is that many men, particularly if they are non-medical, may feel put off or threatened by a competent, often very academic woman who is clearly committed to her career.

As Christians, we must challenge the concept that God is not omnipotent and cannot achieve his perfect will whatever the circumstances. However, God has chosen to work within the constraints of our present world, and the 'worldly factors' in the outworking of his will must be seen as significant. We believe that God has a perfect plan for the life of each of us, and it is our duty and responsibility to wait on him with openness to receive his guidance daily. We must accept, therefore, that those Christian women who remain single do so in accordance with God's will.

What then is the role of the single Christian woman doctor? In the past, many have dedicated themselves to the mission field, and their testimony to God's goodness and strength is a great encouragement to all who hear it. A recent survey of Christian women doctors, however, demonstrated that equal numbers of married and single women are now involved in overseas mission, perhaps confirming the change in mission that has taken place over the last twenty years.

What are the advantages of singleness? The single Christian woman doctor has a unique opportunity to be wholly dedicated to her career or, if God guides, to play a significant role in her local church. The time outside of her work is her own; many single women can testify to the joy of being able to have an open home where those in need can be assured of comfort and counsel.

Surprisingly, in the same recent survey of Christian women

doctors, many single women commented that the local church was not always understanding of them, failing to appreciate that for many, the church family is in a very real way their main family. Single women, like all women, need to feel included and a valued part of the fellowship. Unfortunately, many churches, with their strong emphasis on the family, can leave single women feeling inferior and unwanted.

Single women, free from the commitments particularly of a young family, can provide a tremendous resource for the local church community. Through their training and background, they are usually skilled in group leadership qualities, and also have management skills. They may be able to serve the local church in a number of different ways, such as leading discussion groups, counselling, and chairing committees. It is important, however, that single women are seen, not just as a valuable resource, but also as individuals who need fellowship and support, which can appropriately be received from the Christian family.

Within the workplace, single Christian women doctors also have a vital role to play, acting as a role model for medical students and contributing to hospital committees and working groups. A Christian perspective is often lacking in hospital committees, and it is vital that all Christian doctors prayerfully consider whether they should become involved in the management and organizational structures of the hospital unit. Again, the need for balance is vital. It is no more appropriate for a single Christian woman doctor to devote herself full-time to her hospital career and associated activities than it is for a married Christian woman doctor with a family. Both need to maintain a balance, keeping time for church and home commitments.

Christian women in medicine: the reality

Many women doctors currently feel they are second-class medical citizens. Women statistically are highly unlikely to achieve high academic status, less than 5% of medical chairs being held by women. Only 15% of hospital consultant staff are women, and only 1% of general surgical consultants are women. Women will tend to publish much less than their male counterparts. Many women will work fewer than five sessions a week for a significant part of their medical lives. What should be the Christian response to these facts? Women are called to a particular and special role by the nature of the biological difference that exists between men and women. As Christians we value this difference, and therefore value the contribution made by Christian women doctors who feel called to leave medicine completely to raise their family or who work part-time for a number of years. As Christians, we hold the family in high esteem and encourage all doctors, whether male or female, to take their full responsibility in raising their families, remembering that more Bible passages relate to the father's involvement with his children than to the mother's.

There are many women, however, who feel forced into a role by their medical colleagues or by society, rather than by God. For these women who believe that God is calling them to a full-time career in medicine, every effort should be made to support them and to ensure that no prejudice or bias prevents their reaching their God-ordained goals.

There can be no generalizations; each woman is an individual, and each must discover her individual calling. As part of the Christian body, we each have a responsibility in encouraging one another to fulfil our potential in Christ, not by being conformed to this world's way of thinking, but by being transformed by the renewing of our minds (Rom. 12:1–2).

6 MEDICAL MISSIONS IN A CHANGING WORLD

Peter Green

A young medical student who had just returned from his elective period overseas asked me 'What is the purpose of medical missions and what is the place of the doctor?' He had thoroughly enjoyed his time abroad, he admitted that; but he had many questions. He had been led to expect certain features and had found others. He had expected great enthusiasm for primary health care, and instead found apathy. He had learnt a lot, but he had frustrations and questions he wanted to share. Talking to him enabled me to think out some of the issues facing medical missions today. First, I shall deal with some of the aspects that have changed, and then others that have not.

Changes: medical practice

When I first went overseas, Dr Emrys Thomas of Damascus said how hard I must have found it to adapt to the differences in medical practice between the Edinburgh Royal Infirmary and the Nazareth Hospital. When he first went to Damascus in the mid-1930s, his predecessor was practising much the same kind of medicine as he had found at home. But over the years the gap widened and the stress of adapting to new conditions became harder. When, later, I went to St Luke's Hospital, Hebron, I was delighted to discover Dr Paterson's records from the time when the hospital opened around 1895. The history records, the operating record book and register were all there, and it was fascinating to see how different life was in those days. Many of these changes are common to all medical practice, but others have specifically affected practice overseas in recent years.

From generalist to specialist

I belonged to what was probably the last generation of missionary doctors who were expected to work alone and run a hospital and all its outlying clinics single-handed. We had to cope with every condition, from cardiac failure to depressed fractures of the skull; from kwashiorkor to fetal distress and contracted pelvis with obstructed labour. Fortunately, in most church hospitals this era has passed. Some specialist training is needed, and some division of tasks has been achieved and the burden shared.

From curative to preventive medicine

The emphasis has passed from hi-tech hospital medicine to community healthcare. My own experience of dealing with whooping cough in Maralal showed that it was better to send a team into the community to vaccinate all the children against the disease than to spend much money and time treating those who were ill with pneumonia. The death rate fell dramatically in the next two years. Unfortunately, we were not quite so successful with measles, but it demonstrated to the local people, and especially to the hospital staff, the value of community healthcare in areas such as vaccination campaigns, improving nutrition and malaria eradication.

Changes: buildings

The early missionary doctors practised in very primitive conditions and it was natural to want to improve the situation. Bigger and better hospitals were built and medical care was centred around these buildings.

In very early days the doctor would visit patients in their homes. The early records of Dr Paterson in Hebron show that he would sometimes go with a guide to see a patient in a distant Bedouin encampment, and might be away from the hospital for two or three days at a time. As the doctor became busier, such visits were impracticable and patients had to be brought to the hospital.

In the 1960s, David Morley pointed out that big hospitals were sucking up more and more of the developing countries' resources, and that much more healthcare could be given to the poor in smaller, less sophisticated buildings for the same cost or even less. This applied especially to the Government health services, and to make the point he used to show slides of what he called 'disease palaces'.

Fortunately, in recent years the pendulum has begun to swing back again, as it is realized that curative medicine must be part of community healthcare along with preventive medicine. Betty Cowan of Ludhiana, who pioneered community health in both rural and urban settings in the Punjab, has always maintained that a good preventive service can survive only with a good curative hospital back-up. So now we have what Keith Sanders has called 'integrated medicine'.

It is important not to set up a healthcare scheme which is beyond the capacity of the local church to maintain, or which is too heavily dependent on foreign aid. However, it is not the building or the equipment that produces good medical practice, but the standards maintained by the practitioner, even in the most primitive of circumstances.

Changes: colleagues

Until twenty-five years ago, a doctor sent out from Britain normally expected to have to head a programme, a department or even a hospital. Now, however, he is much more likely to be going out to join a national doctor and to work with him as a colleague. This colleague, especially in Africa, will have been trained locally to a very high standard. This is also true for the nursing profession. Nevertheless, I believe there is still a place for the expatriate doctor.

Mutual co-operation

A Nigerian doctor recently asked me to find a British doctor to join him. When I asked him why, he replied, 'We have different qualities and both are needed. I can speak the language and get close to the people, but frequently the expatriate can organize a service better than I. I have ideas, but he can turn my dreams into reality!' In church life it is good for the people to see black and white working together, giving to each other and learning from each other – truly one in Christ Jesus.

Changing roles

Young national doctors often find themselves in situations of great responsibility for which they have had neither the training nor the experience. As a result, the role of the missionary doctor has changed somewhat, with more emphasis on teaching than on practice. This applies not only in the hospital or clinic but especially in training the trainers of village health workers or the traditional birth attendants. In the long run, these, together with the schoolchildren as they grow up, are the ones who will really alter the whole pattern of healthcare for the next generation.

New ideas such as oral rehydration for babies with diarrhoea may be difficult to get across to older mothers (who may well be under the influence of granny), but teach it to the girls at school, and make sure they know how to make up the solutions, and you will find that the message goes home. It will often be their job to look after the baby anyway, and even granny will listen to the girl at school!

The need and the challenge

What types of doctor are needed? In the bigger hospitals it will be those with higher qualifications in surgery, medicine and paediatrics. But if a young doctor, trained as a general practitioner, and more geared to preventive medicine than to hospital practice, is prepared to go out and supervise and teach in village clinics, he will find more and more openings and challenges. There are great demands on one's medical training and skills in adapting to the real situations of sick people overseas.

The way is open not only for the young to go overseas, but also for those who wish to take early retirement here and give the remaining years of their working life in church-related medical practice overseas. This may be for several years, or possibly a short-term locum while the regular doctor takes leave or time off for postgraduate study. One of the most important tasks now is teaching, and that can be done at all levels.

Dr Muneer of the Menouf Hospital in Egypt proposes four functions for the expatriate western missionary of the future:

● communicating with the local indigenous church and challenging it with the idea of mission;
● discussing with local leaders how to find suitable opportunities and the right people to fill those needs;
● helping in the training of these potential local missionaries;
● working with the local church and helping to provide resources to enable it to send such a missionary.[1]

Changes: relationships

The whole purpose of mission was to plant churches and then hand over control to them. Where this has been achieved, there has been a change in relationships between the home boards and the local churches, and between the expatriate worker and the sending missions. The institutions that were the responsibility of the missionary societies have gradually been handed over to the control of the indigenous church. The title deeds of the land have also been transferred, though this has taken longer because the legal processes were often difficult.

Today, when personnel are sent out they become staff members of the local church. For example, the Church of Scotland Mission in Kenya set up the Presbyterian Church of East Africa (PCEA) in 1943. From that time all missionaries sent out from Scotland became members of the PCEA on arrival in Kenya. They were located by the boards of that church and were subject to its discipline. At the end of each tour they were not reappointed unless requested by the church. A similar system has developed in other churches in their relationship with their sending mission.

The altered pattern of service

The whole pattern of offers of service has changed. When I first went overseas, I offered and was accepted 'for life'. Early retirement was frowned on and considered a betrayal of the call. Nowadays, although societies like offers for long-term service, expatriates are appointed for only one tour initially. Missionaries are sent out to fill vacancies only at the request of the local church, and also have to be invited back, and this has created uncertainty about the future. So there is now a tendency to offer and be accepted for short tours only.

Paradoxically, many overseas churches long to have expatriates who will settle down and become part of the local church as they begin to understand the culture as well as the local language. As one of my African colleagues put it: 'We want your bones!' Yet it is their own insistence on the right to invite workers back at the end of a tour that leads to the lack of security. However, many young missionaries who go out for only a short tour do stay on. In doing so they give stability to some healthcare schemes while they train local workers to take over.

The change of name

The word 'missionary' has become almost a dirty word in some circles, and some societies have aimed to eliminate it from their title and vocabulary. Missionaries have become 'fraternal workers', 'partners in mission' or 'mission partners', but the people remain the same whatever they are called.

There has been a spate of changes in the names of the sending missions. The Bible and Medical Missionary Fellowship (BMMF) had already changed its name once and has now become Interserve. The Sudan United Mission (SUM) has become Action Partners, while Ruanda Mission CMS (Church Missionary Society) has become Mid-Africa Ministry CMS. Some changes have been made in the face of militant Islam, but most have been attempts to end the links between the names 'missionary' and 'missionary society' with the colonial era and paternalism. Just as is happening in India, where the local church is setting up 'missionary societies' within that country, and in some parts of Africa where the church is calling its own people to go as missionaries to other tribes, I believe this phase will pass, and the terms will continue to be recognized for what they are within the life of the church. Local people still refer to expatriate workers as missionaries!

From missionary society to secular appointment

This very significant change began in the educational sphere when many countries nationalized the schools which had been largely run by missionary societies. However, they still welcomed Christian teachers to work in them.

In medicine this change has been slower and not so widespread. In Zambia in 1974 the state nationalized all medical institutions, but hoped that mission personnel would continue to run them. In several of the South African homelands the state has accepted responsibility for the medical work of all the mission hospitals, but they are very anxious to recruit Christian doctors to run them. The state pays all costs, even the doctors' salaries. This is particularly true of KwaZulu, where the Minister of Health and the Chief Secretary as well as others at headquarters are keen evangelical Christians.

In Kenya the Government refused to take over the church medical work on the grounds of cost, but they did give some grants for training purposes. However, they encouraged Christian doctors to join the Government service, and in 1968 two or three other doctors and I were seconded by our missions to work with the Kenya Government and run the health services in several districts of Northern Kenya. This was a thrilling experience which gave me an open door to witness in other ways. For instance, in Samburu district where I was appointed Medical Officer of Health – a rather glorified term, as I was the only doctor in the district – I had to attend the meetings of the District Commissioner, who was very suspicious of what other missionaries were doing. When I remonstrated that I too was a missionary, the reply was, 'But you are one of us!' Here was the opportunity, along with other colleagues, both nurses and administrative staff, for giving a clear Christian witness in a secular setting. It allowed me to go into every part of the district with the gospel along with healthcare, and to be paid to do it, and to show the caring love of God every day, linked to worship in church on Sunday.

Things unchanged

God's call

When Jesus first called his disciples, he simply said, 'Follow me.' At the end of John's gospel we read how Jesus called Peter again with the same simple words, 'Follow me.' But what does this following mean?

During his ministry he sent out the seventy-two with the words, 'Heal the sick . . . and tell them, "The kingdom of God is near you"' (Lk. 10:9). This call has not changed, nor has the need. The world is crying out for someone to show that at the heart there is a God who cares. So God calls us again to 'go into all the world' to heal the sick, to show them that God cares and to tell them about his kingdom.

God's message

Men and women often feel bewildered and lost. In the developing world they cannot understand what has happened. They gained independence twenty or thirty years ago and were promised a wonderful future. It would be their country, and all its wealth would be theirs. Now, several decades later, they are still in slavery to the West because of their crushing debts, and they are worse off.

What does the coming of God's kingdom mean to them? They need to be told that their poverty and the accompanying disease are not changed by independence, since they stem from our rebellion against God and our selfish heart. When a person, whether white or black, puts himself at the centre of the world and uses his power to satisfy his own desires, others suffer. We need to affirm again that everyone has sinned in this way and needs a new heart that only God can give.

Although the message has not changed, the messenger may well have done so. The first missionaries were evangelists who went out to preach the gospel and win men and women for Christ. Now, Christians coming from a country with a long Christian heritage, and often from families with a Christian tradition, have become of more value in building up the church. Often I was in the position of keeping channels open for the local Christians to carry the gospel. They knew the local idiom of language as no expatriate could ever hope to do, and could bring the gospel to their own people in ways we could never match – but we were in the background giving support and keeping the doors open.

God's power

Jesus said, 'As the Father sent me, I am sending you' (Jn. 20:21). And, 'All authority . . . has been given to me . . . surely I am with you always' (Mt. 28:19–20). So many Bible passages give us the assurance that God will be with us, that he has sent us, and that he will give us the necessary strength to fulfil the tasks he has given us.

Of course there are times when we feel stretched to the limit, and not only spiritually. We find ourselves in situations where we are tested by the medical problems we meet. But God will give us what we need to face the challenge.

God's faithfulness

I am often asked by young doctors: 'What about when I come back? Everyone tells me it will be professional suicide to go overseas, especially with a missionary society.' I do not know whether it will be or not, but I do know that if you hear God's call it will be spiritual suicide if you do not go! We trust God in his faithfulness when we are abroad; can we not trust his faithfulness when we come home? God is no-one's debtor; he remains faithful. If you believe that God called you to serve him overseas and has a job waiting for you, cannot you also believe that when he calls you home he will have further work for you here as well? I say this forcibly because I believe it is true. After twenty-five years overseas he called me to come home. I wondered what I would do and where I would fit in, but God had a 'tailor-made' job ready for me in the Medical Missionary Association and at the Royal Free Hospital.

God operates in every sphere of our lives, not just church-related tasks, and he says, 'Do not be anxious' (Mt. 6:25, RSV). We sing with great enthusiasm, 'Great is thy faithfulness, O God my Father', because we have found it to be true. So to those who say 'Yes, but what of the future?' I say, 'Obey God now and leave the future in his hands. He will take care of it then.'

We have looked at the many ways in which the face of medical missions has changed. But in spite of all the changes the need is still there, and God still calls us to follow him and to serve overseas where the need is greatest and the labourers are fewer. He remains faithful to those who answer his call and stands alongside them and uses them to his greater glory.

7 THE CHRISTIAN AND RESEARCH

David Kerr

Why should a Christian doctor engage in research?

For the Christian, truth is not discovered; it is revealed. 'I tell you the truth' (Mt. 5:18, *etc.*), said Jesus Christ; 'I am the truth' (Jn. 14:6). Speaking of the Holy Spirit, he said, 'When he, the Spirit of truth, comes, he will guide you into all truth' (Jn. 16:13).

Knowledge of the truth comes from an act of faith. 'We . . . believe and therefore speak, because we know' (2 Cor. 4:13). 'I know whom I have believed,' said the apostle Paul (2 Tim. 1:12). This act of faith is also stimulated by God: 'God chose the foolish things of the world to shame the wise . . . it is because of him that you are in Christ Jesus, who has become for us wisdom from God' (1 Cor. 1:27, 30).

In Christ we have a limitless source of knowledge. 'All things were created by him and for him. He is before all things and in him all things hold together' (Col. 1:16–17). He knows whether the universe began with a big bang or a whimper, for he created it. He understands the structure of the atom, the forces that keep the electrons in their orbits, the temperature of exploding stars, the wavelength of their radiomagnetic radiation and why they retreat into black holes, for he wrote the laws of nature. There is no part of the biosphere in all its wonder and complexity which is not part of his plan. He can decode the double helix of DNA, for he encoded it.

Above all, he understands the greatest wonder of all, the human mind. 'When [Jesus] was in Jerusalem at the Passover Feast, many people saw the miraculous signs he was doing and believed in his name. But Jesus would not entrust himself to them, for he knew all men. He did not need man's testimony about man, for he knew what was in a man' (Jn. 2:23–24). John, who wrote these words, probably heard in them an echo of the experience of David who said, 'O LORD, you have searched me and you know me . . . you perceive my thoughts from afar . . . you are familiar with all my ways . . . you created my inmost being; you knit me together in my mother's womb. I praise you because I am fearfully and wonderfully made; your works are wonderful, I know that full well. My frame was not hidden from you when I was made in the secret place. When I was woven together in the depths of the earth, your eyes saw my unformed body' (Ps. 139:1–3, 13–16). David seems to have glimpsed the process by which he was created – the elements of the earth transported by the grass and Jesse's flock into animal protein eaten by his mother and converted according to a divine plan encoded in his genes into the physical form and personality of David.

Although he marvelled at this process he was not stimulated to start research into fetal physiology or molecular genetics. His mind was overwhelmed by the fact that God knew intimately his secret thoughts and the workings of his mind. He found the experience frightening, as others have done:

> I fled Him, down the nights and down the days;
>   I fled Him, down the arches of the years;
> I fled Him, down the labyrinthine ways
>   Of my own mind; and in the midst of tears
> I hid from Him.[1]

Echoing those words of Francis Thompson, David exclaimed, 'Such knowledge is too wonderful for me' (Ps. 139:6), and tried to flee from it. But when God's love pursued him to the farthest and darkest hiding-place, he acknowledged in gratitude, 'When I awake, I am still with you' (Ps. 139:18).

That is the story of conversion, of becoming a Christian. It is not surprising that many Christians who have experienced truth revealed in Christ become suspicious of too much curiosity about the things which he has chosen not to reveal. In Genesis 1, God did not impart an estimate of the antiquity of the earth or an understanding of the formation of sedimentary rocks and their fossils, the periodic table, the origins of life on earth, the mechanisms of reproduction, adaptation, ageing and decay, the origins of disease, the characteristics of viruses or bacteria, the functions of immunoglobulins or killer T cells and the neural pathways in the diencephalon. 'So be it,' concluded some of the devout Christians who taught me as a child. 'If God did not reveal it, it is impertinence to seek it.'

In my view, this attitude is unbiblical. The Bible teaches us that we were given enquiring minds with the intention that we should use them. 'Always be prepared to give an answer to everyone who asks you to give the reason for the hope that you have' (1 Pet. 3:15). It is not good enough to say, 'I believe,' urges Peter; 'you must know *why* you believe.' That involves hard study. 'The Bereans were of more noble character than the Thessalonians,' writes Luke, 'for they received the message with great eagerness and examined the Scriptures every day to see if what Paul said was true' (Acts 17:11). If it is incumbent on us to challenge and dissect our Christian faith, which can come only by revelation, it would seem illogical not to exercise our minds in the same manner in understanding the universe in which God has placed us.

This was certainly the view of Isaac Newton who, like Kepler, saw himself as 'thinking God's thoughts after him' as he revolutionized our approach to physics by intensive original thought and careful experimentation. It was the view of Joseph Lister, James Young Simpson and many other pioneer Christian scientists (in the proper sense of those words) who followed in Isaac Newton's footsteps and felt that research was part of their service to God. Clearly, it is my own view, otherwise I would not have accepted the deanship of a medical school which exists primarily to conduct clinical research, and which is not afraid to tackle the most controversial subjects such as *in vitro* fertilization, gene therapy, the diagnosis of brain death, organ transplantation and intra-uterine surgery.

Since I take that view, I would like to encourage young Christian doctors and older ones too – to start a career in medical research, but to do so with their eyes open, knowing the problems that it will raise as well as the fulfilment it can bring. I shall start with a thumbnail sketch of careers in medical research in the UK, and then discuss how Christians can reconcile their research activity with their Christian faith.

First encounter

Medical students hear about research first from their pre-clinical teachers. One morning I arrived for the 9am lecture in biochemistry at the University of Edinburgh. The lecturer was Dr Eggleston, one of the famous husband-and-wife team who discovered the role of creatine phosphate as an energy store in muscle. I am not aware that they achieved any comparable distinction in the rest of their careers, and in his late forties or fifties Dr Eggleston was still a senior lecturer. However, he retained his devotion to research while remaining a charismatic undergraduate teacher. That morning he feigned an apology to the students: 'I did not have time', he said, 'to prepare my biochemistry lecture this morning, so instead I am going to give you a lecture on how to prepare a lecture.' It was obviously one he had constructed with extreme care, not as an afterthought. In the 1940s we shuffled in our seats in slight annoyance at being trapped in a philosophical lecture of no relevance to 2nd MB, but we were too polite to get up and walk out as today's students would do. We were fortunate in our diffidence, for if we had slipped out, we would have missed the most memorable lecture in the five-year course. Dr Eggleston explained how a physiologist carried out an experiment. He produced the lab books in which all his results were punctiliously recorded and which he preserved for all time. He showed how he took the raw data from a series of experiments, analysed the results and wrote a paper for a learned journal. He traced his steps to the library to check the literature, and to the statistician for advice on his analysis. Then he showed how, once in a while, a research worker went broody and incubated a textbook. He pictured the young lecturer going to that textbook to start finding the material for his lecture, working back to the original papers in the process.

I do not recall that he actually said it, but Dr Eggleston left us with the firm impression that lectures were best given by people who had helped to assemble the data, knew the pitfalls and could assess the results.

During the first two or three years of the medical course, the student who has met a Dr Eggleston may be buttonholed by his teacher and asked, 'would you like to take an intercalated BSc or BMedSci in my department?' In London University the more enlightened teachers may even encourage the student to move to another medical school, and have a change of scenery as well as a change of atmosphere during the intercalated. Such students gain a great deal from that year if they choose their supervisor well. They get to know some of the staff of the medical school more intimately than they can ever hope to do during the passive learning process that makes up most of the medical lecture course. They are encouraged to study one subject in depth, and to do so they have to learn to use the library, the wordprocessor and computer, the rudiments of statistics, and at least one scientific discipline. Knowledge is fixed in the most physiological way – by using it to pursue a goal. Students usually have to present their work in seminars, and it is a joy for ageing teachers to learn how much better their students can lecture than they do themselves. Above all, these students learn the ethos of science; the need for thorough verification of methods, honest recording of results, careful analysis of data, scepticism about their own findings – an urge to test them by trying to disprove them before accepting them or commending them to others – and a willingness to change their minds in the face of new evidence.

Of course, not all students benefit from their intercalated year. I have questioned scores at senior house officer and registrar interviews about what they got out of it, in return for leaving their familiar friends and trailing them through medical school and up the earnings ladder by a year. For many, the honest answer would be, 'very little', though they seldom give it at an interview. However, those who choose the right supervisor and conquer the first fit of 'research workers' blues' (the feeling you get when faced with a whole day in which no-one decides the timetable except yourself) earn a rich intellectual reward. A high proportion of all entrants into academic medicine have taken an intercalated BSc or BMedSci.[2] To some extent, that is a self-fulfilling prophecy. Competition for senior house officer posts in teaching hospitals is intense, and those with a science degree have a head start in getting on to the bottom rung of the academic ladder. In a recent intake to the senior house officer posts in medicine at Hammersmith Hospital, eleven of the successful candidates had a first-class or upper second BSc or BMedSci. This is not the only reason science-and-medicine graduates do well in academic medicine; the early start to an apprenticeship in science seems to work better than a late start, when the brain is already cluttered with factual medical knowledge.

Unfortunately, not all students who want to take a science degree and are capable of benefiting can do so. After an enquiry by the Exchequer and Audit Department the Medical Research Council has had to reduce its funding for this extra year of training, and no alternative source of funds has appeared. Some students therefore start the hard way by doing some research in their spare time without interrupting their medical course. Southampton University allots generous time for this in the curriculum, but in most medical schools the time has to be found by sacrificing sport or social activity. Fewer than half the students who set out to do a project actually finish one in these circumstances, and those that are completed are sometimes poorly supervised and scrappy. Nonetheless, I am amazed at what keen students can achieve in their spare time, producing a thesis which would almost merit a higher degree. They learn a lesson in self-discipline in the use of time which is invaluable for young Christians, who will defend their time for Bible study, prayer and meditation from the inroads of other activity, while still doing the same for their research in a day when clinical practice will always seem to take precedence. Supervising this scheme was the greatest privilege I had in the University of Newcastle, and it is no surprise that the Kerr Prize is awarded to the student who turns in the best project.

The well-planned career

Today, the important advances in medicine are made by doctors and other scientists who have a firm grounding in one or more of the basic sciences. At the Royal Postgraduate Medical School, young doctors who show a flair for clinical research are picked out at the senior house officer stage, encouraged to stay on as registrars, put up for training Medical Research Council fellowships, sent off to a basic science laboratory in the UK, USA or continental Europe, and brought back to a Wellcome Senior Clinical Research Fellowship or similar post. Their training takes about seven years. The Medical Research Council has recently agreed to introduce some seven-year training awards which take the unpredictability out of this *à la carte* training menu, at least for the very high flyers who will win these coveted awards. Whichever route you take to a career in medical research, it will be a tough one. The salaries of research workers are well below those of their colleagues working up the clinical ladder and enjoying large extra-duty payments; the hurdles are higher and the jobs less secure at all stages. This will get worse in the near future. University salaries are still linked to the National Health Service basic pay, but without many of the perks, and parity has to be defended each year from increasingly rugged assaults by the Department of Education, which does not back recommendations for pay increases with a permanent increase in university grant. A former Secretary of State said that he envisaged a five-year rolling appointment as the normal new post in the universities, once tenure has been abolished by law. The disparities with NHS appointments will therefore increase and something akin to missionary zeal will be needed by those committed to medical research.

The road to the Celestial City goes up the hill Difficulty, and I do not know of a pathway to success in medical research that bypasses it, but there are some pots of gold at the rainbow's end. The greatest is finding that you have made a significant contribution to the cure or prevention of disease. Many who make great contributions to science will never have the good fortune to see the end results, but the clinical research worker may have the privilege once or twice in his life. For twelve years I toured the branches of the Northern Counties Kidney Research Fund, telling them of the devastating disease that affected patients on regular haemodialysis in our region, causing multiple fractures, wheelchair existence and death from respiratory failure. In the last few years I could tell them that the cause had been found,[3] and that the disease would now disappear, as it has done.[4]

Success brings some other rewards. Fellows come to you from around the world and fill your family photograph album with happy memories of Christmas parties with their children, return trips to their home countries and even the arrival of their sons and daughters as second-generation research fellows. When the International Society of Nephrology held its tenth triennial congress in London, there were reunion parties at Hammersmith and Guy's, with 100–200 alumni returning to pay tribute to Keith Peters, Stewart Cameron and their colleagues – quite a boost to self-esteem.

Is there still a place for the amateur?

Astute clinicians made many of the advances in medicine up to the middle of this century. My own generation of academics contained many – including myself – who had no formal scientific training and became jacks of all trades and masters of none. We would not get on to the academic ladder today, and I would advise no-one to start as I did. However, there are still observations to be made that call for little apparatus and only a modest investment of time and effort. The local Association of Physicians of Region 1 holds three meetings a year at which most of the papers are given by clinicians doing a little research in their spare time and making very useful contributions. Their small requirements for cash are met by the locally organized research scheme which is operated in every health region in England and Wales (Scotland has a similar national scheme) . Two of my own *Lancet* papers – one on improvements in the efficiency of the artificial kidney[5] and one on the mode of action of a new diuretic[6] – represented about six weeks' work by myself and my colleagues and required no research grant. So I encourage every doctor to sustain an interest in research.

However, the future must hold a declining role for the amateur. Scientific equipment is now very expensive. Items installed in, or ordered for, Hammersmith include a nuclear magnetic whole-body spectroscopic scanner and a positron emission tomographic scanner at about £1.5m each, transmission and scanning electron microscopes, mass spectrometers and a fluorescent antibody cell sorter, all at £100,000 or above. The running cost of a research worker in molecular biology – the fastest-growing and most productive basic science in the 1980s – is about £6,000 a year for reagents alone. Consequently, few can now conduct research without the help of research grants won in open competition.

That competition is very stiff. When I first won a Medical Research Council project grant, the cut-off point was a score of 2.5. Today you need a score of 4.2 for an immediate award; that is a colossal score to receive from referees who are your rivals and competitors in the field! It is therefore very hard to win a grant in a field in which you do not already have an established reputation without grant – 'catch 22', to borrow the phrase. I do not believe that my first hero, Dr Eggleston, knew the meaning of 'Publish or perish'. He worked until he felt it was time to produce a paper and in his measured way he produced it. Today's young research worker is under constant pressure to publish fast so that he has a busy *c.v.* to present with his next grant application. Many overstep the mark and clutter up their *c.v.* with trivial papers, abstracts and letters to the editor, apparently unaware that no-one now weighs the papers; quality of publications has rightly come to be valued more than quantity. But that does not make life easier; there is still pressure to produce the bright, clear-cut positive paper that seems likeliest to find its way into the *New England Journal of Medicine*.

That brings me to the first challenge facing the Christian research worker. Some of these problems that confront research workers, whether Christian or not, can be gathered under titles that paraphrase Philippians 4: 8, the most quoted guide to the thought processes that Christians should adopt, and I have used that classification here.

Problems

What is true?

Jesting Pilate was not alone in asking, 'What is truth?' and not staying for an answer. The question has stimulated surprisingly little debate among scientists. There is a bland assumption that science is the dedicated pursuit of absolute truth and that deviation from that path is exceptional. Piltdown Man and the feathers of archaeopteryx are dismissed as bad jokes or the aberrations of amateurs who strayed into science.

Science has therefore taken a nasty shock over the last decade when quite widespread fraud has been exposed.[7] Young research workers have succumbed to the pressure for quick results and have plagiarized the work of others or invented the results. Drs Alsabti and Darsee built successful academic careers on these practices for many years before they were found out and a long trail of falsification was discovered. These celebrated cases had one good effect and a depressing one. The depressing one is that some supervisors who had added their names to the work of these and other 'inventive scientists' have been rather slow to accept their share of the blame and to acknowledge the responsibilities that authorship carries. The good effect has been a tightening of editorial policy in many of the best journals. It is now expected that any author understands the whole paper, even if he contributed to only one section. He should be able to defend its science in public. If that concept is to receive more than lip-service, all collaborating workers must be prepared to expose all their primary data – the original lab books, machine write-outs, clinical case notes, *etc.* – to each of their co-authors. That calls for humility and mutual trust between the collaborators which have been far from universal in the past.

Although a refreshing honesty about this problem is now emerging, I am disappointed by the reluctance of scientists to explore the grey area between honesty and fraud.[8] Absolute truth in science demands absolutely accurate methods, and they do not exist. Revered clinical signs usually have a very high observer error.[9] Even under the best conditions a sphygmomanometer reading differs appreciably from intra-arterial pressure,[10] and many hospital readings are made in conditions that are a long way from the best. Most biochemical methods perform better than clinical measurement, but their weaknesses are underestimated by clinicians. I hear colleagues over-interpreting small changes in serum aluminium, although the coefficient of variation ranged from 12% to 72% over the clinical range in the European quality control system as recently as 1985.[11]

Quality control, and statistical tests to deal with random errors, are improving. But there is an element of personal judgment in deciding when a method is going wrong, so that the data must be discarded, and when it is acceptable, so that the data can be used and published. Such judgments have to be made. The research worker who spends his whole time checking and rechecking for minor sources of error may succumb to academic paralysis, publish nothing, and therefore defeat the whole purpose of conducting research.

I have quoted one example of the dilemma in the *British Medical Journal*.[12] One batch of samples gave satisfactory quality control data, but the clinical results were incredible. After some argument with our colleagues, the tests were repeated on frozen duplicates, and gave clinically sensible answers which were accepted. I have little doubt that on the first run the analyser malfunctioned after the quality control samples had gone through, but it is only a small step from this decision to rejecting all results which do not fit one's preconceived ideas. To guard against this risk, the Christian research worker should be the first to say, 'Let us delay publication and repeat the whole experiment from scratch.' That is fairly easy (though inconvenient) in a laboratory study, but not so easy when ethical approval must be sought again and patients asked to submit to a repeat test.

What is noble?

I have always regretted that it was not a member of the Christian Medical Fellowship who wrote *Human Guinea Pigs*[13] and first challenged the ethical practices of clinical research workers. I appear three times in the book, twice as an unscrupulous research worker and once as a caring physician. I accept the criticism as valid. I started invasive clinical research in the heyday of the human physiological approach when we had exaggerated ideas of what our studies could contribute to knowledge and clinical practice. In our eagerness we carried out studies that demanded more sacrifice by the patients – in risk, discomfort, expense and time away from family or work – than would now be acceptable to any research ethics committee in this country. We justified it to one another; we were slick and well-practised, so the discomfort and risk were minimized. The patients often loved it. One of my supervisors scolded me mildly for my reluctance to include an elderly lady in an invasive study: 'She will love it; you will be the first young doctor who has ever sat for four hours and talked to that old dear.' She was right; not one, but four attentive young doctors chatted her up through a four-hour study, and it was a red-letter day in her life. But that does not justify the study for which she was a control patient whose consent was less than truly informed.

Research ethics committees now tend to err in the opposite direction, labouring over the justification for an extra 2 ml of blood taken during a clinically indicated venepuncture and insisting on written consent. However, they are a vital safeguard to our patients, and are still discovering the many facets of this problem. In Newcastle the research ethics committee appointed its own super-ego – the 'bishop's committee', after its chairman – which sifted through all the applications for a year to detect vulnerable groups, such as acromegalics and patients with chronic renal failure who could be overexposed to investigation in a department interested in endocrinology and nephrology. Again, it saddens me that it did not occur spontaneously to the Christians in my department that these patients, who were so dependent on doctors, could be exploited by being asked to take part in many studies, none individually burdensome, but cumulatively unacceptable. It is another reminder that research workers can become blinkered by the urge for progress.

What is admirable?

The successful research worker wins grants, employs staff on short-term contracts and becomes, against his will, a business manager. Among the admirable qualities now expected of him is being a good employer. 40% of the staff at the Royal Postgraduate Medical School are research workers employed on grants with a tenure of less than three years. Many of these are the non-medical scientists without whom doctors cannot conduct much of modern medical research. They live lives of great insecurity, and the grant holder is responsible for them – and for the wives, husbands and children who depend on them as they struggle to raise mortgages on insecure salaries. It then becomes easy to let one's research programme become dominated by the need to raise grants to support people rather than to do research, and to dodge the unpleasant but necessary task of picking out those who should continue in a research career from those who are not cut out for it and must be directed elsewhere, with the inevitable feeling that you have let them down.

What is right?

There are many occasions when medical and biological research throws up facts which challenge one's cherished beliefs and are uncomfortable for the Christian to handle. The Christian symposium *Creation and Evolution*[14] contains some examples. Piltdown Man, Java Man and other publicized 'missing links' may have been dismissed as fakes,[15] but the undramatic collection of data has amassed some pretty impressive evidence that evolution plays some part in the biosphere. Cytochrome C in the chimpanzee is almost identical to cytochrome C in the human, whereas it is substantially different in other vertebrates and very different in yeasts and bacteria. Variations in haemoglobin follow the same pattern in the species that possess it. How does the Christian who has grown up with Archbishop Ussher's dating of the creation confront this evidence and the equally impressive evidence for the antiquity of the earth?

Should Christians avoid engaging in those areas of research that throw up these awkward questions? Anyone who shares the view of biblical teaching which I expounded at the start would find that idea both unacceptable and impracticable, since tough questions appear wherever one engages in research. The right approach, surely, is to bring these questions to God in prayer acknowledging that we start with an imperfect understanding of Scripture – for some of us are still on a milk diet (1 Cor. 3:2) and have only a glimpse of the scientific knowledge that will one day be revealed to mankind. Like Newton, we are still casting pebbles from the shore while an ocean of knowledge lies beyond us. In humility we can ask him to show us how we can reconcile the truth he has revealed in the Bible with his truth revealed in nature.

What is excellent?

Subjectively, excellence in research is experienced the day one's paper appears in a prestigious journal and one knows one has made an important breakthrough. As I said earlier, that does not happen often in a career. More often, one experiences the disappointment of a negative result. We spent ten years following up women with chronic pyelonephritis, carefully controlling their urinary infections in the hope that it would postpone the onset of renal failure; at the last analysis before I left Newcastle, we could find no evidence that it made any difference at all. The Christian, however, should not expect his work to be judged by positive results or exciting discoveries. His hope is that the final judgment on his work will be, 'Whatever you did, you worked at it with all your heart, as working for the Lord, not for men' (cf. Col. 3:23).

The God of peace be with you

Paul ended his instructions in Philippians 4:8–9 with these words. How does the Christian research worker find peace under the pressures to seek the truth without becoming introspective, to care for his patients while still doing relevant research, to care for his staff but not be distracted by them, to face the awkward questions his studies throw up and get result, but not be dominated and distorted by the rat race? David, disturbed by his first realization of God's knowledge of him, found the answer: 'When I awake, I am still with you' (Ps. 139:18). Happy the Christian research worker who has learned in his undergraduate days how to find time to be with God when he awakes.

Part 2

MEDICAL ETHICS

8 MAKING ETHICAL DECISIONS IN MEDICINE

Peter Saunders

Most medical decision-making is made on the basis of appeal to a body of knowledge derived by experiment and observation. For example, we know that a certain set of signs, symptoms and radiological appearances is consistent with the diagnosis of lobar pneumonia. We know from past clinical observation that lobar pneumonia, if untreated, may well be fatal. We know from microbiological investigation that the disease is caused by the bacterium pneumococcus, and we know from pharmacological research that this pathogen is sensitive to penicillin G, and from clinical experience that patients with lobar pneumonia who are treated with penicillin G will generally recover.

These are medical facts, the truth of which has been established by repeated careful observation – and no properly trained doctor, at least one who has examined the evidence available at the time of writing, would dispute them. But it does not immediately follow from these observations alone that we should always treat a given patient suffering from lobar pneumonia with penicillin G. This is to move from the realm of medical knowledge (what we know about disease) to the realm of medical ethics (what we ought to do).

Medical ethics are obligations of a moral nature which govern the practice of medicine[1] – principles of conduct prescribing what we ought to do. In the not-too-distant past, at least in western society, there was a broad consensus about what these principles should be. They were formulated in such ethical codes as the Hippocratic Oath, and its modern restatement, the Declaration of Geneva,[2] which made certain presuppositions about such issues as the value of human life. Despite the fact that such codes were framed and adopted by secular bodies, they were nonetheless broadly consistent with biblical principles of conduct. In other words, as recently as the beginning of the century there was a broad consensus between doctors. This roughly approximated to the Judeo-Christian ethic, and there was therefore little disagreement about the right way to behave in a given situation. This is no longer the case.

Why ethical decision-making is more difficult

Both medicine and society have changed dramatically over the last century in ways that have made ethical decision-making much more complicated than before.

First, medical knowledge and technology have advanced tremendously. The general practitioner managing a case of lobar pneumonia at the turn of the century did not have to make a decision about whether or not to give antibiotics. There were none. We now have surgical operations for the patient with an aortic aneurysm, ventilators for the premature infant with respiratory distress, and phenothiazines for the schizophrenic, and we have to decide in which circumstances to use them.

Secondly, because of the influence of the mass media, medical knowledge is growing less secret and more public. An increasingly educated public knows what technology is available and is demanding it. This heightened scrutiny is making our decisions more visible and our practice more accountable.

Thirdly, the specialization that has resulted from the increase in knowledge and technology available has meant a move to team decision-making. The solitary doctor at the bedside has been replaced by a team of sub-specialists, a hierarchy of medical staff, a host of paramedical specialties and a vast array of technical and management personnel, each expert in his or her own small field.

Fourthly, financial and resource constraints in the face of rapidly advancing knowledge and technology have meant that we have more acute decisions of resource allocation to make. What should our priorities be – heart transplants or hypertension, ventilators or venereal disease, geriatrics or gene therapy?

Finally, and most importantly, all this is taking place in a moral vacuum. We live in a post-Christian society where there is no agreement on the underlying basis for decision-making. The plurality of religious traditions, cultural backgrounds, worldviews and ideologies makes any real consensus impossible. Tolerance is paraded as the supreme virtue in such an ethical environment, but tolerance of mutually contradictory views is both ludicrous and unworkable when decisions have to be made. It is simply impossible to please all of the people all of the time. So whose view should prevail?

These factors combine to create a minefield of ethical conflicts for the Christian doctor. Every new advance in knowledge and tech-

114

nology creates new dilemmas. His (or perhaps more accurately 'her', as most medical graduates are now female) patients have higher expectations, and he must make his decisions in an atmosphere of increasing financial constraint, growing public scrutiny and in consultation with those who are ever less likely to share his faith. What is he to do?

Different bases for ethical decision-making

Before we examine the principles governing the behaviour of the Christian doctor, it is useful to have a broad understanding of the ways our various non-Christian colleagues make their ethical decisions.

Gut feeling: 'It feels right'

In a society as obsessed with the pursuit of pleasure as our own, it is inevitable that some believe that their emotions should rule their behaviour. Of course, having feelings is part of being created in the image of God (Gn. 1:27), but problems arise when they are made the sole basis for decision-making. They can be perverted, as in the case of the sadist who derives pleasure from inflicting pain on others. They may disagree – witness the passion felt by those on both sides of the abortion debate – and they may change. The girl who wakes up with a hangover, and then finds she is pregnant after a one-night stand, knows with certainty that what 'felt so right' was not right at all. 'The heart is deceitful above all things,' says Jeremiah (Je. 17:9). It is no guide to ethical conduct.

Reason: 'It's logical'

If not the heart, why not the mind? Can human reason be our basis for ethical decision-making? I argued previously that the fact that penicillin G has been observed to cure patients with lobar pneumonia does not in itself logically lead us to the conclusion that we ought to treat a given patient who has the disease with the antibiotic. In reaching this decision we are (perhaps even subconsciously) making several other decisions along the way.

We are first deciding that we can trust our own senses to give us reliable information, and that those other observers on whom we are relying are truthful and not deceived themselves. Even if we are sure about this, we are then deciding that it is reasonable to expect the future to resemble the past – that, for instance, the pneumococcus has not mutated in the intervening period in such a way as to render it resistant to penicillin G. Finally, we are deciding that it is right to kill millions of bacteria in order to save the life of one sick person.

It is not reason alone which is leading us to these conclusions. Reason may help us to know whether our arguments are logical or illogical, or alternatively strong or weak – but we still need to make assumptions of the sort outlined, or 'steps of faith', before we can begin to make decisions at all. The beliefs that our senses are trustworthy, that others are reliable, that nature is uniform and that helping people is right are all steps of faith. They are not self-evident truths established by reason alone. They are presuppositions which we all make when deciding to treat patients. But if these assumptions from which we start are wrong, then even if our powers of reason are faultless our conclusions will be flawed – and whose powers of reason are faultless? Even the best of minds are not always reasonable. So reason also has its limitations.

Conscience: 'But I don't feel guilty'

Our capacity to feel guilt is a reminder that we are fallen creatures, and there is no doubt that God can use conscience for our good. 'Train a child in the way he should go,' says the writer of Proverbs (Pr. 22:6). However, conscience also has weaknesses as the only criterion for making moral choices. It may become blunted. Many of the Nazi doctors who presided over the killing of millions during the Second World War felt they had done nothing wrong. They were nonetheless judged to be guilty. On the other hand, there is the danger that conscience may become over-sensitive, as in the case of the neurotic patient who is paralysed with feelings of guilt despite having done nothing wrong. Consciences need educating. 'There is a way that seems right to a man, but in the end it leads to death' (Pr. 14:12). People are capable of suppressing the truth and exchanging the truth of God for a lie (Rom. 1:18, 25).

Consensus: 'Everybody's doing it'

The desire not to appear different is a strong one, but majority opinion may not be correct. It was once believed that the earth was flat, that the sun revolved around the earth, and that there was no connection between smoking and lung cancer. Every major scientific discovery initially has to challenge the *status quo* of incorrect consensus opinion. Furthermore, popular opinion varies across cultures. Female circumcision is regarded as barbaric in

Britain and civilized in parts of Africa, but opinions about abortion vary in the opposite direction. Consensus opinion may change over time within any one culture. Euthanasia for handicapped children and the demented elderly is perfectly acceptable in Holland today, but during the Second World War many Dutch physicians willingly chose imprisonment in preference to being involved with it. Oscar Wilde rather cynically called democracy 'the bludgeoning of the people by the people for the people';[3] it can be simply a euphemism for mob rule. The Bible sternly warns us: 'Do not follow the crowd in doing wrong . . . do not pervert justice by siding with the crowd' (Ex. 23:2). Consensus opinion, after all, crucified Christ.

Consequences: The best outcome

The fact that following gut feeling, conscience or consensus opinion may lead to undesirable consequences has led some to suggest that *outcome* should be the determinant of whether actions are judged right or wrong. But does the end always justify the means? In the 1970s, Pol Pot successfully eradicated leprosy from Kampuchea (a noble aim), but he achieved it by diabolical means (killing the leprosy sufferers). In our own society, we are attempting to reduce the level of handicap by prenatal diagnosis and selective abortion. Is this justified? Doesn't the consideration of consequences alone also ignore the fact that means and motives are also important? What of the person who does the 'right' thing for the 'wrong' reason? Furthermore, the real consequences of our decisions may not be apparent until years afterwards. The heavy drinker does not have cirrhosis foremost in mind, nor does the promiscuous student consider that his actions may be leading to gonorrhoea or emotional hurt. The Bible is full of stories of entire nations who remained blind to the consequences of their actions until it was too late.

Relativism: What's true for you

With the loss of a common consensus and the infusion into our culture of an extraordinary range of religions and philosophies, many have responded by choosing to believe that right and wrong are entirely private matters. Over 75% of pre-clinical medical students in a recent survey answered that in their opinion there were no absolute moral standards, but that it was rather up to each person to develop his or her own, relative to the individual, the period of history, the culture and the situation. This sounds a nice idea, but let us think about it a moment. If there are indeed no absolutes, then the statement that 'there are no absolutes' can be only relatively true. Similarly, to claim that 'all things are relative' is to make an absolute statement. This position is first and foremost logically absurd. But it is also unworkable in practice. Nobody in reality is a true relativist. Everyone makes moral judgments about others. No-one sincerely believes that a belief that is diametrically opposed to his own can be as valid as his own. Virtually every decision we make as individuals has repercussions for other people. If we were complete relativists, we would be unable to make any objective decisions at all, and we certainly could not be doctors with this perspective.

Authority: What so-and-so says

What many do in practice, given the difficulty of making moral decisions themselves, is to choose some reliable authority figure to follow. In practice in the healthcare team, the ultimate responsibility for ethical decisions lies with the consultant. However, there are problems with this. The presence of technical expertise and knowledge does not imply the possession of moral integrity. Just as there are politicians who cheat on their wives, embezzle funds and betray their countries, so there are consultants who make decisions in their own interests rather than the patient's. Even well-meaning people may be deceived or misinformed. I remember once being pressured by a nurse to prescribe megadoses of vitamin C for a patient with leg ulcers, on the ground that 'Linus Pauling believed in its efficacy and he was an eminent chemist'. If medicine has taught me anything it is to have a healthy distrust of all authority figures – most of all myself. We are all susceptible to being misled or deceived, and to having our judgment impaired by impure motives of which we ourselves may not be aware. 'All a man's ways seem innocent to him, but motives are weighed by the LORD' (Pr. 16:2). So, while believing that all authorities have been instituted by God, we must not fall into the trap of thinking that their decisions, even in their own areas of expertise, are therefore infallible. Doctors may possess godlike power and knowledge, but it does not follow that they also have godlike character and judgment.

Where does this leave us? We are not completely discounting these means as guides in human conduct, but merely recognizing their limitations. Emotions buzz and fade. Reason may fail, or start from flawed premises. Conscience can be blunted or over-sensitive. Consensus is subject to prejudice and prevention. Consequences are often difficult to judge before the event, and human authorities are not infallible. Is there then some morally pure, perfectly reasonable,

118

all-knowing, benevolent, non-human authority we can trust to guide us through our moral dilemmas?

Knowing God's will: which voice?

The theistic religions (Christianity, Judaism and Islam) and the multitude of denominations, divisions, sects and cults associated with them would answer that question in the affirmative. They all hold that there is an all-knowing, all-powerful, morally perfect, benevolent God who has made and is making himself known through the course of history in an intelligible way. They also have, to a greater or lesser extent, other concepts in common: a shared thread of history in the ancient Middle East, a belief in divine revelation, and a belief in an afterlife of some sort, with a judgment based on decisions or choices made in this life. The similarities, however, end there.

There is major disagreement between the theistic faiths on how God makes himself known. All would hold that he has revealed himself through the created order, which tells us something of his majesty, power and complexity – but only in very general terms at best. To enable us to know God in any coherent way, he would have to reveal himself to us more specifically, in language we can understand. Each theistic faith claims that he has done just this, and accordingly has its own prophets, scriptures and associated literature and gives varying weight to past and contemporary prophecy, oral tradition and the role of reason, conscience and mystical experience. The Muslims have the Qur'an, the Jews the Old Testament and the Christians the Bible. But then within each group there are further divisions: for example, within Islam the Shi'ites emphasize ongoing revelation, the Sunnis oral tradition, the Mu'tazila the importance of reason and the Sufis mystical experience.

It is not my intention here to debate the strengths and weaknesses of the other theistic faiths, apart from saying that in a pluralistic society such as ours it is imperative that the Christian medical student has some idea of the spectrum of belief that exists – not least because some of his patients will come from this range of traditions. Our purpose here is rather to lay a foundation for a distinctively Christian approach to decision-making in the area of medical ethics. The Christian medical student or doctor is then concerned with two principle questions: What would God have me do? How would he have me do it? The first is a question about what God has specifically commanded and the second is a question about character, the first about doing and the second about being.

Imitating Jesus Christ: his commands and character

It is worth making a few preliminary comments about what a Christian is (Eph. 1:3–14). Each of us is a person chosen by God and adopted into God's family as a result of God's own initiative, to which we have responded by repentance (turning from sin) and faith (trusting belief). As a result of Christ's death on the cross on our behalf, and Christ's subsequent resurrection, we have received God's forgiveness for our sins, and have been given the Holy Spirit both as a guarantee of our inheritance of eternal life and as the agent helping us to live in obedience to our new master. As chosen children of God, loved, saved, forgiven and empowered, we are now committed to serving God for ever. While we have been saved by God's grace through faith (and this is God's doing not ours (Eph. 2:8–10)), nevertheless this faith finds its expression in obedience and love (Gal. 5:6). There is thus an inextricable connection between the faith that saves and the good works that are the evidence of its existence (Jas. 2:14–24). The Christian has become in effect a love-slave of God (Rom. 6:15–18). As we grow in faith, and as understanding of what God does and who he is develops, so we will be progressively transformed into the likeness of Christ (2 Cor. 3:16–18), becoming more like him in both obedience and character.

This path will not be easy for us however, especially in a world which is becoming more antagonistic to Christ and his message. It will involve following Christ in the shadow of the cross, increasingly standing out as different from the world, and experiencing its rejection of godly obedience and belief. As part of this, Christian medical students or doctors in a multi-faith, post-Christian society will discover that our beliefs, decision-making and practice will create conflict for us. Despite this, our supreme loyalty will always be to God (Mt. 10:32–40).

Now to the specific questions of the Christian doctor's behaviour and character. How should we act and be? The short answer is that we should act and be like Christ. God, Paul tells us, has predestined us (Christians) 'to be conformed to the likeness of his Son' (Rom. 8:29), to be imitators of Christ (or alternatively imitators of God (1 Cor. 11:1; Eph. 5:1), as Christ is 'the exact representation of his being' (Heb. 1:3), the one who 'has made him known' (Jn. 1:18)).

Fundamentally, therefore, the most important question to ask in making ethical decisions in medicine as in any other area of life must be: 'What would Jesus have done in this situation?' Obviously our ability to answer such a question will depend on our knowledge of the person of Jesus. How are we to obtain such knowledge? Christ's own teaching on this matter is clear: we grow in our knowledge of him by holding to his teaching – by hearing his words and obeying them (Jn. 14:21). In other words, to be growing in our understanding of how he would have us behave, we need to be obeying the teaching we have already received from him.

Jesus Christ's view of the Bible

Christ's teaching has been diligently and painstakingly recorded for us by the apostles and early leaders of the church in the pages of the New Testament. We can be confident that what they recorded was what Christ said (Lk. 1:3; Jn. 20:30–31; 2 Pet. 1:16), not only because they were eye-witnesses of all that he said and did, but more importantly because he personally commissioned them and gave them the authority to teach in his name (Mt. 16:18–19; 18:18; 28:19–20; Gal. 1:11–12). To doubt that what they recorded is true is to doubt the very words of Christ himself. The fact that what is recorded in the New Testament is the testimony of eye-witnesses means that we can be confident that no errors of a 'Chinese-whisper' type have crept into the text. Nor can there be errors of written transmission which alter the meaning of what they wrote, since we have copies of parts of the New Testament that date from the lifetime of those who knew the apostles personally.

We have not only the apostles' own testimony that what they wrote were the words of Christ, but also Christ's own testimony that he would enable them by means of his Holy Spirit to teach them all things, remind them of everything he said, take what was his and make it known to them, and guide them into all truth (Jn. 14:25–26; 16:12–15).

Furthermore, we should do the same with the Old Testament, because Jesus believed and taught that it was equally the Word of God. He treated its historical narratives as straightforward records of fact. Interestingly, the stories that are the least acceptable to the 'modern mind' are the very ones he seemed most fond of choosing for his illustrations (e.g. Abel (Mt. 23:35), Noah (Lk. 17:26–27), Jonah (Mt. 12:39–41)). He repeatedly quoted it as the final court of appeal in debates, not only with his earthly opponents but with the devil himself (Mt. 4:1–11). He believed that its prophecies were fulfilled in him (Lk. 24:44), and used them as proof of his claims to be the Messiah (Jn. 4:25–26; Mt. 16:20). He obeyed its ethical teaching. It follows then that part of holding to the teaching of Christ and imitating him must involve having the same respect for the Old Testament that he had.

In summary, Jesus put his stamp of approval on the Old Testament as God's inspired Word, and commissioned the writing of the New Testament. In view of Jesus' own attitude, is it then possible to be a Christian and not accept the Bible's authority? If Jesus himself has underlined the authority of the Bible, can we claim to live under his authority (because this is what having him as Lord means) if we do not have the same attitude to it? A logical corollary of being Christians is that we share Jesus' own high regard for the Scriptures. We want regularly to hear, read, study and meditate on what God has revealed in the Old and New Testament, so that our thoughts and actions are increasingly in line with those of Jesus himself.

It does not follow from the fact that Jesus has given his stamp of approval to the Bible that all people will be able to agree about what it says. It is clear from the teaching of both Jesus and the apostles that it is quite possible to hear God's Word and not understand it – even to study it over a lifetime and not do so (Jn. 5:39–40; 2 Cor. 3:14–16). The Bible can be legitimately understood and applied only with the help of the Holy Spirit – in other words, by those who are already true believers. A person can clearly claim to be a Christian, even or passionately believe himself to be a Christian, and yet not be one. Jesus made this fact perfectly clear (Jn. 7:21–23). However, one need not go beyond the pages of the New Testament to see that even true believers may have strong disagreements.

There are accordingly very stern warnings in the Bible about adding to or subtracting from what God has already revealed (Dt. 4:2; 12:32; Pr. 30:6; Rev. 22:18–19). But it also clear that the Bible does not tell us everything. There are things that God has revealed and there are things which he has chosen not to reveal (Dt. 29:29). As Christians we must diligently seek to know what lies in each category, and then be dogmatic about what the Bible does say and agnostic about what it does not say. It requires great wisdom and maturity not to let the revealed encroach upon the secret, and *vice versa*. If we make the first mistake, we add to Scripture. If we succumb to the second, we subtract from Scripture. Either way, we hinder the work of the gospel, which, according to Christ, is dependent both on the unity of true believers and the preservation of truth.

Why disagreements among Bible-believing Christians?

Why then do Christians who accept the authority of the Bible add to or subtract from Scripture? There are three main reasons.

First, not all people who accept the authority of the Bible have necessarily studied it sufficiently to know what it says. Secondly, some believe that Jesus Christ exercises his authority and rule in ways that complement the Bible – for example, through the teaching of the church, through reason and conscience or through contemporary revelation. Thirdly, some Christians who accept the supreme authority of the Bible and have studied it in depth may still disagree on how it is to be interpreted. Let us consider each of these in turn.

Knowing what the Bible says

The Bible is of course not one book but a collection of sixty-six, written by some forty different authors in three languages over a period of 1,400 years. It consists of historical narrative, law, poetry, proverbs, prophetic literature and apocalyptic, and takes over fifty hours to read through, let alone study. It was written in a cultural setting and at a time in history which are completely foreign to us, and long before the advent of modern medicine. Applying it to contemporary situations is no easy task, but if we are to bring our whole lives under the lordship of Christ, we can and must work hard at understanding it. Having our deeply held convictions challenged and changed by interaction with God's truth may at times be very painful. However, it is essential that we come to the Scriptures with a readiness to be reshaped by God. If God is not speaking to us freshly from his Word, if at any stage we feel we have mastered its teaching, then we need to be humbled once again. Jesus and the apostles lived and breathed Scripture, and if we are to bring glory to God in our professional lives, we must do the same. Ignorance of God's Word in responsible Christian professionals dishonours Christ and hinders the gospel.

Christian authorities outside the Bible

As already argued, we believe in the authority of the Bible because Jesus Christ himself gave his stamp of authority to the Old Testament and commissioned the writing of the New. As Christ will not contradict himself, we can be sure that anything which is not consistent with the teaching of the Bible cannot be coming to us with the authority of Christ. Some Christians would hold that

Christ may speak to us in ways other than by the written Word which has faithfully been passed down to us. There is good support for this thinking in Scripture itself, but much which should lead us to exercise caution. Everything must be carefully tested against the Bible, and anything inconsistent rejected. The three main extrabiblical categories of God's speaking are church teaching, conscience and contemporary prophecy. Each of these deserves consideration on its own.

Church teaching. In this category I am including everything from church creeds and councils, ecclesiastical officials and the great Christian teachers throughout history, to respected contemporary church leaders and Christian friends. Now there is no doubt that God can speak to us through the writings and words of all of these, but it does not follow that this teaching is infallible. If even recognized biblical prophets and apostles can be led astray at times (1 Ki. 22:19–23; Gal. 2:11–13), we should take note and be continually on our guard about teaching which comes from any lesser authority. No denomination is immune to this.

It is one thing, for example, for the council of bishops of the Roman Catholic church to give ethical teaching consistent with Christ's own. It is quite another to expound doctrines which blatantly contradict the teaching of Jesus and the apostles (such as the immaculate conception of Mary). Such teaching must be roundly rejected. Protestants can make similar mistakes if they uncritically accept the words of Christian teachers without testing them against Scripture.

Helpful as the writings and words of great Christian teachers are, our study of them must never take precedence over our study of the Bible itself. All human beings are fallible and can be misled and deceived – a fact which the apostle Paul recognized. 'Even if we . . . should preach a gospel other than the one we preached to you, let [us] be 'eternally condemned' (Gal. 1:8). It follows that we should maintain a healthy suspicion of all that we hear, even from those we most respect within the church, having the attitude of the Bereans who, when they heard the teaching of the apostle Paul, 'examined the Scriptures every day' to see if it was true (Acts 17:11). All church teaching should drive us back to the Bible, knowing that if any Christian teacher and the Bible ever disagree, then the teacher is wrong and the Bible right.

Reason and conscience. Some people parody Christianity as mindless obedience, but nothing could be further from the truth. Of course, God does expect from us childlike faith and obedience, but he expects us to use our minds in applying his Word to the specific decisions we make. The fact that God knows best is no excuse for laziness in Bible reading, study and interpretation. Rather, it should produce in us more diligence to develop these disciplines, so that we can glorify our creator, deepen our obedience and strengthen our evangelistic witness. Having the mind of Christ involves making reasonable deductions about how we should live on the basis of the truth he has revealed. Problems arise when, instead of looking to God's revelation, we trust our own judgment or insight (Pr. 3:5–6). Reason may be a gift of God, but it is not infallible if it starts from unbiblical premises or disregards logical principles.

Conscience, like reason, is a God-given faculty through which God can guide us, but we need to ensure that our consciences are being continually shaped and moulded by exposure to God's Word. Christians who claim to 'have peace' about a certain course of action may simply have consciences which are uneducated through lack of exposure to God's Word, or blunted through habitual disobedience. Similarly, those who 'feel convicted' may actually have over-sensitive consciences which are more informed by human authority than God's law.

While we should use reason and take notice of conscience, both have their limitations and must always be tested against God's Word. If given the wrong place, both can lead people astray.

Contemporary prophecy. There is a broad diversity of opinion among Christians about the contemporary function of the gifts of the Holy Spirit mentioned in Romans 12 and 1 Corinthians 12. At one extreme are those who hold a 'cessationist' view, believing that the use of certain gifts such as prophecy ceased in New Testament times. At the other extreme are those who have jettisoned the Bible and rely entirely on 'prophetic words' for guidance. The first group despises all prophecy, while the second group capitulates uncritically to everything claiming to be 'from the Lord'.

The Bible reveals that there were 'prophets' in New Testament times (Acts 13:1; 21:8–10; Eph. 2:20; 3:5), and gives us no reason to believe that this ministry should not operate today. There are detailed instructions about the functioning of prophetic gifts within the church (1 Cor. 14; 1 Thes. 5:19–21), and also about the discernment of true and false prophecy (Mt. 7:15–20; 2 Pet. 2; Jude 3–16). God clearly did speak to his people directly, to warn them (Acts 11:27; 21:10), to encourage them (Acts 15:32; 1 Cor. 14:3) and specifically to direct them (Acts 16:6–10). Jesus and the apostles also warned repeatedly about the dangers of false prophecy, however, and throughout the whole of Scripture we are given principles for assessing it. Prophets who make false predictions are not speaking

God's word (Dt. 18:21–22) but neither are those whose true predictions are accompanied by false teaching (Dt. 13:1–5). True prophecy exalts Christ (1 Jn. 4:1–3), edifies the church (1 Cor. 14:4), is consistent with existing Scripture (1 Cor. 14:37–38) and is accompanied by a godly life (Mt. 7:15–20) and a teachable spirit (1 Cor. 14:29–33) – for even those who have been used by God as his mouthpiece may be misled (Gal. 2:11–13). What the speaker sincerely believes to be a prophetic word may in fact have its origin in his imagination (Ezk. 13:1) or, worse still, in some ungodly source (1 Ki. 22:19–23).

This is why it is so important that all 'words from the Lord' be carefully weighed and tested (1 Thes. 5:19–21; 1 Cor. 14:29). This involves exercising caution and seeking the confirmation of others with gifts of prophecy and discernment, and of Christians wiser than ourselves. Most importantly, such 'words' must be tested against the words of Jesus and the apostles in the Bible. Any 'word' which is inconsistent with the teaching of the Bible cannot be from God and must be firmly rejected. Similarly, any Christian who claims that 'the Lord told me' something contrary to the plain teaching of the Bible is simply wrong, regardless of the depth of his or her conviction.

When Christians still disagree

Among mature Christians who have studied hard and know their Bibles well, there may still be disagreement, and here great wisdom is needed. It may be because the issue is something that God has not spoken clearly about, and in this case we must simply agree that we do not know (Dt. 29:29). It may be some issue of secondary importance to the gospel where each Christian is free to act according to his or her conscience (Rom. 14; 1 Cor. 8; Col. 2:16–23). However, it may an issue where the very authority of Christ himself is being questioned. In this latter situation we must be as committed to resolving it and to reaching a godly consensus as the apostles were (Acts 15:1–35). This can require a vast amount of courage, grace and humility. If Peter and Barnabas could be led astray, as they clearly were over the circumcision issue (Gal. 2:11–13), then how much more may we! We must be aware of our own capacity for error, but if we are concerned about the gospel, we will also be anxious to discover the mind of God and will not tolerate a variety of opinions where the Bible does not allow it.

For Christian doctors who know their Bibles well, and are seeking to obey God in every area of their lives, there remain several areas of difficulty, and I will conclude with some words about six of these. What do we do when God's commands appear to conflict? Which commands in the Bible still apply to Christians? How can we apply its commands to our own twentieth-century technological society? Does the end ever justify the means? To what extent can we impose our Christian morality on our patients? How do we practically handle the inevitable conflict our obedience to Christ will create with colleagues and patients?

1. *When God's commands conflict.* The question addressed here is whether God's commands ever conflict in such a way that it seems impossible to obey one while not at the same moment disobeying another. If such conflict exists how should we act in such situations?

Much has been made of moral conflicts by situation ethicists such as Joseph Fletcher. Is it ever right to tell a lie to preserve innocent life? Is it ever ethical to kill in order to relieve suffering? Is it right temporarily to compromise one's values in order to stay in a position of influence?

There are examples of each of these in medicine. Take abortion. Should a doctor who believes that abortion is wrong give false information to prevent it happening? Should he perform abortion anyway in some situations to relieve other people's suffering? Should he perform some in order to get to a position where he can prevent a greater number of others?

It is clear biblical teaching that it is wrong to tell lies (Lv. 19:11), right to relieve the suffering of others (Lk. 10:37), and wrong to disobey the governing authorities (Rom. 13:1–5) – yet the Bible mentions examples of godly men and women apparently acting counter to these divine directives when faced with conflicting priorities. It seems that deceiving an evil person can be justified to protect innocent lives (Ex. 1:15–20, Jos. 2:2–7; 2 Sa. 17:17–22), causing suffering through a word of rebuke or act of discipline can be justified to save a person from greater evil (Heb. 12:7–11) and disobeying the governing authorities can be justified if it is to honour a direct command of God (Dn. 3:13–18; 6:6–10; Acts 4:19; 5:29).

Did Jesus face moral conflicts of this kind? If we deny that he did, we are in effect denying that he was tempted in all ways as we are (Heb. 4:15). Did he then sin by neglecting one duty to perform another? If we say that he did, we are in effect denying that he was the perfect sacrifice (Heb. 10:12–13). It seems that we must accept that Jesus faced moral conflicts and that he did not sin in his choice of priorities. As we might expect, the gospel accounts bear testimony to this fact.

On occasions he used his miraculous powers to resolve the conflict and somehow perform both duties. When confronted by a choice between attending to a chronic illness near at hand or a rapidly fatal one at a distance, he healed the first patient and raised the second from the dead (Lk. 8:40–56). When faced with a crowd hungry for both food and teaching he fed 5,000 people with a handful of fish and bread rather than turn them away (Jn. 6:1–15). But there were clearly other occasions when he made a choice between two apparently conflicting priorities. He gave priority to God rather than his family (Mt. 12:46–50) or the governing authorities, prayed rather than went on responding to desperate need while exhausted (Lk. 5:15–16), healed and relieved hunger rather than resting on the sabbath (Lk. 6:6–11; Mk. 2:23–28), and offered mercy rather than insisting upon justice (Jn. 8:1–11). He went to the cross because he refused to submit by lying about his identity (Lk. 22:70–71) or by speaking out in defence of his innocence (Mk. 15:1–5).

What can we learn from this? First, that all God's laws are important. Jesus said that he had not come to abolish Old Testament law but to fulfil it, and that anyone who relaxed 'the least of the commandments' and taught others to do the same would be called least in the kingdom of heaven (Mt. 5:17–20). Obedience to the more important of the commandments was not an excuse for neglecting those of lesser importance (Mt. 23:23).

Secondly, there are higher and lower moral laws. There was a range of punishments for sin in the Old Testament depending upon the severity of the offence (Ex. 22:23–25). Jesus himself spoke of the 'greatest commandment' (Mt. 22:38), the 'more important matters of the law' (Mt. 23:23) and the 'greater sin' (Jn. 19:11). This pattern is also evident in the apostles' teaching. Although it is never denied (but rather affirmed) that all wrongdoing is sin, there were nonetheless some sins that called for excommunication (Mt. 18:17), some which led to or did not lead to death (1 Jn. 5:16–17) and some which were unforgivable (Mt. 6:15; 12:31–32; Heb. 10:26–31).

Thirdly, we sometimes face conflicts of priorities where we must choose between one duty and another.

Fourthly, in making these choices, we should choose to honour the higher rather than the lower duty.

Finally, Scripture does not leave us in the dark concerning the way God apparently grades moral duties: love for God takes precedence over love for parents and family (Mt. 10:37), obeying God is more important than obeying government (Dn. 3:13–18; 6:6–10; Acts 4:19; 5:29), mercy triumphs over judgment (Jas. 2:13), preserving innocent life takes precedence over veracity (Ex. 1:15–20; Jos. 2:2–7; 2 Sa. 17:17–22), preaching the gospel is more important than healing (Lk. 4:38–44) and obedience to God's commands is more important than exercising spiritual gifts (Mt. 7:21–23; 1 Cor. 12:31–13:3).

In the teaching and the life of Jesus himself we see these principles worked out to perfection. He seemed to understand the exact meaning and application of every commandment. It was the failure of others to understand and apply them that led them to replace God's own authority with their own and ultimately to judge Jesus as deserving of death. The teachers of the law and the Pharisees were criticized because they introduced an unbiblical hierarchy of moral duty (Mt. 23:23), failed to obey God's law and replaced it with their own oral tradition (Mt. 23:3). Furthermore, they repeatedly tried to trap Jesus in situations of moral conflict (Lk. 11:53–54; Mt. 12:9–14; 22:15–22) when they themselves had made deliberate choices to obey one commandment over another in similar situations (Mt. 23:1–39; Mk. 7:5–13; Lk. 11:37–54). This is an area where great wisdom is needed. We do well to echo the psalmist's prayer: 'I am your servant; give me discernment that I may understand your statutes' (Ps. 119:125).

2. *Which biblical commands still apply to Christians?* Jesus taught that he had come to fulfil the Old Testament law (Mt. 5:17–20), and that in effect the entire Old Testament Scriptures bore witness to him (Jn. 8:39–40). Through his death and resurrection he established a new era and a new covenant whereby we are put into a right relationship with God not through obedience to Old Testament law but through faith in Christ (Rom. 3:20–22). This is because no-one is capable of obeying the law fully: the Jews fall short of the written code they received through Moses, and the Gentiles fall short of what their own consciences reveal about what God requires (Rom. 2:12–13).

Relationship with God, however, implies obedience to his commands (Jn. 14:15; 1 Jn. 2:3). The fact that we have been saved by God's grace through faith is not a licence to sin (Rom. 6:15); rather, obedience is the evidence of genuine faith. The reality is that in moving from being under law to being under grace, although we have died to and become free from the law that we could never before obey, we still have an obligation to God. As Paul puts it, we are not under Old Testament law but rather under Christ's law (1 Cor. 9:21) to love one another as he has loved us (Jn. 13:34–35). This is a much higher obligation than the one the Jews had in the Old Testament – but we are privileged to have knowledge and power

129

which they could only speculate about. We have not only the knowledge of Jesus but also the power of the Holy Spirit to help us to be 'imitators of Christ'. Because of what God has done for us, we are now 'slaves to righteousness' (Rom. 6:18) and must walk in the way of the cross as Jesus himself did (1 Jn. 2:6).

To fulfil this law of love is a duty which goes far beyond Old Testament legalities. It is wrong not only to murder but also to hate (Mt. 5:21–22), not only to commit adultery but even to lust (Mt. 5:27–28). We are enjoined to go far beyond mere legalistic obedience so that our lives fulfil the very principle of self-sacrificial love which Christ's own life exemplified. In this endeavour, Old Testament principles are not to be relaxed, for they are divinely inspired to teach, rebuke, correct and train us in order that we may be thoroughly equipped for every good work (2 Tim. 3:16–17). It follows that the Christian should have a high view of all Scripture, taking all commands seriously and avoiding the extremes of legalism (where we are satisfied to neglect the spirit of the law for the letter) and presumption (where we are tempted to redefine morality in accordance with what we perceive love to be). Both errors can be avoided if we make the life and teaching of Jesus our standard.

The Old Testament law is prophetic. As Christians, we are not expected or commanded to make animal sacrifices, for example, or to observe the complex rituals pertaining to temple worship. This would be to deny the New Testament teaching that Jesus is the one perfect sacrifice for all our sins (Heb. 10:11–14) and that his own body, the church, is the true temple of God (1 Cor. 3:16–17).

Nor are we obliged to observe Jewish dietary laws or celebrate Jewish festivals (Col. 2:16–17), although we may choose to do so, as Paul did in certain circumstances, to further the gospel (1 Cor. 9:19–20). Nor in fact are we obliged to obey the purely moral teaching of the Old Testament simply because it is in the Old Testament. The commandments not to murder, commit adultery or steal are to be obeyed because they are underlined by Jesus (Lk. 18:18–20) and the apostles (Rom. 13:8–10) as being part of what is involved in loving as Christ loved us. We will seek as Christians to go beyond them to the very spirit behind them without relaxing them in the process (Mt. 5:19).

In summary, our highest authority is to be that of Christ and the apostles. We are not under the old covenant, but (as Christ did) we will seek to be as fully conversant with its teachings as possible in order to love as Christ himself loved.

3. *Applying God's commands today.* Even if we have a good grasp

of what God's commands are, and how to resolve situations where they appear to conflict, we still have a lot of hard thinking to do in applying them to contemporary ethical dilemmas. The Bible was written primarily to a middle-eastern, pre-industrial culture and therefore specifically addresses middle-eastern pre-industrial problems. There is much about cows but little about cars. Infanticide gets mentioned but not abortion, vineyards but not ventilators, silver but not smart cards, stone tablets but not silicon chips. However, the principles remain the same. It is only the context in which these unchanging moral principles are to be applied that is different. We are faced with this hermeneutical task – sorting out how God's unchanging principles apply to contemporary situations which may not have been envisaged by the human authors, but were nonetheless prepared for it in the mind of God. All this involves hard work and skill. But if we are to live in obedience to God in today's society (and we have no choice, because this is exactly what knowing and loving him involve), then we have a responsibility to use our minds to work out contemporary codes of conduct based on the revealed principles we find in Scripture.

We know that murder, adultery, stealing and idolatry are wrong. This is no problem. The crucial questions are these: is euthanasia for compassionate motives murder? Is the use of donor gametes adultery? Is lending at interest stealing? Is materialism idolatry?

Genetic engineering is not mentioned in the Bible but there are principles about stewardship (Gn. 1:26–28; Mt. 25:14–30), and cross-mating of different species (Lv. 19:19). Abortion is not specifically dealt with but there is much about intentional killing (Ex. 21:12–14), pre-natal life (Ps. 139:13–16) and child sacrifice (Dt. 18:10; 12:31). AIDS was not known, but there is a lot about sexual morality (1 Cor. 6:18) and compassion for sinners. Kwashiorkor does not feature, but there is much about feeding the hungry and the causes of injustice. We can and must use our minds to apply these biblical principles to contemporary problems.

As we think about contemporary problems in the light of biblical principles and with the help of God's Spirit, answers will be forthcoming. A useful approach is to consider each problem within the framework of biblical history, particularly in relation to the four great events of creation, fall, redemption and consummation. Take disease as an example. Christians begin by thinking of health as the good gift of a good creator, a blessing of providence over which we have some control. Secondly, we recognize that disease has entered the world as a result of the fall, but that God in his grace has revealed principles of prevention and cure that can to some extent ameliorate it. Thirdly, the gospel offers forgiveness, and the will and compassion to work with God to relieve spiritual and physical suffering. Finally, Jesus has revealed that in the new world we will possess resurrected, non-decaying bodies (1 Cor. 15:35–54; 2 Cor. 5:1–10) and that there will be no more death or crying or pain (Rev. 21:1–4). As our minds are increasingly renewed by thinking biblically, we will find contemporary ethical dilemmas less and less confusing.

4. *Ends and means.* Secular ethicists classically divide ways of making ethical decision into two categories: deontological and consequentialist.

The deontologist judges an action right or wrong on the basis of whether it conforms to a set of rules or principles. Immanuel Kant was one of the first advocates of deontological decision-making. In the 1980s, Beauchamp and Childress first enunciated four *prima facie* principles of ethics in health care which have become the basis of most contemporary secular ethical discussion. They are beneficence (the obligation to do good); non-maleficence (the obligation not to do harm); autonomy (the obligation to respect the decision-making capacities of autonomous people) and justice (the obligation of fairness in the distribution of benefits and risks).

The consequentialist, on the other hand, judges an action by its outcomes. John Stuart Mill and Jeremy Bentham are usually associated with this category of decision-making, and it would be fair to say that most popular contemporary ethical discussion gives far more weight to consequences of decisions than to the principles underlying them.

The Christian will obviously respect the authority of Christ and Bible above Kant and Bentham, but it can legitimately be asked whether Christian ethics are deontological or consequentialist. In fact, the Bible has elements of both. Take for example the question 'Is adultery right?' On the one hand the seventh commandment states, 'you shall not commit adultery' (Ex. 20:14). Why not? Because God prohibits it and we have a duty to obey God. This is a rule-based or deontological argument. However, the writer of Proverbs takes a different approach. 'Think about the consequences of adultery,' he says in effect. 'Consider the shame and disgrace not to mention the fury and rage of a jealous husband. Is it really worth it for a few moments of pleasure? You'll probably end up destroying your marriage. What about the children? How can it be right?' (*cf.* Pr. 5:1–14; 6:20–35). This is a consequentialist argument. So the Bible sees rules and consequences as being intimately connected. God is loving, trustworthy and profoundly concerned with human welfare. It therefore makes sense to obey his commands, since to ignore them is to choose unpleasant consequences.

However, recognition of this is not enough. We must also recognize that because God is a far better developer of deontological principles and judge of consequences than we are (Pr. 3:5–6), it follows that we should trust his judgment rather than our own. This will mean that even when the consequences of a course of action seem to dictate that we should ignore the rules and trust our own judgment rather than God's, we should nonetheless abide by the rule. This is to acknowledge the limitations imposed on us simply by virtue of being human and sinful. This is the way of faith, and this is what makes Christian ethics so diametrically opposed to secular ethics. It is based on God's revelation rather than human wisdom. God is a far better judge of principles of conduct and consequences of action than we are. It follows that we must trust his Word and not our own judgment.

Scripture is full of examples of this. The great men and women of faith are commended for their faith in obeying God's word despite the perceived consequences (*e.g.* Abraham's sacrifice of Isaac (Gn. 22:1–19), Moses' return to Egypt (Ex. 3:7–4:31), Daniel's persistence in public prayer (Dn. 6:6–10)). Conversely, those who exhibited lack of faith were the ones who chose not to obey, but to trust their own judgment of consequences (Saul's attack without Samuel (1 Sa. 13:1–14), Aaron's golden calf (Ex. 32)). Perhaps the best example of all is Christ's third temptation. Satan offered him all the kingdoms of the world if Christ would worship him (Mt. 4:8–10). We know that to rule over the kingdoms of the world was Christ's destiny. But the way to it was not through worshipping Satan but through submitting to God on the cross. With God the end never justifies the means. We must do his work in his way.

5. *Imposing our morality?* We live in a pluralist culture where religious belief is seen as a private matter and the supreme virtue is tolerance. It is not surprising that when we submit to God's rule in the way we behave, we will be accused of attempting to 'impose our morality' on our colleagues and patients. Of course we must not impose our beliefs in the sense that we force others to do what we say. After all, the gospel is an invitation, not an imposition. But neither must we let the world 'squeeze us into its mould' (Rom. 12:1–2. JBP). We must resist having the morality of others imposed on us to the extent that we refrain from speaking the truth or become a party to things which we know are wrong for fear of causing offence. The gospel is offensive, and our allegiance to Christ will cause us at times to do things which others find offensive (Mt.

5:11–12). We must be careful to ensure that the only offence we cause is that of the gospel, that our manner is not ungracious (Col. 4:5–6), but we must realize that sometimes people will dislike or even hate us simply because of how our beliefs lead us to behave (Jn. 15:18–21; 16:1–4).

There are two main areas where we can be tempted to compromise in our allegiance to Christ. The first is in giving medical advice which challenges our patients' or colleagues' lifestyles, and the second is in participating in unethical practices to which society has given tacit approval..

First, giving medical advice. As well as having skills in the diagnosis and treatment of disease, doctors also possess knowledge about the aetiology, progression and spread of disease. Because before God all knowledge confers accountability, doctors have a responsibility to educate and warn patients about lifestyle factors and prognosis. If we fail to do so, we are denying them the opportunity to change their behaviour or prepare properly for the future. A patient's illness may well be linked to some lifestyle factor such as alcohol, smoking, fat consumption, stress or sexual promiscuity, and he himself may not be aware of the link. Some patients will take such advice well, but others may be offended at our suggestion that they may have contributed to their illness in some way. Either way, it is our duty to inform them sensitively and firmly in the hope that they will take our advice and change their behaviour.

Secondly, participating in unethical practices. There are situations when our patients or colleagues want us to help them do something we regard as unethical. It may also be illegal, such as making false statements on an official document or certificate, or it may be something quite 'legal', such as being party to an abortion. If we refuse to cooperate in such situations, we may be putting our relationships, reputations or careers at risk. In these conflict situations, we have to remember that we are ultimately God's servants and not primarily the servants of our patients, colleagues or superiors. Although we must never be rude or disrespectful, there are times when we are obliged politely to refuse to act improperly, remembering that 'we are not trying to please men but God, who tests our hearts' (1 Thes. 2:4).

6. *Handling conflict*. How then should we handle the conflict situations which will inevitably arise in our work as a result of our faith?

First, we must be sure that the difficulty has arisen as a result of our being faithful to God rather than unfaithful (1 Pet. 2:19–20). If we are genuinely at fault ourselves, then we need to apologize for our part in the disagreement. This may be difficult to discern in the heat of the moment, and it may be wise to take some time to reflect on the situation, perhaps with the advice of an independent Christian whom we respect. If we have been accused of wrong-doing, it does not follow that we are necessarily at fault (Rev. 12:10).

Secondly, we should expect conflicts to occur (2 Tim. 3:12), and try to anticipate them. We should ideally think through the issues involved biblically, and well ahead of time, so that we know exactly where we stand and why. Some conflicts arise completely out of the blue, and in these we need simply to trust that God will give us the words to say (Lk. 21:14–15). If we are unsure, it is best to err on the side of caution (Rom. 14:23), saying that we are unhappy and would like to give the matter more thought.

Thirdly, we should look for some way to defuse conflicts before they arise – as Daniel did so masterfully early on in his career (Dn. 1:8–16) – or to suggest some ethical alternatives to our patients or colleagues.

Fourthly, we need to make our stand and take the consequences. Usually we will find that our fears do not eventuate. Sometimes God may use the circumstances to vindicate us, and our stand may result in some positive change in other individuals or in the system. Occasionally we may stand to lose our popularity, reputation, place on a training scheme, job, or worse. This is what carrying the cross is all about.

Finally, we should always look for some compassionate third way out of the dilemma. Some ethical decisions may seem like choosing between two equally undesirable alternatives: for example, between letting a patient die in severe pain or giving him a lethal injection. Referral to a more experienced colleague or transfer to a hospice specializing in pain relief may resolve the problem. Similarly, practical support and adoption constitute a viable alternative to the undesirable options of either abortion or keeping a child a woman is unable or unwilling to support. Jesus was remarkable at discovering the third way no-one had contemplated in so many of his ethical dilemmas, and will help us by his Spirit to do the same. Not rushing into diabolical quick-fix solutions will make us much better researchers in the long run.

On the one hand, then, we need to resolve to obey what the Lord has commanded, and on the other we need to be searching for compassionate Christian alternatives. This is the way Jesus walked. It is the path of the cross – obedience regardless of the cost (Lk. 14:28–33), and a willingness to be part of the solution by bearing the burdens of others ourselves (Gal. 6:2).

9 ISSUES OF EARLY LIFE

David Cahill

This chapter addresses several issues which pertain to fertility treatments and early embryonic and fetal life. These are approached from a biblical perspective, based on words just as alive and applicable to our lives at the close of the twentieth century as when they were written 2,000 or more years ago. Whatever opinions are voiced are based on the study of the Scripture verses, filled out by a distillation of conservative evangelical thinking. Recent debates in the literature of the Christian Medical Fellowship illustrate the diversity of opinion that exists within Christian circles. An open, humble attitude and a non-dogmatic approach are required in these very difficult and confusing issues. In addition, there may be the difference of opinion between those in clinical practice, who have to face these issues daily, and those thinkers who have the time and training to approach the issues philosophically. Both groups are necessary to bring about an informed opinion. Dialogue is important; these groups need to listen and relate to each other.

Our patients are unlikely to share our beliefs and, moreover, may resent the imposition of our opinions and values. This may lead to a conflict of approach, because of differing attitudes. There will always be situations of special need or circumstance to which we ought to respond with love and compassion – not always acquiescing to someone's request, but certainly conveying to them that we understand their circumstances.

Finally, there is the question of whether or not individuals have the right to have a child. This has important implications for the use of resources – manpower, finances and so on. It is a crucial aspect of the whole debate on the ethics and morality of infertility treatment and management.

Fundamentally, we have very few rights. The most fundamental must be the right to life and to live. Integral to this is the necessity of eating, drinking, and breathing. We may have a longing or an overwhelming desire for our own child, even an obsession with our need for a baby. We may have a biological urge to reproduce, but there is no clear evidence that we have any individual right to fertility. Biblically, the commitment of a married couple to each other is for companionship. Children are an expected part of the marriage but are not guaranteed.

Infertility

Background, investigation and treatment

Infertility is the failure to become pregnant when desired. It affects at least one in every ten couples and has two main areas of classification: before a woman has ever become pregnant (primary infertility), or after a previous pregnancy (secondary infertility). The causes of infertility are sperm-related (25%) or unexplained (30%), the remaining 45% being female-related: ovulation failure (20%), damage to the Fallopian tube*† (15%), endometriosis* (5%) and others.[1]

The investigation of infertility does vary somewhat depending on an individual unit's own philosophy and areas of interest. Most, however, would agree that a general assessment would include a test of sperm numbers and quality (usually a sperm* count), perhaps a test of sperm function (their ability to survive in biological media*), a test of the quality of ovulatory function (usually the amount of progesterone* produced on the twenty-first to twenty-third day of the menstrual cycle), a test of normal stimulation to the ovaries (by blood sample in the first week of the menstrual cycle) and a test of tubal patency (either by laparoscopy* or hysterosalpingography*). If these investigations are performed, it should be possible to reach a diagnosis.

Treatment of infertility is based on the underlying problem. Some problems are more amenable to treatment than others. Thus ovulation* problems respond well to treatment. Tubal damage can be repaired although the more severe the damage, the lower the chance of success. Problems of sperm numbers or function are generally difficult to treat, although some treatments are claimed to be effective. Conditions where sperm or oocyte* production fails are generally not amenable to treatment without recourse to the use of donor gametes.* On the part of men, this failure may be because of a congenital failure of spermatogenesis,* injury, medical treatment, or previous sterilization procedure (16% of requests for donor insemination*).[2] On the part of women, donor eggs are used in the case of premature menopause, primary ovarian failure, or where ovaries are non-functional as a result of surgery or chemotherapy.

The long-term likelihood of success (pregnancy) with problems of

†An asterisk * refers to a term listed in the glossary on pp. 157–159.

sperm numbers or function is low, in the region of 5% or less; with problems of failure to ovulate 40%-50%; surgical repair of tubal damage up to 25%, depending on the severity of the damage; treatment of conditions such as polycystic ovarian disease or endometriosis up to 30%. While some couples may be prepared to wait to see if they conceive on their own or after some simple treatment, others are not prepared to do so and opt for assisted conception techniques.

Assisted conception

In general, attempts to treat the more severe forms of subfertility (*e.g.* tubal damage or sperm disorders) and failure of human conception* were quite ineffective until the birth of Louise Brown in 1978 by *in vitro* fertilization (IVF). This was hailed by the popular press as a miracle and as the answer to every infertile couple's problem. She had been conceived as a result of fertilization of her mother's egg* by her father's sperm outside the body in a laboratory, and the resultant embryos* were replaced into the cavity of her mother's womb several days later.

Unfortunately, the promises of 1978 have not really come true. For a greater investment in time, effort and money, these treatments offer a much higher chance of success in one single cycle. In the best possible circumstances, these treatments offer up to a 45% chance of success, though this is significantly reduced if the woman is older or if sperm quality is poor. More likely, however, is an average 'take-home baby' rate of 15%–20%. The main techniques are IVF*, GIFT* (gamete intra-Fallopian transfer) and IUI* (intra-uterine insemination). All of these treatments use 'fertility' drug injections to stimulate a number of eggs to develop and are consequently very expensive. The choice of treatment will depend on a balance of a number of parameters including cost-effectiveness. IVF is usually more expensive than GIFT, and both are usually more expensive than IUI (costs are of the order of £1,000–£3,000 per cycle). However, GIFT is considered to be more effective than IVF, and both are more effective than IUI, although GIFT and IUI are not appropriate for every couple. The numbers of cycles and successful outcomes for IVF and GIFT are given in table 1 (p. 159). These are obtained from the most recent available Human Fertilization and Embryology Authority report.[3]

Why have fertility-related issues become an area of interest?

To a greater degree than before, people are coming out into the open and admitting that they are infertile. For many years, this information was considered to be something to be ashamed of, a secret to be kept hidden away from others. The more general openness on other aspects of our behaviour since the 1960s has led to more open discussion of this area of infertility.

Secondly, more traditional ways of dealing with infertility are being eroded. Since the Abortion Act (1967) passed into law, the number of abortions* per year has increased steadily. As a result, the number of babies placed for adoption has fallen steadily (Table 2, p. 160). Furthermore, due to the increase in social acceptance, the number of unmarried mothers has risen (570,000 in 1971 to 1.15 million in 1989). Therefore, those who in the past might have accepted adoption as an answer to their childlessness are now forced to seek alternative approaches to alleviate their infertility.

Finally, advances in technology, skills and scientific resources mean that medical intervention is more likely to succeed than in the past. Those involved in research at the forefront of knowledge often continue to forge ahead without giving adequate time and consideration to discuss these issues. Controversy and concern result when the full implications of any treatment are not fully evaluated before that treatment is widely available to the public. One of the beneficial aspects of the introduction of the statutory UK regulatory body, the Human Fertilization and Embryology Authority (HFEA), has been to bring new or proposed treatment methods to public notice so that at least some degree of public response can be obtained.

Biblical reference material

Early fetal life

What does Scripture say about the unborn child and early intra-uterine life? God's relationship with us may begin before our birth. There are many references in the Old and New Testaments which suggest that God was aware of individuals and had set them apart while still within the womb and even before they were created (e.g. Samson (Jdg. 13:1–25); Jeremiah (Je. 1:5); the psalmist (Ps. 139:13–16); Isaiah (Is. 49:1); Paul (Gal. 1:15); and non-specific references (e.g. Is. 44:2, 24)).

In Luke 1, God knew that John the Baptist would be conceived and that his life was already destined for service to the Lord (Lk. 1:13–17). John, as yet unborn, responded with a leap within Elizabeth's womb when he heard the voice of the virgin Mary. Was this because he sensed the presence of the Messiah within her womb? Does this imply that we can respond to God's presence at that time? If so, this must be with our spirit or our soul.

Many passages refer to our being formed in the womb and indicate that God knows us and can set us apart even before that. In their context, the phrase 'being formed' seems to be equivalent to taking on a recognizable human shape, perhaps at six to ten weeks. Being human (as opposed to animal) implies having both a physical and a spiritual element to our existence. Much thought has gone into the point at which the soul might enter the body, marking the beginning of human life. When does it take on a spiritual aspect? Even before we are formed, God knows us (Je. 1:4–5). Perhaps the non-implanted morula* (that undifferentiated mass of cells) is the stage at which we become human. For a more in-depth discussion than is possible here, the reader is referred to a molecular biologist, John Medina, who discusses the position of early fetal life and its relationship to God.[5] He comes to the conclusion, however, that we cannot know, as Scripture does not provide satisfactory 'scientific' answers to these questions. God, being outside time, is not constrained by whether an individual is a child or a baby, or unborn or even conceived. His purposes and plan for any individual human being surpass the physical constraints we are under.

We are created in God's image and likeness (Gn. 1:26–27; 5:1; 9:6). While the implications of this truth are beyond the scope of this chapter (and discussed elsewhere)[6] we can summarize the content of the verses. We are made in the likeness of the Creator, we are not exact replicas, and we are capable of relating to that Creator. These verses suggest that rights are conveyed on individual people for existence simply because of that relationship; furthermore, we should not use others or value them simply on the basis of their possible usefulness to us or to others.

Fertility and infertility

Before the fall, God gave humankind first a responsibility for ruling the earth and then a command to increase in number and to subdue the earth (Gn. 1:26–30; 9:7). From earliest times in the Scriptures, children were regarded as a blessing and gift from God (Ps. 127:3) and their withholding as a sign of disfavour before God and a mark of disgrace and ridicule among the people round about. Sarah (Gn. 16:1), Rebekah (Gn. 25:21) and Rachel (Gn. 29:31) in the Old Testament, and Elizabeth (Lk. 1:25) in the New, were all childless for much of their life. They suffered inwardly and outwardly because of this, even expressing that feeling of shame and disgrace (Gn. 30:23). It is, however, important to recall that these situations I have just mentioned are in the context of the Old Testament, with the significance of the blood-line of the people of Israel to the covenant made by God. The shame felt by these people in the Old Testament was not just on the part of the individual, but had a more corporate meaning, because of the implications of childlessness for the future people of Israel. The emphasis on the nature and cause of physical disease in the New Testament (Lk. 13:1–5; Jn. 9:1–3) is less specific to the individual, although particular examples of illness following sin do occur (Acts 13:6–12).

There is an overriding principle in the Bible which should also be considered. Those who are weak or disadvantaged should be given particular care and attention, so that their needs are looked after. The poor, the elderly, the orphaned or strangers (Ex. 23:7; Lk. 19:32; Ex. 23:21–24) are prone to exploitation and are therefore more in need of our particular protection. This principle is probably as applicable to the fetus* as it is to these others, although it is not specifically mentioned.

The role and importance of marriage

The role of marriage is particularly relevant to the use of donor gametes. Some of the passages which refer to marriage (Gn. 1:28; 2:20–25; Mt. 19:3–12; Eph. 5:22–33; 1 Pet. 3:1–7) and, more specifically, adultery (Lv. 20:10–21; Dt. 5:18) teach that marriage was instituted by God, for the purpose first of companionship and then procreation. Most would also agree that these passages suggest that marriage is heterosexual (only) in nature, that it is monogamous and exclusive, that it represents a public promise of a lifelong commitment, and that its intimacy is expressed by sexual intercourse. Adultery is the 'sexual relation of a married person with one who is not his or her lawful spouse' (*Shorter Oxford English Dictionary*). Even the sexual act with a prostitute is adultery (1 Cor. 6:16). Adultery has to do with breaking of the unity of the marriage bond, and not with procreation.

What then is marriage? It arose because of a need for companionship which is felt by all humans, and is intended to answer it. Within the marriage relationship the partners grow together, mature together and help each other to move closer to God, each safe in the knowledge of acceptance by the other. John Stott[7] points to the teaching of Jesus and of Paul that marriage is permanent, and that the only ground for divorce (and remarriage) was sexual immorality or the desertion of a believer by an unbelieving partner. It is clear from the degree of emphasis placed on adultery in both Old and New Testaments that in God's view it is the foremost cause of the interruption of the marriage bond. In his teaching, Jesus was more restrictive than the teaching of the rabbis had been. He ruled out divorce for all the reasons permitted in Deuteronomy, and permitted it only for sexual violation of the marriage bond.

The fundamental question that needs to be answered in the matter of gamete donation is: does the use of donor eggs or sperm constitute a sexual violation of the marriage act? Physically, it is not a sexual act. Emotionally and spiritually, it is difficult to understand how it could be so interpreted. But (and this is important) individuals will differ in their understanding of this situation, and that difference needs to be accommodated.

Surrogate motherhood in Scripture

Very little mention of the practice of surrogacy is made in Scripture. In Genesis 15, God had made a covenant with Abram promising him many descendants. Abram's doubt in that promise made him take alternative action. At Sarai's suggestion, Abram took his servant-girl Hagar to his bed and she conceived. The result of this was distress and emotional turmoil for all concerned. Hagar despised Sarai, after which Sarai ill-treated her. Hagar gave birth to Ishmael, and the ensuing family conflict continued down through the generations. Abram's action was not out of step with the cultural mores of the time; his sin was his failure to wait for God to fulfil his covenant.

Jacob also had children by the servant-girls of his two wives (Gn. 30). This came about because of jealousy between his wives. While Jacob does not appear to have directly contravened God's direct promises here, the result of his action was continued dissension and dissatisfaction in his family.

God's attitude to the marriage relationship is that it is for companionship and for procreation (Gn. 2:18; 1:28). The practice of surrogacy in the cases of Abram and Jacob is quite different from what we see happening in the twentieth century. Nonetheless, the inference seems to be that it involved either a failure to wait for God to fulfil a very specific promise, or sinful attitudes in a marriage relationship. Is it too much to deduce from this that the practice is viewed by God as at best a poor second, or at worst outside his will for us because of its effects?

Summary of biblical principles

● God knows us before our birth, and sets apart some individuals even from then to serve him.
● We are created in the image or likeness of God.
● We are commanded to increase and multiply, and children are a blessing and a gift.
● We have a responsibility to protect the weak and disadvantaged within society.
● Marriage is God-ordained for companionship and for procreation.
● Marriage is heterosexual, exclusive, and public.
● The practice of surrogacy was generally a result of human impatience with God's revealed plan and had undesirable consequences.

Historical setting, ethical codes of practice and the current legal situation

The events (medical and otherwise) that bring us to the present day with regard to fertility treatment within the UK are summarized briefly below and outlined in appendix 1 (p. 160). The ethical codes of practice which refer to pregnancy, embryos and related issues are outlined in appendix 2 (p. 161).

The use of donor sperm for insemination, as a medical alleviation of male infertility, has been possible since the 1940s. From that time in the UK and elsewhere, several scientists sought to achieve extra-corporeal fertilization. Although the work was initially carried out in animals, human work began as techniques became more refined. Between 1970 and 1978, a number of researchers (with Professor R. G. Edwards at the forefront) published papers describing the fertilization of eggs outside the body. It took until 1978 for the first IVF live birth to occur, the result of collaborative work by Cambridge University scientists, led by Edwards, and Patrick Steptoe, a gynaecologist in Oldham. The possibilities of abuse of this knowledge, however, came to the fore. As a consequence, a committee of inquiry was established under Dame Mary Warnock to determine what policies should be drawn up on the issues of human fertilization, embryology and donor insemination, though not abortion or contraception*. Its report was published in 1984. In the following year, 1985, the Surrogacy Act was passed. This Act made it an offence to set up, agree about or take part in a commercial arrangement for surrogacy. It is not, however, an offence to participate in such arrangements when there is no element of gain or commercial interest. Surrogacy is carried out on a commercial basis (according to this Act) if payment is received by a third party for it, or if it is carried out with a view to payment being received. Payment for the necessary expenses of the (prospective) surrogate mother is allowed. It is also an offence to advertise either that one is looking for, or willing to be, a surrogate mother, through any medium (television, radio, newspapers, etc.), apart from word of mouth.

As a result of the Warnock Report, a Voluntary Licensing Authority was established in 1985 under the auspices of the Medical Research Council and the Royal College of Obstetricians and Gynaecologists to regulate IVF and embryo research. Once this was in place, steps were taken to formalize matters. The Human Fertilization and Embryology Bill passed through Parliament, becoming law in 1990. Prior to this, the Voluntary Licensing Authority became the Interim Licensing Authority, leading to the Human Fertilization and Embryology Authority (HFEA), which was established in 1991. The majority of centres took out licences to practice IVF or donor insemination or both. Since its inception, the HFEA has published several documents for public discussion and response, including those on sex selection and donation of tissue for the alleviation of infertility.

The HFEA is composed of professionals and non-professionals, men and women, whose function is the regulation of treatment using IVF techniques and of any treatment using donor insemination. Under their control, a secretariat and inspectors enforce the Act. Each hospital or clinic which practises IVF or donor insemination may do so only under licence granted by the HFEA. This licence is conditional on yearly inspection, with attention being paid to details like confidentiality of patient affairs, maintenance of clinical and scientific standards and the provision of ancillary services such as independent counselling of patients. The HFEA keep records of each and every treatment cycle performed, together with the result (successful or not, multiple pregnancy, and so on) in every licensed unit, and publishes the success rates for the country, though not for each unit, in an annual report.

One of the HFEA's functions is to emphasize the importance of the welfare of the child who may result from treatment. One factor in this is that the welfare of the child is implicitly bound up with the presence of a father, and therefore the practice of treating single women is not looked on favourably, although not banned.

Until the Warnock Report was published, there was no regulation of surrogacy practices in the country. The members of that body strongly recommended that the 'activities of agencies and individuals to arrange for surrogacy services be [regarded] criminal, professionals knowingly assisting in this be [regarded] criminal and all such contracts to be [regarded] illegal'. The Human Fertilization and Embryology Act also amended the Surrogacy Act so that surrogacy arrangements cannot be enforced by law. The commissioning couple may become legal parents of a child born as a result of a surrogacy arrangement, but the child is legally the surrogate mother's until then. The areas of social and legal concern relate to the wide constraints placed on the practice of surrogacy by the law (as already pointed out) and to the inability of either party to enforce the arrangement. In essence, this means, first, that it is very difficult to find a surrogate or to offer oneself as a surrogate and, secondly, that if the surrogate mother decides she wants to keep the child, she cannot be prevented from doing so; likewise, if the commissioning couple decide they do not want to take the child, they cannot be forced to do so.

The current legal status concerning IVF treatment and surrogacy may be summarized thus:

● Surrogacy arrangements are not enforceable in law; commercial interest or advertisement regarding the arrangement is illegal, although surrogacy of itself is not illegal.
● A child born as a result of surrogacy is the legal child of the surrogate mother, but can, through a court order, be treated in law as the child of the commissioning couple.
● It is permitted to create embryos for the purpose of treating a woman, and to replace no more than three embryos (or eggs in the case of GIFT) at any one time. Excess embryos can be frozen for the couple's further use, may be used for research, or may be discarded by means of a well-defined protocol.
● Embryos may also be generated specifically for the purposes of research. In either case, a specific licence is required for the research. In addition, embryos are never allowed to develop further than fourteen days, and embryos used in research are never replaced in a uterus.
● Strict penalties exist for infringement of licensing arrangements,

including a prison sentence. Infringements include performing unlicensed treatments and breaking confidentiality.

Implications of the treatments used, recent advances and research possibilities

There are ethical dilemmas bound up in these new techniques to help infertile couples. But agreement with the use of IVF in the alleviation of infertility need not entail agreement with all its possible applications. Some of these are unacceptable from a Christian point of view. For instance, some researchers will deliberately fertilize eggs with sperm and use the resultant embryos for research purposes only. The unacceptability of such practices relates, first, to considering these embryos as commodities to be used at will, and secondly, to a failure to recognize the inherent value and status of the human embryo. This is to some extent related to humanistic and evolutionary philosophy, which suggests that humans are no better than animals and of no greater value than them, and therefore disposable at will.

The element of human control in IVF could be regarded as dehumanizing or as supremely human, as we share, to a minor degree, in God's work of creation.[8] Whichever approach one adopts, it certainly converts what should be intimate and personal into something impersonal and no longer intimate. (The same comments could be, and are, made about childbirth.) Arguments against the use of IVF make the point that there is laboratory interference in the physical and sexual aspect of love in a couple's relationship. However, the children of assisted conception can be as much products of marital love as those of natural conception, although in a different way. While clinical IVF (its use to improve fertility) is an interference in the natural order, it could be regarded as a further extension of the interference involved in normal medical practice.

The practice of IVF causes concern because of the financial and emotional expenditure which is a part of the treatment. Costs are high because of the expertise required. Is it right to spend so much public money on the treatment of a desire when other needs, perhaps more deserving, are present? Even if it is privately funded, spending so much is still an ethical issue. The build-up of hopes followed by disappointment is very much a part of the treatment. Patients will always be upset by failure, and occasionally this can be very severe. Whether IVF and fertility treatments generally cause any long-term physical harmful effects is not yet clear, and further evidence is required before we can decide on this. Short-term morbidity (and mortality) does occur, though rarely. When it does occur, it is usually either a result of the operative procedures to collect oocytes or from over-stimulation of the ovaries.

Any ethical guidelines for treatment need careful thought and consideration. There must be some screening process, however, which determines who is treated, and to what level of technology. Is it appropriate to treat unmarried couples, single women, and homosexual couples? What treatments can we offer? Is the success rate high enough to warrant offering a treatment as a service? These are questions which need to be faced at the inception of a service, but also on a regular basis as new treatments come on the scene. Furthermore, these treatments cause ethical and social dilemmas because one person has to judge another's suitability for parenthood. This may seem patronizing, but the HFEA now asks all centres to judge the client's suitability for parenthood, as the welfare of the child is paramount.

Conception and the status of the embryo

Our knowledge of the physical events of conception is derived from animal and more recently human studies. Conception is not fertilization alone; it is the process of becoming pregnant. It is somewhat easier to understand the process of conception if we think of it in terms of a chain of physical events: hormonal changes within the woman leading to ovulation, intercourse around that time, a small number of sperm reaching the egg within the Fallopian tube, one sperm penetrating the egg, and the chromosomal contents* from the egg and sperm fusing (fertilization*) to form the zygote,* formation of a two- cell structure (30 hours), rapid growth by division through the morula* stage (8–16 cells in 3 days) to about 32 cells when it enters the cavity of the womb from the Fallopian tube (4 days), formation of a cavity within the structure (4–4½ days), and the particular differentiation of a few cells (inner cell mass*) which will go on to become the fetus and baby.

Implantation into the wall of the womb will occur on or about the sixth day. Further growth of the differentiated cells will lead to the development of the true embryo, and ultimately the fetus and infant. (In general conversation and in the press, the term 'embryo' is often erroneously used to describe the pre-implantation zygote, not, as is scientifically correct, the post-implantation embryo.)

One of the most contentious issues of IVF is the creation of embryos, more particularly the creation of extra embryos. These latter arise because only three embryos are replaced in the uterus (to reduce the incidence of multiple pregnancy). Spare embryos can be frozen for future use if pregnancy does not result (a procedure acceptable to most couples and practitioners), donated to other couples for their use (a concept similar to adoption of children), used for research (for many, an unacceptable option, although current techniques have come about only through such research) or discarded (sometimes necessary if embryos are abnormal or fail to develop, but something which would be deplorable if it were routine). What is crucially at issue here is the nature of those embryos. Are they fully human, with all the rights to survival and existence that an adult has? Are they simply little groups of cells with the potential for human life? Or are they something in between?

What can be agreed about the status of an embryo? An embryo, or more correctly, a zygote, is alive, and is not cellular material from the male or from the female partner but something uniquely distinct in chromosomal content from its parents. It has the ability and the potential to grow and become a recognizable human being. What is more difficult to agree upon is the point at which it is to be accorded the full protection and rights of a human being. One interesting way to approach this is the 'retrospective' approach. Few would deny the newborn child full human status (even though it is still very dependent on others). Even at 24–26 weeks' gestation, most would strive as hard as possible to protect that child (or fetus). Going any further back into early gestational age, however, we find that things are not so simple. Any form of extra-uterine existence is essentially impossible. Do we then accord full human status when the mother feels life (16 weeks), when (primitive) behavioural responses can be observed on ultrasound, i.e. when it is capable of responding to external stimuli in an observable manner (12 weeks), when a distinct fetus can be distinguished with a heartbeat (it is definitely alive; 6 weeks) or when neurological development begins (with the formation of the notochord and therefore the possibility of neurological response, i.e. brain birth (2 weeks)? Should it be at the time when implantation into the uterine wall occurs (it is now capable of growing and developing; 6 days), when the blastocyst stage is reached (the cells start to differentiate into those destined to become the baby and those destined to become the placenta; 4–4½ days)? Perhaps it is at fertilization when the chromosomal contents of the egg and sperm combine and form a different, genetically unique, creature, having the possibility and potential to develop through all these stages to become a baby? Many do choose one of

148

these points to mark the start of human life. The HFEA uses 14 days (the development of the primitive streak) as the cut-off point for embryo research. Like the others, this is an arbitrary point to take. Several of these are outstanding milestones in early fetal development, but only one is unique – fertilization. So do we regard the recently fertilized oocyte as being fully human, made in the image of God and deserving of full human rights? Some certainly do.

In discussing the status of the zygote or morula, it is helpful to examine some eventualities which can arise in its development. These include identical twins, 'missed abortion', the hydatidiform mole* and early fetal loss (miscarriage*). Discussion around some of these issues will illustrate the difficulties.

Identical twins arise by the separation of the early growing zygote/morula in two parts, any time from the two-cell stage on (though most commonly at the early blastocyst stage). This occurs in about 0.5% of all deliveries. Each becomes a fetus in its own right. The twins have identical genetic make-up and will undoubtedly in later life have marked similarities. They are not, however, the same person (even if they are joined!), and do not share the same soul or spirit. They are both complete and individual in themselves and will have different talents and abilities. Difficulties arise when we try to comprehend what is going on here. Should we consider that what was there before their separation was one person with a soul and spirit and afterwards, two persons with two souls and two spirits? Or, should we understand that before this point, there was no person with soul and spirit as such?

At least two other situations raise questions about the nature and status of the zygote/morula. A 'missed abortion' (anembryonic pregnancy*) will continue for several weeks after the embryo should have differentiated from the blastocyst. When this happens, there is placental tissue, the woman feels pregnant, and a pregnancy test is positive, but there is no embryo developing in the pregnancy sac* within the uterus. Sooner or later, inevitably, this pregnancy will miscarry. A 'hydatidiform mole' is a condition where pregnancy occurs but the tissue which is destined to make up the placenta undergoes a type of cancerous change and grows rapidly. More and less severe forms of the condition occur, but in the more severe form, no trace is ever found of any embryonic tissue. In these situations an embryo never forms. Does this imply that the blastocyst stage is pre-human?

Until recently, it was accepted that at least one-fifth of recognized pregnancies (missed period with a positive pregnancy test) miscarry. IVF data suggest that at least 50% of zygotes/morulae are lost before the woman even knows that she is pregnant or has missed a period. This high wastage is used by some to justify a less caring attitude to these zygotes/morulae.

These situations illustrate the problems that exist in understanding what the status of the pre-implantation 'embryo' is. The Bible is not a biology textbook. It cannot provide precise answers to these deep questions about the status and value of the early human embryo. We must balance the scientific knowledge we have about the biology of this being with what Scripture says about it. As passages in Scripture suggest that God may have a plan for some of us before we are born, before we are 'formed', and perhaps before we are conceived, using the point of 'being formed' is not really valid. Because we know that once the inner cell mass* develops (about 4–4½ days) and implantation occurs (fifth or sixth day), the pregnancy will not be anembryonic or unlikely to twin or be a molar pregnancy, then from that point onwards there is a developing human being. Before that, from the zygote stage to the morula stage, its fate is less sure both in nature (*in vivo*) and *in vitro*, when created in the laboratory. I would then suggest that at this stage the developing 'pre-embryo' or zygote/morula be accorded the utmost respect due to a potential human being, with due recognition of its less certain fate. Bearing in mind the biblical injunctions to care for those who are weak or disadvantaged, and its teaching that we are created in God's image, the status of potential human being is a high one. I realize that others could interpret this position to justify doing anything with the embryo, as it is only a 'potential' human being. I want to emphasize that it *is* a potential human being and that we need to do all in our power to permit it to take its natural course of development, whatever that may ultimately be.

For these reasons, I believe that the only acceptable destiny for apparently healthy cleaving embryos created *in vitro* is to be replaced in the uterus during the cycle in which they were created, or in a future cycle after being stored in a suitable deep-frozen environment. Some embryos will clearly be degenerative or malfunctioning in some way. By this, I mean that these embryos are undergoing cellular break-up or are failing to divide at anything like normal rates of development. I think it is not inappropriate that these should then be allowed to perish in an approved manner. The remainder should be used immediately or at some later stage. I believe that it is not appropriate within the guidelines of Scripture to generate large numbers of embryos for a couple who wish to have a baby and use only a few. Neither should one regard these embryos as commodities, to be disposed of should a defect (such as cystic fibrosis) be found. Certainly, it is unethical to generate embryos simply for the purpose of scientific experimentation.

One rare dilemma is worth mentioning (if only because of the headlines arising when it occurs). What of the couple who have IVF and have some embryos frozen, and then undergo separation or divorce? To whom do these embryos belong? If the couple can agree on their management, and provided that this allows for upbringing within a two-parent family, their use may be acceptable (perhaps by the woman herself in a new relationship in the future, or by donation to another couple). If not, then sadly we may be forced to consider allowing these embryos to perish.

The use of donor gametes and the sanctity of marriage

The use of donor gametes has not met with general approval in Christian circles. This is partly due to the implications for the marriage relationship should donor gametes be used (although, interestingly, it is generally the use of sperm that elicits this response). Objections are based on a contravention of the spirit of Scripture, the practice being considered close to adultery and an interference in the bond of 'one flesh' referred to in Scripture (Gn. 2:24; Eph. 5:31).[9] The proponents of its use suggest that it does not represent adultery, as there is no sexual intercourse and no impingement on the emotional and spiritual relationship between man and woman.[10]

There is also concern about the complexity, the confidentiality and the secrecy which surrounds this treatment. The use of donor sperm, in the past and today, has some degree of stigma attached to it. The need to use donor sperm is seen as the man's inability to procreate, a reflection of his own masculinity. Not surprisingly, then, there is a wish to keep secret the use of donor sperm, but the reasons for this must be recognized and acknowledged. In all these infertility treatments, the welfare of the child is very important. The child resulting from the use of donor sperm will ask questions about his or her origins and couples must be prepared for this. The attitude of the 'social' father to the future child is important. He should be willing to accept him or her as his own, but may be under pressure from his wife (perhaps covertly) to acknowledge this willingness, without being totally comfortable with it himself.

Other problems arising from the use of donor sperm may be that donors get paid expenses for their donation and that the donation arises from masturbation. Sperm donors are generally younger and therefore possibly less emotionally mature than oocyte donors, and might not have considered all the implications of their actions. An important consideration is the information which may in twenty years' time be given to any genetic child of the donor. The current legal situation is that no identifying information is available and no grounds for inheritance claims are possible. The HFEA is particularly keen to move recruitment of sperm donors into an older age group, preferably those who have already fathered children. Furthermore, all prospective donors are counselled at length about their attitudes and motives, and any degree of hesitance on the part of the candidate generally leads to rejection (only 33% of prospective donors end up as actual donors). Attitudes of the recipients of donor sperm have not been widely researched, although a recent publication by Snowden[11] discusses recipients' perceptions, some of which are positive, some negative. They reflect a wide spread of reactions from the experience.

The use of donor gametes is an extra-ordinary treatment, and must be regarded as such. It should only be resorted to after exhaustive counselling and discussion, and should not be readily available to all and sundry as a means to pregnancy. My own response to a request for donor gametes within the context of a stable married relationship is that I cannot rule out such use. Marriage was given to us by God primarily for companionship, but also for procreation. If this latter element is lacking because of some physical reason (azospermia* or premature ovarian failure), then it is difficult to see any malfeasance or anything improper in using donor sperm or eggs to bypass the problem. The decision to use donor gametes is a joint one, the relationship still maintains the monogamous nature, and the couple can now find expression for the procreative side of their relationship. Consider an analogy. Adoption is a process whereby a child conceived outside and separate from the couple is taken into that relationship; the use of donor gametes takes the principle of adoption back several steps and, in a sense, legally adopts the sperm for use within the relationship. In *Manufacturing Humans*, Gareth Jones considers that the use of donor gametes is not adultery, although neither is it as simple and straightforward as blood donation (his comparison). He is not convinced of any biblical teaching against the use of donor gametes, but, on a personal level, cannot support it. In general, there is a need for more openness about such treatments and a greater awareness of why couples need to undergo them. Less secrecy would be more healthy, now and for the future.

Surrogacy

Surrogacy means simply taking 'the place of another' (*Shorter Oxford English Dictionary*). A surrogate mother 'carries a fetus and bears a child on behalf of another person, having agreed to surrender that child to this person at birth or shortly thereafter'.[12]

The procedure involves a couple who wish to have a child and a woman who offers to carry that child through pregnancy for them. The couple are known as the commissioning couple, and the woman as the surrogate. The oocyte (egg) and sperm which unite to form the embryo may come from a number of sources. The egg may come from the surrogate, from the female partner of the commissioning couple or from a donor source. The sperm may come from the male partner of the commissioning couple or from a donor source. Fertilization of the egg may be by sexual intercourse, artificial insemination or *in vitro* fertilization (IVF).

The availability of surrogacy is very limited in Britain. In the small number of units where it is available, the general practice is to carry out IVF on the commissioning couple by collecting the woman's eggs after hormone stimulation and mixing the eggs with the man's sperm after those involved have been screened for HIV and hepatitis B infections. The resulting embryos are transferred to the uterus of the surrogate mother, usually after freeze storage for a number of months so that the HIV and hepatitis B status of those involved can be confirmed as negative. Surrogacy may be an option when an individual couple are unable to conceive or the female partner is unable to carry a pregnancy (usually because of a past hysterectomy). Other possible indications for its use include ovarian failure, major uterine anomalies or the absence of a uterus.

The ethical dilemmas relate to asking one woman to carry the pregnancy of another who for some reason is unable to do so. Within the context of a heterosexual (married) relationship, the responsibility and the small risk involved are accepted as an integral part of the relationship. However, to bring in a third party who is not a part of this relationship means that the woman takes on these risks and responsibilities voluntarily without the benefits of companionship and support. It is this major step, I think, that makes surrogacy so contentious. Difficulties arise when counselling both the prospective surrogate mother and the commissioning couple to ensure that they understand what is involved. The areas which need to be covered include the physical and psychological risks to the surrogate mother from the pregnancy and the effect of the surrogate pregnancy on the surrogate mother's existing family (especially her husband, if she has one). The surrogate mother must be screened for various conditions related to health in pregnancy. Whether or not the couple and the surrogate mother should meet or remain anonymous is another area of concern. Anonymity may protect the two parties involved from further distress should problems arise. The knowledge that the child may be able to discover his or her natural mother (because he or she will be legally adopted) is also important and may dissuade many from going through with the surrogacy process. For the child, the principal risk is that neither the surrogate nor the commissioning couple may want to be responsible for him or her.

Given the ethical and legal concerns that must be clearly understood by both parties, it is difficult to see how the process can be performed without someone getting hurt. That may be an acceptable risk for the adults involved. The child who may be born as a result of this arrangement will not have been consulted, and his or her rights must be defended by someone. Although over seventy surrogacy arrangements have now been carried out, the potential for hurt is, I believe, too great. If this process were handled like adoption, with confidentiality being maintained between the couple and the 'natural' mother, then it might be acceptable. It may be better to avoid the situation completely by not permitting the arrangement to proceed, rather than to do so while unsure about it.

Sex selection, use of fetal gametes for infertility purposes, and other areas of interest

Several forms of treatment have recently been publicized. Some of these are likely to be considered ethical, some less so. The introduction of these techniques provides examples of the situation mentioned earlier in this chapter – that having the technology to do something entails the right to do it without thought for the consequences of the action. Several examples arise: sex selection, the use of fetal gametes for infertility purposes, the treatment by IVF of women beyond their normal reproductive years (usually post-menopausal), pre-implantation diagnosis and micromanipulation.

Sex selection employs techniques which either separate sperm into male or female, or identifies male or female embryos. It is therefore useful either in electively planning a child of a particular sex or in excluding a particular sex because of genetic risks associated with that sex. The sperm separation techniques are currently commercially available in this country but regarded by the HFEA as unreliable.

The use of fetal gametes for infertility purposes involves the removal of the ovaries from fetuses that have been aborted (medically or surgically), the identification of the follicles* within those ovaries and the development of those follicles to mature the oocytes within them. These oocytes can then be used by women who need oocyte donation. The same sort of procedure can be performed on cadaveric ovaries. The procedure has been carried out but is still only at the developmental stage. The background to its consideration is the large number of women whose own ovaries have failed prematurely – often in their early twenties – and whose only hope of their own child is the use of oocytes from a donor. There is a relative difficulty in the provision of adequate numbers of suitable oocyte donors, hence the search for oocytes from other sources. The HFCA commented on this in July 1994 (see below).

The treatment by IVF of post-menopausal women is usually by their own husbands' sperm but with oocytes from a donor. The resultant embryos are transferred back into the uterus of the post-menopausal woman after suitable preparation. The reasons for this treatment vary considerably from individual to individual. The widely publicized case in late 1993 of the career woman who delayed having children is probably unusual. This treatment is not available in the UK at present.

Pre-implantation diagnosis is used in situations where there is a risk of genetic disease and IVF is carried out. The embryos so produced are examined and one cell removed and the chromosomal contents examined. If that embryo is found to be the carrier of the disease in question, it is not replaced and is discarded. The rationale behind the procedure is that it is less traumatic to the couple to replace only healthy embryos at this stage than to carry out chorionic villus biopsy* or amniocentesis* later in pregnancy, with the possibility of an abortion if the results indicate that the disease is present. In the UK this procedure is available to a very limited extent and for certain diseases only (*e.g.* cystic fibrosis). However, with the passage of time and further determination of the entire human genome, it is possible that more and more diseases will be available for examination and 'eradication' in this way.

All these examples suggest a 'commodity' approach to fertility treatment. They represent a stretching of the boundaries of acceptability for IVF treatment. While few would deny a couple who are infertile the opportunity to alleviate their situation, these examples are different; they might even represent an abuse of the knowledge we have gained. They fall very clearly into the category where the end justifies the means and should, I believe, be regarded as unethical and immoral.

Regarding the donation of ovarian tissue from fetal or cadaveric sources, several specific issues arise, including the impossibility of adequate consent, the concerns about 'skipping' generations, the bypassing of the normal protective elements of reproduction, and the potential difficulties of informing a resulting child about his or her origins. The British Medical Association issued a statement to the effect that it did not consider that fetal oocytes should be used for treatment, but had no concerns about such use for research purposes.[13] The HFEA issued a statement in July 1994 which summarized their attitudes to the use of ovarian tissue. In research, use of such tissue (including oocytes), requires that specific consent be obtained from live donors, from the individual prior to death for post-mortem use, and from the mother of aborted fetal tissue. Minors should not be approached with such a request. In the treatment of patients, the HFEA found it acceptable to use ovarian tissue from live donors who give informed consent, and, in principle, to use ovarian tissue from adults who have died but gave specific consent prior to death (though they were less than happy about agreeing to this without in-depth psychological research into the possible effects on children who might result from such treatment). The HFEA did not find it acceptable to use ovarian tissue from minors who have died or from aborted tissue in the treatment of infertile patients requiring oocyte donation.

The HFEA admitted in its report that one of the features of the responses to their discussion document they received from the public was the 'yuk' factor to the use of ovarian tissue from fetuses. As Christians we are equally likely to judge things using the 'yuk' factor. But (and this is a major concern) the 'yuk' factor can change as a result of lobbying and 'education'. What is not acceptable now may in five years' time be so, as a result of apathy or a genuine shift in public opinion. It is to be hoped that biblically based attitudes would not change with the 'yuk' factor. As a more concrete safeguard, a Private Member's Bill has been passed in Parliament, proposed by a Conservative MP, Dame Jill Knight, which effectively bans future research on fetal oocyte harvesting and development.

Micromanipulation is a procedure which uses standard IVF techniques up to the point of oocyte collection. Thereafter, each individual oocyte is identified. Using very fine and minute instruments, the oocyte is punctured and a single sperm is introduced into it (intra-cytoplasmic sperm injection, ICSI), or several sperm are injected into the potential space just next to the oocyte (subzonal injection, SUZI). The rationale behind this form of treatment is to allow men with very poor sperm quality an opportunity to use their own sperm in the conception of a baby. These treatments are available in the UK though few can emulate the results of van Steirteghem's group in Brussels. Of themselves, these treatments do not present any problems. However, some issues do arise from this form of treatment. They represent very invasive techniques and may bypass some of the normal safety mechanisms inherent in normal penetration and fertilization of an oocyte by a sperm. They also are very expensive, current charges being up to £10,000 for ICSI. Whether it is right for any one individual to spend such a large sum in pursuit of a desire is debatable.

Where do we go from here?

The scientific advances and techniques described above are undoubtedly of enormous value to those couples who desire a child. But none of those techniques would be available without the research which preceded them. Great care must be taken as new techniques and knowledge become available. Christians should be fully involved in their evaluation even if it means being criticized and misunderstood. How can they do this? By a prayerful approach, seeking wisdom and discernment, by being aware of developments (through membership and support of organizations like CARE), and by responding to developments by writing to MPs and to the HFEA. Society is being allowed to determine what is acceptable. Who makes up society but us? Many of the attitude changes on important issues are brought about as a result of motivated individuals and vocal minorities. We must not be silent.

Glossary

Abortion: the deliberate removal of the products of conception* from the uterus. Spontaneous abortion (miscarriage*) is a natural process.
Amniocentesis: a technique during which a small needle is passed into the amniotic fluid (surrounding the baby) to collect fluid or shed cells from the baby, usually for diagnosis purposes.
Anembryonic pregnancy: fertilization* and early division of the cells and implantation occur, but separation of the embryo* away from what will become the afterbirth/placenta fails to take place.

Azospermia: the complete absence of sperm in seminal fluid.

Biological medium: any fluid which is based on or derived from a body fluid, particularly in this context, the mucus present around the cervix.*

Blastocyst: that developmental stage of the fetus* where fluid collects within the 'pre-embryo' and the cells destined to become the embryo* are clearly distinguishable from those destined to become the placenta.

Cervix: a fibrous circular structure at the lower end of the uterus, often called the 'neck of the womb'.

Chorion villus biopsy: a diagnostic technique during which a tube is passed through the cervix or across the abdomen into the uterus, to collect cells from the placenta (afterbirth). Compared with amniocentesis,* the results are obtained faster, though with less accuracy.

Chromosomal contents: The 46 chromosomes carry the genes which provide all the information determining the development and genetic characteristics of the adult.

Conception: the process of becoming pregnant.

Contraception: any technique to prevent the process of becoming pregnant while having sexual intercourse.

Egg: more correctly, an oocyte;* a cell produced by the ovary which contains half the normal amount of genetic material (and is designed to be complemented by the donation of the male half of genetic material at fertilization*).

Embryo: specifically, the developing fertilized ovum from about two weeks after fertilization* until the end of the eighth week, while organ development is occurring; less specifically, the term is loosely applied to the developing structure at any stage of its development.

Endometriosis: a condition where tissue resembling that which lines the cavity of the uterus is present in the pelvis and causes distortion of the structures and occasionally infertility.

Fallopian tube: a round tube with finger-like endings which picks up the oocyte* at ovulation* and directs it down to meet the sperm.

Fertilization: union of sperm* and egg* with progression on to a two-celled and four-celled unit.

Fetus: the developing organism from the eighth week onwards, fully formed but maturing further to the time of birth.

Follicle: a fluid-filled area in the ovary which grows in each menstrual cycle to about 2.5 cm (1 inch) in diameter, and produces a mature egg, capable of fertilization.*

Gametes: covers sperm* and oocyte,* each containing a half set of chromosomes.

GIFT (Gamete intra-Fallopian transfer): a procedure involving oocyte* collection, and subsequently, in the same procedure, surgical placement of three oocytes and sperm* directly into the Fallopian tube.

Hydatidiform mole: a condition where pregnancy occurs but the tissue which is destined to make up the placenta undergoes a type of cancerous change and grows rapidly.

Hysterosalpingography: a procedure in which a dye is passed into the uterus and thence into the Fallopian tubes, which can then be seen on X-ray.

Inner cell mass: a group of cells, also known as the cytotrophoblast, with single-nucleus cells, which will eventually differentiate to become the fetus.

Insemination: placing of sperm* within the vagina at the cervix,* often used with an artificial connotation.

IUI (Intra-Uterine Insemination): a process whereby prepared sperm* are placed at the top of the uterine cavity, usually at the time of (artificially induced) ovulation.*

IVF (*In Vitro* Fertilization): a procedure involving oocyte* collection, preparation of sperm and then mixture of the two; the eggs* are then inspected some hours later to check for signs of fertilization* and then allowed to develop further outside the body until transferred back into the uterus at the 4–8 cells developmental stage.

Laparoscopy: an operation requiring an anaesthetic and involving the passage of a small telescope-like instrument into the abdomen, allowing direct visual inspection of the internal genital organs, an assessment of patency of the Fallopian tubes,* and of disease processes such as endometriosis.*

Miscarriage: loss of a pregnancy before the fetus* is capable of surviving outside the uterus (before 24 weeks of pregnancy), used to imply the absence of deliberate action.

Morula: intermediate stage of pre-embryo, between zygote* and blastocyst,* around 8–32 cells in size.

Oocyte: *see* egg.*

Ovulation: release of a mature oocyte* from the ovary following various hormonal influences.

Pregnancy sac: a term used to describe the outer layer of cells destined to become the placenta, the amniotic cavity and the developing embryo.*

Progesterone: a hormone produced in the second half of the woman's menstrual cycle, crucial to the maintenance of an early pregnancy before the placenta begins to function.

Sperm: the cells produced by the male in the testis containing half of the normal genetic content.

Spermatogenesis: the process whereby sperm are produced in the testis.

Zygote: the fertilized egg.*

Table 1

Numbers of cycles, pregnancies and live births in the UK from IVF, GIFT and donor insemination, 1991 (GIFT results for first six months only) and IVF and donor insemination.[14]

	IVF(a)	GIFT(b)	DI(a)
Cycles	13301	1094	16024
Pregnancy rate	2186(17%)	178(16%)	1023(6.4%)
Live births	1604(12%)	124(11%)	797(5%)

Sources: (a) HFEA, 1.1.92–31.12.92; (b) OPCS, 1.1.91–30.6.91

Table 2

Number of abortions performed and babies placed for adoption, 1968–90

	Abortions performed (a)	Babies for adoption(b)
1968	23641	—
1975	139702	21299
1980	160903	10609
1990	186912	6533

Sources: (a) HMSO; (b) Life.

Appendix 1

Historical, medical and other events in fertility treatment within the UK

1884: First recorded use of donor sperm insemination to achieve a pregnancy.

1930: Anglican bishops accept artificial contraception as an economic necessity, but deplore the use of abortion as a form of contraception. This served to illustrate that the act of procreation can be separated from that of sexual intercourse.

1948: A commission of the Archbishop of Canterbury judged that, as donor insemination made a personal act into a transaction, it should be made illegal.

1958: An Edinburgh court ruled that donor insemination did not constitute adultery.

1960: A Department of Health committee suggested that donor insemination be discouraged though not banned.

1968: The papal encyclical *Humanae vitae* objected to the use of donor insemination as it split procreation from sexual intercourse.

1970–78: Efforts on the part of several individuals (with Professor R. G. Edwards at the forefront) to bring about the fertilization of eggs outside the body, with many failures over those years.

1978: The first IVF live birth, the result of collaborative work by Cambridge University scientists, led by Edwards, and Patrick Steptoe, a gynaecologist in Oldham.

1982–84: As a consequence of public disquiet, a committee of inquiry was established under Dame Mary Warnock to determine what policies should be drawn up on the issues of human fertilization, embryology, and donor insemination, though not abortion or contraception. Their report was published in 1984.

1985: The Surrogacy Act was passed.

1985: As a result of the Warnock Report, a Voluntary Licensing Authority was established under the auspices of the Medical Research Council and the Royal College of Obstetricians and Gynaecologists to regulate IVF and embryo research.

1986–90: Passage of the Human Fertilization and Embryology Bill through Parliament

1989: The Voluntary Licensing Authority becomes the Interim Licensing Authority, with the same remit.

1991: The Human Fertilization and Embryology Authority (HFEA) came into being, and the majority of centres take out licences to practise IVF and donor insemination or both.

1992–93: Several more centres gain licences to practise IVF and donor insemination. The HFEA publishes several documents for public discussion and response, including those on sex selection and donation of fetal tissue for the alleviation of infertility.

1994: Private Members Bill passed to ban use of fetal tissue for research or treatment.

Appendix 2

Ethical codes of practice referring to pregnancy, embryos and related issues

Hippocratic Oath (400 BC): 'I will not give a woman a pessary to produce abortion.'

Geneva Declaration (1948): Doctors should have 'the utmost respect for human life from the time of conception'.

UN Universal Declaration of Human Rights and Freedoms (1948): 'Everyone has the right to life.'

International Code of Medical Ethics (1949): 'A doctor must always bear in mind the importance of preserving human life from conception until death.'

Declaration of Helsinki (revised 1975): 'Biomedical research involving human subjects cannot be legitimately carried out unless the importance of the objective is in proportion to the inherent risk to the subject. Concern for the interest of the subject must always prevail over the interests of society and science. In any research upon human beings, each potential subject must be adequately informed of the aims, methods, anticipated benefits and potential hazards of the study. The subjects should be volunteers. It is the duty of the doctor to remain the protector of the life and death of that person on whom biomedical research is being carried out. In research on man, the interest of science and society should never take precedence over considerations related to the well-being of the subject.'

UN Convention on the Rights of the Child (1989): The child is entitled to 'legal protection before as well as after birth'.

Code of Practice of the HFEA (1991): 'The welfare of the child is a crucial element. Treatment of gametes or embryos prior to use is circumscribed.'

10 ABORTION

Siân Kerslake

Abortion is the removal of the fetus from the womb with the intention of causing its premature death. One third of British women have abortions. One pregnancy in five ends in abortion, and over four million abortions have been performed in England, Wales and Scotland since the passing of the Abortion Act in 1967.[1] Abortion is now such standard practice in British hospitals that many are unaware that legalized abortion is a comparatively recent phenomenon.

The Soviet Union was the first to introduce legalized abortion in 1920. Sweden and Denmark followed in the 1930s, Japan in 1948 and China in 1957. Singapore, India and Korea made similar moves in the next two decades. Britain was the first non-Scandinavian western country to liberalize its abortion laws (in 1967), and was followed by the USA (1973), Austria (1975), Germany (1976), Italy (1978) and Holland (1981). As a result of this worldwide trend, by 1982 only 28% of the world's population lived in countries where abortion was largely illegal, mostly Muslim countries, Africa and Latin America. It is now estimated that 55 million legal abortions are performed each year worldwide.[2]

In England and Wales the annual total has stabilized at about 180,000. The majority (98.6%) are performed on the grounds of risk of injury to the mental or physical health of the pregnant woman or her existing children. Only 0.1% are done because of fetal handicap and 0.013% to save the life of the mother. For 58% of women it is their first pregnancy, and 67% have never been married. Most abortions (61%) are carried out in the private sector.[3] The typical British woman having an abortion is single, under 25 years of age, and in her first pregnancy, with the procedure being performed for social reasons.

Methods of procuring an abortion

Abortion may be induced mechanically, with drugs (abortifacients), or by external injury to the mother or cervix. In the UK the vast majority of abortions (90%) are performed by vacuum aspiration or dilatation and evacuation (D&E) but the techniques employed vary

163

with gestation. 87% take place before 12 weeks' gestation. Suction termination may be performed under local anaesthetic up to eight weeks following the last menstrual period. Between 6 and 12 weeks vacuum aspiration through the dilated cervix under general anaesthesia is usual. More recently, early abortions have been induced pharmacologically using mifepristone (RU 486) in conjunction with the prostaglandin gemeprost. This has been shown to effect a 95% complete abortion rate up to 9 weeks' gestation, the same as with a surgical procedure.[4] Dilatation and evacuation of the uterine contents is safe (for the mother) up to 20 weeks in skilled hands.[5]

The fetus is usually alive during these procedures, but often dies when drugs are administered to carry out the abortion. Sometimes these are specifically injected into the amniotic cavity (urea or hypertonic saline solution) or the fetal heart (potassium) in order to kill him or her before the delivery. Later terminations are performed using these drugs along with intra- or extra-amniotic prostaglandins. Because multiple pregnancies are prone to a higher incidence of spontaneous miscarriage, selective reduction (the abortion of one or more of the fetuses) is sometimes carried out in order to improve the chance of survival of those who remain. Rarely, a hysterotomy (opening the uterus as in a Caesarean section to remove the baby) or hysterectomy (uterus and baby removed at the same time) is performed.

Ethical codes

Historical codes of medical ethics have until recently been uniformly opposed to abortion. The Hippocratic Oath states: 'I will give no deadly medicine to anyone if asked, nor suggest such counsel, and in like manner I will not give to a woman a pessary to procure abortion.' The Declaration of Geneva (1948) states: 'I will maintain the utmost respect for human life from the time of conception even against threat,'[6] and the International Code of Medical Ethics (1948) affirms that 'a doctor must always bear in mind the importance of preserving human life from the time of conception until death'.[7] 'Everyone has the right to life'[8] and 'legal protection before as well as after birth' are principles that are affirmed in United Nations declarations.[9]

A fundamental change occurred in the way doctors thought about abortion when countries began to adopt more liberal legislation in the second half of the twentieth century. This found its expression in the Declaration of Oslo,[10] which was formally adopted by the World Medical Association in 1970. It states that in situations 'where the vital interests of the mother conflict with those of the unborn child', 'therapeutic' termination of pregnancy is admissible 'according to a doctor's individual conviction and conscience', provided that the law and local medical association allow it. This declaration opened the gateway for relativistic thinking and a flexible approach to abortion.

As the number of legal abortions performed by doctors increased exponentially in this new ethical environment, it was apparent that traditional codes had to be revised. In 1983 the 35th World Medical Assembly in Venice amended the words 'from the time of conception' in the Geneva Declaration to 'from its beginning'. At the same meeting the words 'from the time of conception until death' were deleted from the International Code of Medical Ethics.

All of these amendments were adopted by the British Medical Association, which has now rejoined the World Medical Association after a period of absence.

The law

The law on abortion in Britain is enshrined in the Abortion Act (1967) and in various amendments to it in the Human Fertilization and Embryology Act (1990). For an abortion to be carried out legally, two doctors must affirm in good faith that the case falls into one of the following categories:

A. The continuance of the pregnancy would involve risk to the life of the pregnant woman greater than if the pregnancy were terminated.

B. The continuance of the pregnancy would involve risk of injury to the physical or mental health of the pregnant woman greater than if the pregnancy were terminated.

C. The continuance of the pregnancy would involve risk of injury to the physical or mental health of any existing child(ren) of the family of the pregnant woman greater than if the pregnancy were terminated.

D. There is a substantial risk that if the child were born it would suffer from such physical or mental abnormalities as to be seriously handicapped.

E. In emergency to save the life of the pregnant woman.

F. The termination is necessary to prevent grave permanent injury to the physical or mental health of the pregnant woman.

Conditions A to C apply up to 24 weeks' gestation, and conditions D to F apply up to birth. In England and Wales, 98.6% of abortions are carried out under categories B and C.

One of the aims of the law was to decrease the number of illegitimate births. However, these have increased threefold since the law was introduced in Britain. There was a vain hope that all children would be wanted, but the incidence of child abuse has doubled. There were no maternal deaths from back-street abortions in 1984, and so it is believed that they have been eliminated in Britain.[11]

In 1973, the United States Supreme Court gave women abortion on request. In Sweden this is permitted up to 18 weeks. France has allowed abortion on demand up to 12 weeks since 1975. In Italy, abortion in the early weeks of pregnancy has been permitted from 1977. Other countries have more restrictive laws.

Embryology and viability

How developed is the fetus at the time abortion is usually carried out? Implantation takes place between 5 and 7 days after fertilization. The neural crest develops by 14 days. The 'tubular heart' is present by 17 days, and at 21 days primitive circulation is in place. The embryo is called a fetus at six weeks of intra-uterine life, and by 8 weeks all the major organ systems are present and beginning to function. Fetal movements begin at about this stage, but are not felt by the mother until about 18 weeks' gestation, when the baby is over a third of his or her birth size. The frontiers of viability outside the womb are constantly being pushed back by advances in technology and currently stand at about 23 weeks. Only one eighth to one sixth of the adult number of alveoli are present at birth (40 weeks) and the myelination of the spinal cord continues to develop in the first post-natal year.

All these processes are part of a continuum. It is not possible to ascertain an absolute moment for the beginning of life apart from the fact that human development is an event which begins at fertilization. Before this time a human being will not develop. After fertilization it will, unless a miscarriage occurs.

The majority of abortions (87%) are performed between 6 and 12 weeks' gestation. The attitudes and practice of individual doctors vary. A survey of gynaecologists' attitudes revealed that 21% stopped doing abortions at 12 weeks or less in certain circumstances and only 10.2% would perform them after 20 weeks.[11]

Complications of abortions

Physical sequelae

The maternal mortality rate of first-trimester abortion is less than 1 per 100,000,[12] so as a procedure it is safer than having a hysterectomy. This compares with the maternal mortality figures of 7.6 per 100,000 total births for the years 1985–87. Early abortion is thus safer (for the mother) than natural childbirth, and this fact provides in Britain a legal loophole which has been fully exploited by the pro-choice lobby. (See conditions B and C under 'The law' above.) Complications do occur, however, and include effects on the woman's life which may be temporary or permanent. Uterine perforation (0.1%–2%), haemorrhage, sepsis of the uterus and Fallopian tubes, the need for a second procedure to empty the uterus of retained products of conception, lacerations of the cervix, and, in second-trimester abortions, complete retained placentae have been noted.

Long-term complications include chronic pelvic inflammatory disease and tubal blockage (although one prospective study failed to find any reduction in fertility due to terminations).[13] There is evidence of a higher incidence of subfertility in women who developed infection after the procedure (10% as compared with 2% in controls).[14] Cervical incompetence, Rhesus isoimmunization, endometriosis and menstrual disturbances also occur.[15] There are also the added anaesthetic complications. The prospective and joint study of the Royal College of General Practitioners and the Royal College of Obstetricians and Gynaecologists showed that 10% of women had some complication within 3 weeks of an abortion, and major complications occurred in fewer than 1%.[16] This study, though large, seems not to have been representative of women having abortions, since 30% refer themselves to clinics, and only general practitioner referrals were studied. Cervical incompetence seems not to be a problem in early termination of pregnancy according to a prospective study of 745 women,[17] though the long-term complications of late terminations on the cervix are not known. Other long-term emotional complications, and some physical ones as ectopic pregnancy, hysterectomy and miscarriages, were not studied by this survey.

The Rawlinson Report pointed out that complications should be reported by one week on the statutory 'yellow' form. Most occur after this time, and, with a shifting population who may not tell their subsequent carers about the termination, it is obvious that under-reporting occurs. The true outcome in terms of complications may not be known.[18]

Emotional sequelae

A Danish study demonstrated a low incidence of admission to hospital for serious emotional disturbance, at 1.84 per 1,000 compared with 1.2 per 1,000 after delivery.[19] Early psychiatric morbidity appears to be about 10%.[20] The long-term sequelae are difficult to evaluate, as follow-up rates are low for a number of reasons. It is thought that many do not wish to be reminded of their experience. The Rawlinson Report stated that a number of risk factors predispose to emotional and psychological problems: younger maternal age; previous pregnancies; previous history of psychiatric or depressive illness; ambivalent attitude to the procedure; abortion done for fetal handicap or genetic reasons; and socio-cultural disapproval, a religious background, or both. Representatives of the Royal College of Psychiatry who gave evidence to the Commission stated that there were no psychiatric grounds for abortion. This is in spite of the fact that most abortions are carried out on alleged grounds of damage to the mental health of the mother.

Why women seek abortion

In an ideal world all pregnancies would be both planned and wanted, but our fallen world is far from ideal.

Unplanned pregnancies very rarely result from rape, incest or sexual abuse. The vast majority result from sexual intercourse between two willing partners when contraception has either failed or been forgotten. Sex education has not stemmed the tide of unplanned conceptions any more than public-health campaigns about smoking and alcohol have stemmed the incidence of unplanned lung cancer and cirrhosis. In Britain during the last twenty years, contraception has never been more freely available, yet abortion and conception rates continue to rise, especially in young people. The younger the age of commencing sexual activity, the greater the risks taken and the worse the outcome.

On occasions, women may deliberately choose to become pregnant. This may be to prove to themselves that they are fertile (especially if it is culturally important or if there is a history of past pelvic infection), to avoid intercourse, to have a child to nurture, or to force a change in their relationship with their partner or family. Pregnancy may result when two people fail to take proper precautions while 'making up' after a breakdown in their relationship.

Why do women choose to have an abortion? According to the Rawlinson Report, the most common reasons are as follows:

- Partner pressure or an unstable relationship (45%)
- Financial circumstances (26%)
- Family pressures or situation, study, career or age (15%)
- Various reasons (40%) in order of priority:
    Unplanned or not wanting children
    Emotionally unstable
    Illness or previous problems with pregnancy
    No apparent alternative
    Lack of counselling
    Deformed or Down's baby
    On drugs, taken 'morning-after pill' or rape

These results, along with the experience of those involved in crisis pregnancy counselling, suggest that most women who choose abortion do so because there is no male partner willing to share responsibility for the child. Abortion is in large part the problem of the absent man.

Biblical teaching related to abortion

Although the Bible does not mention abortion specifically, there are nonetheless clear biblical principles which we can apply to the problem.

Committed family relationships

The first principle is that of committed family relationship. God ordained marriage as a public, lifelong, heterosexual, committed love relationship (Gn. 2:24). It is the context not only for sexual union, but also for the raising of children (Dt. 6:5–7). Sex without lifelong commitment is contrary to the nature of God, who through Christ commits himself to his people for ever (Eph. 5:31–32). Reproduction without taking responsibility for one's offspring is similarly abhorrent to God. He, by contrast, cares for all his children, even though they may reject him.

This is why the Bible promotes chastity before marriage and fidelity within marriage. All sexual behaviour outside this pattern is roundly condemned. The vast majority of abortions are performed on pregnancies resulting from unions outside the limits God has set.

The sanctity of life

The second principle is the sanctity of life. All men and women are made in the image of God (Gn. 1:27; 9:5–6), and as such are not to be killed (Ex. 20:13). Although Old Testament law allowed for the killing of *guilty* human beings in certain special circumstances (*i.e.* holy war, Dt. 20:10–18; capital punishment and self-defence, Ex. 22:2–3), the shedding of innocent blood is universally condemned throughout Scripture. Abortion clearly involves the shedding of innocent blood.

The status of life before birth

The third principle is the status of life before birth. Psalm 139:13–16 affirms God's creation of, and communion with, the unborn child as well as implying the continuity of life before and after birth. These principles are reinforced by many other references to life before birth (*e.g.* Gn. 25:22–23; Ps. 51:5, 119:73; Jb. 10:8–9, 18–19; Ec. 11:5; Is. 49:1, 5; Je. 1:5; Lk. 1:15, 41–44) and by over sixty references to the event of conception. God is completely just and impartial, and commands special respect for easily exploited groups within the human family (Pr. 22:22–23; Ex. 22:21–24; Lv. 19:14). The essence of Christian love as fully expressed in Christ's death on the cross is that the strong lay down their lives for the weak. The developing child in the womb is arguably the weakest and most defenceless human being that there is. There is no biblical basis whatsoever for the belief that life before birth has any less status in the eyes of God than life after birth. It must follow that if we would not consider infanticide for a given set of circumstances, then we equally should not consider abortion.

There have been many attempts to undermine these three principles, from sources both inside and outside the church. A discussion of these is outside the scope of this chapter, but interested readers are referred to comprehensive reviews elsewhere.[21]

Compassionate care

The fourth principle is that of compassionate care. In not condoning abortion, the Christian doctor cannot refuse to take responsibility for the pregnant woman who is in a state of crisis with her unplanned pregnancy. Even when her pregnancy is the direct result of ignoring God's principles of right living, our model must be that of Christ, who did not condemn but offered forgiveness and grace.

170

We need to become involved in easing the burden that the pregnant woman carries, helping her to find solutions which do not involve the taking of innocent life. This will be elaborated later.

Our technologically sophisticated society has developed the techniques necessary to end the lives of its children even before they are born. The Bible tells us that covetousness is idolatry (Col. 3:5), and abortion is the price we have been prepared to pay in our desire for 'sexual freedom', affluence and personal peace. God surely views our society, which sacrifices children in pursuit of our western gods of career, money and pleasure, just as seriously as he did those Canaanites in the Old Testament who sacrificed to images of wood and stone (Lv. 20:1–5).

Handling the practicalities

Unplanned pregnancy constitutes a major life crisis for the majority of women, and it is not surprising that those with feelings of ambiguity are tempted to search for an easy way out. The vast majority of our non-Christian colleagues will have no hesitation in recommending abortion, especially if the social circumstances are poor. It can be very difficult for the Christian doctor or student to stand against the tide, especially when subjected to the ridicule and coercion of other staff.

Our ethic, however, is that of the cross, and the suffering that this necessarily entails.

First of all, it means taking the consequences of refusing to disobey God by being party to the shedding of innocent blood. Legally, in the UK, we do have the right conscientiously to object to being involved directly in the abortion process. However, the full extent of this legal protection has not yet been tested in law. The General Medical Council has ruled that doctors do have an *ethical* obligation to refer patients requesting abortions to other doctors if they are not willing to authorize them themselves.[22] A court has ruled that a doctor's receptionist does not have a legal right to refuse to type a referral letter on conscientious grounds.[23] The application of the law between these two extremes will no doubt be more clearly defined as more conscientious objectors are forced to answer charges. As Christians we must be prepared to be discriminated against at all levels for our stand on this issue.

Secondly, the cross means being willing to be part of the solution to the unwanted pregnancy in helping the woman to find alternatives to abortion. This is costly. Fortunately, as doctors we are not alone in this. In the UK we are particularly fortunate to have at least two organizations[24] which run crisis pregnancy centres throughout the country. These are equipped to offer the counselling, support, accommodation, practical and financial help and adoption advice which we as individual doctors may be unable to provide. Most of all, women in crisis need time.

Specifics of counselling

Jesus loved sinners with a passionate love which took him to the cross. Abortion counselling is an opportunity to befriend and get alongside people whom God loves, when they are in a difficult situation. Here we have Jesus as our model, who did not condemn the woman caught in adultery but rather offered her forgiveness and the power to change (Jn. 8:2–11). We need to beware of adopting the judgmental attitude of the Pharisees, or of seeing the woman as the only guilty party. In the case cited the equally guilty man was absent, along with all the others who may have contributed to the woman's sexual sin through their failure to instruct or their unwillingness to confront lovingly. If we do not start by remembering our status as sinners saved by grace, we will be of little help to women in crisis.

We need to be factual in the information we impart, not only making sure that the woman is aware of the fact that her baby is fully formed and alive but also ensuring that she is aware of all the alternatives (adoption, financial assistance and help available to keep the baby) along with all the organizations that are there to support her. We also need to inform her of what the law allows if she is unaware of it. As Christians we have an obligation to submit to the laws of the state (Rom. 13:1–5), although we cannot use this as an excuse for disobeying God if there is conflict between what the law demands of us and what the Lord demands (Acts 4:19, 5:29; Ex. 1:15–21). When asked a medical question about the risks involved, we must be accurate, statistical and factual in the information we impart. If we do not know the answers, we must be prepared to refer to more senior colleagues. Ideally, if at all possible, the male partner should also be involved in the discussion. After all, his willingness to share responsibility is probably the most important factor in persuading the woman to change her mind.

As Christians, we can appeal to conscience which, even if the woman is not a Christian, is nonetheless God-given. She may think she is having the abortion to please a relative or parent, and a role of the counsellor may be to re-focus the responsibility on her choice. She is the one who will live with the decision, not her friends. Her conscience holds sway over the decision whether to go ahead or not. We may well be able to help her find the courage she needs to stand up for what she knows is right in the face of family pressure.

We need also to be aware that in trying to encourage a woman to make the decision to spare her baby's life, we are entering a spiritual battle. It is therefore imperative that we pray before and throughout counselling any patient, and are completely reliant on the Holy Spirit as to how much it is wise to say. Sometimes God may give us a special word for that person and situation. We need to be aware also that even in Jesus' presence, some found the challenges he gave too hard, and walked away, rejecting his offer of salvation. He gives us all choices and free will to obey or disobey. Like Jesus, we can lovingly try to convince our patients freely to choose the right course. There may rarely be an opportunity to share something of our own faith, not in a legalistic way, but in terms of showing them what gives us hope even in crisis situations.

One of the most satisfying rewards in medicine is to witness an unwanted pregnancy become a much loved and wanted child through a change in the attitude of the mother. God can work in the most difficult situations and people can be persuaded by his grace to change their minds. A number of women have become Christians. We need to be honest in explaining to the woman why we cannot help her further in obtaining an abortion. This is not imposing our morality. It is simply putting God first and desiring God's best for her also. It is not uncommon for women in these circumstances to return to us later because we are 'the only ones who ever listened' to them. Some who have regretted their decisions suffer great guilt over what they have done, and later in life may be open to receive Jesus' love and forgiveness.

The British Medical Association has stipulated that doctors have an ethical obligation to refer patients to other doctors if they are unwilling to authorize abortion requests themselves. The full legal position is not currently clear, and doctors will need to decide before God what they should do in this situation.

Colleagues may be very angry with us for choosing not to be involved in abortions, because it involves them in more work. We need to be able to explain to them the rationale for our stand. In reality it should not be we who are called to account. We are simply trying to act in accordance with the ethical codes which doctors have historically embraced. We need to help them see that abortion is not only a betrayal of the Hippocratic Oath and Declaration of Geneva, but in fact contrary to the whole strategy of medicine which is to care, cure and console. We need not feel guilty for not participating in something which is not part of medicine. However, we need to understand why our colleagues believe what they believe, and how strange our beliefs seem to them. The public conscience has shifted so much that we must not be surprised if we are accused of being unprofessional, uncaring or even un-Christian. Nor should it dissuade us from entering obstetrics and gynaecology and related specialties; the need for consistent Christians here is greater than ever. It is the most effective way of turning the tide.

Problem areas

Let us conclude by considering a few key problem areas.

Screening

A large number of women will not now consider having a child with any form of handicap, and so tests to detect anomalies are increasingly available, including biochemical screens, pre-implantation screens, chorionic villus biopsy and amniocentesis. Apart from the small number of tests done in order to prepare parents in advance for the arrival of a child with special needs, or to identify surgically correctable anomalies, most screening is performed to identify handicapped fetuses so that they can be aborted. This Darwinian approach is quite at odds with Christian love whereby the strong make sacrifices on behalf of the weak. All obstetricians have to decide how involved to become in the diagnosis of these anomalies, knowing that a small number of normal children will be sacrificed in the process. Once the cascade of intervention has begun its relentless course, a price has to be paid whether results are acted upon or not. One baby in a hundred will die as a result of an invasive diagnostic procedure such as amniocentesis or chorionic villus sampling. Following a cordocentesis (blood sampling from the umbilical cord), this may be as high as 3%–5%.

We need to ensure that our patients are aware of the risks posed by these procedures, and of their true purpose. The way parents are counselled can make all the difference to the attitude they will have to a handicapped child – whether they see him or her as an encumbrance to be disposed of, or a human being who needs a special degree of love and care. Ultimately, all societies will be judged on the basis of how they treat their weakest members.

Contraception

Post-coital contraception is probably abortifacient since it may well act by preventing implantation of an already fertilized ovum. The morning-after pill causes shedding of the endometrium, and both it and the intra-uterine contraceptive device (IUCD) render it hostile to the developing blastocyst. Doctors who are asked to insert IUCDs as a contraceptive or post-coitally need to understand that they may technically be facilitating abortions, albeit at an early stage. The combined pill usually acts by preventing ovulation, and the progesterone-only pill primarily makes the cervical mucus hostile as well as affecting the endometrial receptivity. It is essential that Christian doctors think through all these implications very carefully in coming to a decision before God about what they will do.

Rape and incest

Thankfully, rape and incest are extremely rare, and pregnancy resulting from them even more so. In the USA in any one year, one woman in a thousand reports rape, and of these a similar proportion become pregnant. The physical and, in particular, the emotional trauma can be extremely severe. In Old Testament times both these crimes were punishable by the death penalty (Dt. 22:25–27; Lv. 18:6–23, 20:10–21), an indication that God views them as seriously as he views murder. Any woman who chooses to carry such a pregnancy to term, or to bring up the baby as her own, needs a tremendous degree of courage and considerable support. It is a cross that few can bear, and yet the alternative, that of taking the life of an innocent party in abortion, is an action which is wrong in itself. As one author has put it: should the child die for the crime of its father? I am forced to the conclusion that the Christian solution, difficult though it may be , is to care for the child at least until birth, when adoption can be considered (especially if the mother is young). However, one cannot advocate this without at the same time realizing that it puts a great onus on us as Christians to do everything we can to help an equally innocent (and much sinned against) mother.

Abortion to save the mother's life

On very rare occasions it may be necessary to perform an abortion in an emergency in order to save the life of the mother. Here we are not saying that the baby's life is less important than that of the mother, but simply (since the baby will die regardless) that it is better to intervene to save one life rather than to stand by and watch two die. Thankfully, these situations are very rare (0.013% of all abortions in the UK). When the mother's life is at risk, the baby is usually viable and so can be successfully delivered alive. As obstetric and neonatal care advances the call for this sort of intervention should become rarer still.

Law reform

A more just society cannot be finally secured without abortion law reform. The law is a very powerful educator, and whereas just laws cannot change human hearts, they do nevertheless restrain them. Not all are called to be engaged in the political process, but God will equip some of us to do just this. We cannot expect the same standard of behaviour from our society that God justifiably expects of us as Christians who have known his grace, but we should certainly aim for legislation which restricts abortion considerably more than at present.

Conclusion

In a society which long ago jettisoned the Judeo-Christian ethic, there are few issues which will test the Christian doctor more than that of abortion. The world will struggle simply to understand our view, let alone respect it. We are called, however, to walk in the shadow of the cross, which means not only suffering the consequences of refusing to participate in what society has sanctioned, but also being prepared to be part of the solution in providing compassionate alternatives to women in crisis. It is a high calling, and one which can be fulfilled only in the power of the very same Holy Spirit who filled our Master before us.

11 HUMAN GENETICS

Alan W. Johnston

The importance of genetics in and to clinical medicine is still not fully appreciated, even though it was at the beginning of the century that Mendel's laws were rediscovered. In the first decade Sir Archibald Garrod published his seminal papers on what he called 'inborn errors of metabolism'.[1] The significance of this work was such that it was recognized and acknowledged by Beadle and Tatum in 1958 when they received the Nobel Prize for demonstrating the principle of 'one gene, one protein' (or enzyme). This concept lies at the heart of all single-gene (Mendelian) defects. Garrod, however, went further with a second book, published in 1931, entitled *The Inborn Factors in Disease*.[2] He pointed out that there are factors in our chemical structures – genes, in modern terminology – which confer on us our predispositions to and immunities from diseases. This in essence is multifactorial disease, in which there is interaction of genetic and environmental factors in the production of abnormality.

These two concepts, embodied in the phrases 'single-gene disorder' and 'multifactorial disease', are of fundamental importance for the practice of clinical medicine today. The third principle for genetic disease had also been laid down early on in a classic paper by Bridges[3] entitled *Non-disjunction as Proof of the Chromosome Theory of Heredity*. This work had been carried out on the fruit fly Drosophila. However, it had generally been assumed that the higher animals were too complex to survive in the presence of a chromosome abnormality. Following the discovery of the correct chromosome number of man (46) in 1956 by Tjio and Levan,[4] abnormalities of number were found three years later, first in Down's syndrome (47, +21), and then in Klinefelter's syndrome (47, XXY) and Turner's syndrome (45, X).

The recent introduction of the techniques of molecular biology has been accompanied by a much greater public awareness of their value, while their application to clinical genetics has resulted in an explosion of information in this area. However, their impact outside this field has so far seemed small, but their application will undoubtedly come.

Incidence of genetic disease

In order to set the background for our discussions, we must begin by asking how common are diseases of genetic or part-genetic origin.

At birth, a baby's risk of having serious disease already present, or of developing it during the first years of life, is at least 1 in 40. It has been estimated that in the UK 21,000 children are born each year with a significant genetic defect such as cystic fibrosis or haemophilia (Human Fertilization and Embryology Authority). Lifetime risks for having a genetic disorder rise from 5% of the population by age 25 to as high as 65% when common diseases with a strong genetic component (multifactorial) are included.[5] The loss in pregnancy from conception onwards is even higher, at least 71%. Jacobs and Hassold[6] comment that the reasons for this high loss rate are unknown, but that it is reasonable to suppose that many early losses are attributable to a chromosome abnormality with its associated lethality. It is well-documented that in European women about 50% of spontaneous abortions before twelve weeks show a chromosome abnormality; about half have an extra chromosome.[7] About 6% of stillbirths are also associated with a chromosome abnormality, but when congenital heart disease and the like are included, about one half of these stillbirths are genetic or part-genetic in origin.

Many of the inborn errors of metabolism, such as galactosaemia, become apparent during the first year of life. Most are inherited in an autosomal recessive manner, *i.e.* the abnormal gene is carried at both loci on the pair of chromosomes. Some are X-linked recessive, *i.e.* carried on the X chromosome and causing disease in males, such as haemophilia. Autosomal dominant diseases, where the abnormal gene is present at only one locus, but where the disease develops nonetheless, become apparent from childhood onwards to late adult life. There tends to be rather more variation in extent of the disease, though there are certain notable exceptions, particularly Huntington's disease. Multifactorial diseases, whether presenting as congenital abnormality or in adult life, show considerable variation in severity.

Given the frequency of genetic disorders, it is likely that within the reader's wider family there is at least one individual with such a condition. However, that information may not always be forthcoming unless specific enquiry is made, perhaps when another member is found to have the disease. It is wholly understandable that such information may not always be common knowledge in the family.

Incidence of genetic disease

Single gene	*per 1000*
Autosomal dominant, *e.g.* hypercholesterolaemia, Huntington's disease	7
Autosomal recessive, *e.g.* cystic fibrosis	2.5
X-linked recessive, *e.g.* haemophilia	0.5
Chromosome , *e.g.* Down's syndrome, fragile X syndrome	6
Multifactorial disease	
Congenital malformations, *e.g.* spina bifida	10
Adults, *e.g.* hypertension, ischaemic heart disease, duodenal ulcer	>20
Total	>46

At least 1:20

Screening programmes

The recognition of the overall frequency of these diseases, with their consequences and implications, has led to a large expansion in the genetic services, including counselling. This would often involve studies of the whole family and the parallel development of screening programmes. These are carried out not simply on total populations but also on selected groups, such as a family or pregnant women.

Prenatal diagnosis

In antenatal clinics, screening for syphilis has for long been standard practice. Testing for rubella and genetic diseases, particularly neural tube defects and sometimes Down's syndrome, are now usual. Specific counselling is not normally given, but the fact that screening will be undertaken is simply included in the booklet given to mothers by antenatal clinics. Whether this is adequate is debatable. If there is a positive family history, counselling should have been given prior to pregnancy, and the whole area of prenatal diagnosis (with its options) explored with the couple – though it has to be said that the occurrence of pregnancy is often the stimulus for referral to the genetic clinic.

No single technique will screen for all the major abnormalities. A choice has therefore to be made, based on a number of factors including cost, yield of abnormalities, complications and reliability. While most screening is carried out on blood (*e.g.* triple testing for Down's syndrome) other methods may be used, particularly in certain subgroups (for example, amniocentesis in older mothers for chromosomal abnormalities). Of the established techniques only ultrasonography in its various forms is non-invasive. Its value does depend on the skill of the operator. In good hands it can detect (but as late as 19-20 weeks) as many as 70% of major defects, including neural tube defects and those due to a chromosome abnormality.

The best-established and safest of the invasive techniques is amniocentesis at 16–17 weeks for neural tube defects and chromosomal abnormalities. The additional risk to continuation of the pregnancy is only 0.5%–1%. Earlier series had also suggested an increased risk of congenital malformations. However, a most comprehensive series from British Columbia[8] recently showed that the only additional risk was of haemolytic disease due to ABO isoimmunization.

Chorion villus biopsy has been developed in order to obtain a diagnosis by 12 weeks of pregnancy. However, it does carry a slightly higher extra risk of miscarriage occurring, say 3%. It can be used not only for chromosomal abnormalities, but more important-ly for molecular diagnosis. It cannot, strictly speaking, be employed for screening purposes because molecular techniques require that the abnormal DNA sequence is already known for each family.

This constraint also applies to the earliest form of prenatal diagnosis, called embryo biopsy. Here a single cell is removed at the eight-cell stage and the DNA obtained, amplified by the polymerase chain reaction and tested for the specific sequence of importance in that family. The embryo was created and, when normal, would be implanted using *in vitro* fertilization technology. Embryos containing the abnormal sequence causing a particular disease would be allowed to perish. Some couples find this approach to be more acceptable than termination of the implanted fetus of an established pregnancy. While one consequence of prenatal diagnosis may be termination, the more common outcome is the reassurance to the couple at high risk that, within the limits of the tests employed, the baby is normal. For instance, for a couple carrying the cystic fibrosis (CF) gene, 75% of fetuses will be normal (3:1).

Termination, even when the fetus would be unlikely to survive, is always a very serious step to take, and some Christians consider it unacceptable in all circumstances. It may, however, be regarded as simply completing the normal, natural process of rejection of abnormal embryos and fetuses. It is known, for example, that the incidence of Down's syndrome is higher at amniocentesis than at birth. This issue needs to be thought through by the reader and especially by the Christian practising in obstetrics or in clinical

180

genetics. Prenatal screening programmes especially need scrutinizing because of the implied termination of an abnormal fetus. Christians do hold differing views, but it is probably fair to say that those who are prepared to recommend termination when appropriate do so with reluctance. It should also be noted that discussing the serious nature of the step is often welcomed by couples, even when they have no religious beliefs.

Population screening

Population screening for genetic disease began in specific ethnic groups in which there was a high incidence of a certain condition. Early programmes met with a mixed response, an important factor being how information had been provided to that community. Successful programmes have included those for Tay-Sachs disease among Ashkenazi Jews and thalassaemia among Cypriots. Screening of whole populations for any disease raises significant problems, but there are somewhat different aims for genetic disorders. In the Nuffield Report,[9] three goals are given. The screening should contribute to improving the health of persons who suffer from genetic disorders, and/or allow carriers of a given abnormal gene to make informed choices regarding reproduction, and/or move towards alleviating the anxieties of families and communities faced with the prospect of serious genetic disease.

Although there are special problems of consent and consequences in screening children, let us take some examples from neonatal screening, since it has been standard practice in some form for many years. Screening for congenital hypothyroidism (which is not usually genetic) provides an excellent example of its value, since treatment with thyroxine is simple and effective, allowing the development of a healthy individual. Screening for phenylketonuria (PKU) is also effective, but dietary management in childhood and in adult life (at least in any pregnancy) has to be strict. Although screening for Duchenne muscular dystrophy (DMD) has sometimes been strongly advocated, its main value is in terms of counselling with a view to prenatal diagnosis and determining the status of other members of the family. The burden of the knowledge, primarily for the parents, that their apparently healthy boy is destined to be in a wheelchair by age eleven and probably dead by twenty-five is arguably one that should not be inflicted on them. They will become aware all too soon. Where the disorder is of late onset and where treatment is available, a case can be made for screening children. Familial hypercholesterolaemia (FHC) is the commonest autosomal dominant disorder, with an incidence of 1 in 500. Identification of these individuals in childhood could enable healthy patterns of eating to be established early with the aim of delaying the onset of arterial disease. Finally, screening for a particular disease does allow identification of those individuals with the gene who can then be kept under appropriate surveillance, for example in familial adenomatous polyposis (FAP) for the development of carcinoma of the colon, or in ovarian/breast cancer families.

It is the ability to alter the environment which is the principal reason for screening for multifactorial disorders in adult life. The avoidance of obesity in type II diabetes and the availability of drug treatment in mild hypertension are possible options, for example. Such possibilities as the early detection of disease or modification of the environment, *e.g.* by diet or drugs, are likely to be developed in many specialties over the next few years. Yet the individual's right not to be involved has to be respected, just as in other spheres of medicine.

Genes and therapy

Clearly, modification of the genetic component would be the better option still, since it would restore normal genetic function regardless of the mechanism by which the disease is produced. Initial enthusiasm in the early 1990s that somatic gene therapy would soon be in routine use waned with the realization of the practical difficulties. Severe combined immune deficiency disease (SCID) is the success story, but, for the commoner disabling diseases such as cystic fibrosis (CF) and Duchenne muscular dystrophy (DMD), practical progress has been less encouraging so far. But it will come.

In somatic gene therapy, the healthy gene is carried by a vector. For example, a liposome or an adenovirus, of a type commonly found in the respiratory tract, can be used to carry the CF gene and be administered via an inhaler – which sounds simple. However, there are possible disadvantages, the relevance and seriousness of which are not yet known, but which might be anticipated in view of what we already know about the organization of the genome. First, there is no control over where the gene is inserted. It is uncertain whether controlling mechanisms, either inserted with the gene or already present, will function normally. It is possible that an excess of the gene product could be produced so that, in theory, a boy with haemophilia could, after replacement of the factor VIII gene, develop a clotting disease because of excess production. Another problem is one to which parallels are already recognized. In both chronic myeloid leukaemia (CML) and in Burkitt's lymphoma, there are translocations involving chromosomes 9 and 8 respectively. The break in the chromosomes allows unmasking by translocation of the oncogenes c-abl to chromosome 22 and c-myc to chromosome 14 respectively. Similarly, the insertion of a new gene at random could expose an oncogene, with the risk of development of malignant disease.

With factors such as these being unknown for somatic cell therapy, germ cell therapy involving egg and sperm, with its implications for future generations, has been proscribed by the Gene Therapy Advisory Committee until much wider experience has been obtained with the former. In contrast, it should be noted that, like a transplanted kidney, somatic cells treated by gene therapy will die on the death of the recipient.

The Gene Therapy Advisory Committee

This Committee was established in 1993 after the UK Government had accepted the Report on the Ethics of Gene Therapy (Clothier Report).[10] This stated that somatic gene therapy was not thought to be fundamentally different from other advanced therapies such as organ transplantation. The Committee is responsible for approving applications for gene therapy to patients. The first to be approved was for its use in a child with an inherited immunodeficiency disease (SCID) due to lack of the enzyme adenosine deaminase.

The perfect baby

It is wholly understandable that a couple should desire more than anything else a healthy baby. In the presence of a family history of a genetic disease, some even go so far as to say that they would avoid a pregnancy unless there is a guarantee of a perfect baby. Yet such perfection can never be assured or assumed. It is unobtainable because of the frequency of all types of genetic disease. Every child deserves and needs to be loved, and especially is this essential should the child be handicapped in any way. A consumerist approach is totally out of place. Seeking perfection by the use of eggs or sperm regarded as 'superior' because of the type of individual from whom they derive is largely thwarted by the infinite variations that meiosis entails as well as by any mutations which occur. This is why children differ from their parents. Similarly, even when it becomes possible to identify the genes involved in the traits for normal variation (*e.g.* eye colour) or minor defects (*e.g.* excessive moles) no attempt should be made to select or correct them. The Clothier Report has so recommended.

Handicapped people

The care of handicapped, weak and underprivileged people continues to constitute a most important and necessary commitment of the work and witness of the Christian church. This must continue regardless of the circumstances. For instance, if a couple choose not to take the opportunity afforded by prenatal diagnosis and where an abnormal baby is then born, they should still be supported in every way. Most regrettably, commercial pressures have sometimes produced a scenario in which (US) insurers have refused to cover the care of an affected child – but they would have paid for prenatal diagnosis and, if appropriate, termination. Financial considerations have triumphed over ethical ones. In every respect, the Christian's compassion for the handicapped and disadvantaged, and for those caring for them, should be evidenced by their whole attitude.

Synthesis of therapeutic proteins

As an alternative to gene therapy, recombinant DNA technology has made possible the synthesis of therapeutic proteins free of any contaminant, whether virus or foreign protein. The relevant gene is inserted into the genome of another species (a transgenic organism) such as a bacterium or another mammal. Human insulin is now synthesized in this way, with the gene inserted into the bacterium E. coli. Other products so produced are factor VIII for haemophilia A, human growth hormone for some types of shortness of stature, and hepatitis B vaccine. Another approach has been to attach the desired gene into the DNA sequence involved in the synthesis of the milk protein casein. After insertion into the DNA of a fertilized egg from a sheep, the egg is placed into the uterus. Any resulting female, when lactating, then produces the desired protein in its milk.

Human Genome Project

This ambitious project aims to sequence every chromosome by the year 2000. It is a costly exercise, made possible only by advanced technology such as automatic DNA sequencing machines with computerized recording and correlation of the results. Laboratories in many parts of the world are collaborating. There are estimated to be some 3000 million base pairs and 50,000–100,000 genes. Yet only 2%–3% of the genome is known to code for amino acids, and the function of more than 90% is unknown. The argument was initially advanced that it might be more effective – not least in cost – to concentrate on those sections of DNA known to contain disease sequences. Such a strategy could possibly produce early benefits for patients and their families.

Christian principles and biblical interpretation

In accepting that God created the earth and the universe and that Christ sustains it (Gn. 1:28; Rom. 1:19–20; Col. 1:16–17), we accept the responsibility of being stewards of that creation. This includes using our minds and applying them to bridge any apparent discrepancy between our understanding of God and of his creation. 'Thinking God's thoughts after him' reminds us that this is no new area of debate. It was when Galileo was attempting to understand the universe that he stated that the Earth revolved around the sun. Such a radical theory brought him into conflict with the church leaders of his day, who interpreted Scripture as stating that the Earth was the centre of the universe. Excommunication was the penalty for such heretical views – and only recently has he been rehabilitated. Yet his theory has become established fact. Last century, Sir James Simpson was criticized for the introduction of anaesthesia into labour wards: did not Scripture say that with pain children would be born (Gn. 3:16)? That is not the approach of today's church to the relief of pain.

The Bible was written not as a scientific textbook but to make us wise to salvation and to equip us thoroughly for every good work (2 Tim. 3:16). But it was written for those of any century. God has spoken, still speaks and will speak, to every generation, regardless of its culture, through his Word. It is our responsibility to respond to that Word. Yet we need to be careful not to insist that there is only one correct interpretation of Scripture, lest thereby we diminish its authority. We should also be aware that our own prejudices – ecclesiastical, scientific, social or gut reaction – can influence or even determine our interpretation. Many of our problems arise from faulty interpretation of either Scripture or science – our imperfect understanding of the word God gave or of the world God made – as well as from our lack of humility in theology and science. In the final analysis, there can be no conflict between the discoveries of science and our Christian faith. Until that time comes we all need to show the greatest love and respect for our fellow Christians who accept the authority of Scripture and yet take a different view from ourselves.

Status of embryo and fetus

Nowhere is this more important than in the continuing debate on the status of the fertilized egg. Is it a new person? Or a potential new person? The new person view in many ways represents the simplest approach, including as it does the development into baby and adult. Questions, however, need to be asked. Does it represent an over-simplification, or is it merely a semantic solution, perhaps heightened by the Warnock debate? Does it truly do justice either to what little Scripture actually teaches on the subject or to the scientific facts as we understand them? Here, then, are some points relevant to the debate.

Such definitions of a person, as an individual capable of thinking and relating – commonly accepted attributes – do make it difficult to include a fertilized egg or indeed any stage until the fetus is capable of independent existence.

The Bible does refer to the body as a tent or tabernacle prepared for the spirit, as if the two are not necessarily coextensive. (This is also one explanation for there being two accounts of the creation of human beings in Genesis, namely as physical bodies and then as living souls.)

In considering the various references in Scripture to intra-uterine existence, it is essential to recognize that they are all retrospective – looking back from the standpoint of individuals whom God has chosen. It is not surprising that there is no mention of fertilized eggs, whether destined to develop or not. Yet the distinction between these two groups is important, as Donald MacKay[11] has persuasively argued. While development of the central nervous system is essential, it should not be correlated directly with being a person, though there is a decisive moment after which there is a person. As Jones[12] emphasizes, MacKay's contribution to the debate is a reminder that our own early history as embryos is shrouded in mystery and uncertainty. We can reflect retrospectively on God's provisions for us as embryos, since each adult 'I' has historical continuity with an embryonic 'I'. In attempting to move prospectively from an embryonic 'I' to a future adult 'I' we have to exercise great caution. Others, of course, such as O'Donovan[13] and Stott,[14] take the conservative position of the embryo as a person. Wilkinson[15] concludes: 'We may describe the embryo as a human being but not a human person. It is a human being in the pre-personal stage of its existence.'

Another argument is that because there is a continuity between the fertilized egg and the living adult, there can be no alternative to the former being a new person. Yet this ignores the discontinuous nature of that continuity. The fetal heart is recognizable before it beats, and the kidneys before they produce urine, while the lungs do not complete their development until after birth. Similarly, there are stages in the maturation of the central nervous system. Is there, as MacKay suggests, a stage before which the fetus cannot become a person? How also does one view the fetus without a brain (anencephalic)?

A further relevant area is that of twins and chimaeras and also hermaphroditism. Identical (monozygotic) twins have the same DNA, being derived from a single fertilized egg. Yet they are clearly independent persons and sometimes have distinguishing features such as handedness, like the Gullikson twins of Wimbledon fame. Equally, there are individuals who are chimaeras, that is, derived from two fertilized eggs which may even be of different sex, and yet give rise to a single person. Again, there are hermaphrodites and pseudohermaphrodites in whom the genetic sex is at variance with the anatomical sex or with the gender. Perhaps the most striking example is virilizing congenital adrenal hyperplasia. Here, when the diagnosis is not made, the 46, XX (female) zygote develops into an apparent male, though internally they have uterus and ovaries. However, when correctly diagnosed and treated, they become females capable of bearing children (though plastic surgery to correct the male-type external genitalia will be required). What constitutes the person can clearly be modified by the consequences of the genetic abnormality.

The final point, as already mentioned, is the generally accepted high wastage rate in pregnancy. Jacobs and Hassold[16] quote at least 71%, with geography and ethnicity having little influence on the frequency. They state that at least 25% of all conceptuses are lost prior to implantation and a further 30% in the early post-implantation stage prior to the woman recognizing that she is pregnant, while at least 15% are spontaneously aborted between 6 and 28 weeks, with a further 1% in the later stages of pregnancy. Survival to term of embryos with a chromosome abnormality (other than balanced structural rearrangements and boys with 47, XYY constitution) is exceptional, 94% being lost when present in clinic-ally recognized pregnancies. They concluded that chromosome abnormalities account for the great majority of pre-embryonic,

embryonic and fetal wastage. Chard,[17] after reviewing the literature, derived similar estimates – 30% of embryos failed to implant, another 30% produced chemical evidence of pregnancy but only 10% clinical abortion, while 30% resulted in a term pregnancy. A figure of 8% has been given currency, apparently based on the work of Whitaker, Taylor and Lind,[18] but this paper appears to refer only to the loss during the second week after conception and prior to the onset of menstruation. Given the difficulties in assessing early loss, it is prudent to be cautious in the interpretation of all such figures, but the occurrence of such a sizeable loss clearly cannot be ignored in theological debate.

During a pregnancy, there is a hormonal dialogue between the developing embryo and the mother, such that if the former is or becomes abnormal, the pregnancy will probably be discontinued. (We should incidentally marvel at the wonders of such a control mechanism!) In some, there is never even any differentiation of the embryo but only of the membranes, a blighted ovum.

Even taking just the loss subsequent to clinical recognition of the pregnancy and recognizing that many are abnormal, we need to ask what is the theological status of these abnormal embryos and fetuses – particularly if it is the fertilized egg which is regarded as a person? In such discussions the scientific facts cannot be ignored. I would suggest that these pointers from the divine Book of Nature support the view that it is at a later stage that the fertilized egg becomes a person during the course of its normal development. An excellent review of this whole area is provided in A. C. Berry, *Beginnings: Christian Views of the Early Embryo*.[19]

We turn next to some practical aspects.

Counselling

The objectives of genetic counselling are first and foremost to establish the diagnosis as precisely as possible, then to identify the mode of inheritance and finally to communicate this information to the family in a way that can be comprehended. This then enables each individual or couple to make informed decisions regarding their own future, particularly whether to have children. It is not surprising that some individuals and some families do not wish to receive such information (and this attitude must be respected), but the majority come to welcome it, even when treatment is not available. Knowledge is preferred to ignorance.

The counselling should be non-directive, leaving individuals to make their own decisions once they have been given the facts. But it has to be recognized that such emotive information can never be given in a wholly neutral or impartial way.

Confidentiality

While confidentiality is a cardinal principle of all medical practice, in clinical genetics it should be scrupulously observed because of the sensitive nature of much of the information. Yet, ironically, it can be much more difficult to maintain within a family setting. Some disclosure may be inevitable, since this is how members of the family are recognized as being at risk, and the consultation may appropriately include the whole family. During the course of taking a detailed family history, however, information may be obtained which is both highly sensitive and significant: for example, the illegitimacy of a first child (which is not uncommon) who has an autosomal recessive disease such as cystic fibrosis. This fact greatly reduces the risk of a second affected child from 1 in 4 to the low-risk category (1 in 80). Such situations produce problems. The response to this sensitive information is that in the consultations with other members of the family the counsellor may have to be economical with the truth. This may be the only way to preserve a confidence and yet honestly and accurately counsel other members of the family – regrettable, perhaps, but necessary.

Another type of complication can arise because a family member will sometimes refuse to allow key information to be passed on, for instance that a relative might carry a particular gene. This can produce major problems and even litigation. We try to resolve such situations by persuading the patient, asking for the help of the family doctor where appropriate.

A further area of failure in cooperation is in refusing to provide information about the family or by refusing to give a blood sample. Sometimes the reason given is that since it has happened it must be the will of God. These refusals were particularly difficult when it was necessary to track the passage of a gene through the family. With recent advances enabling the gene itself to be identified rather than a marker (restriction fragment length polymorphism, RFLP), refusal has become less important. The advances do, however, produce a new problem! For example, if an individual wishing to start a family has, based on the pedigree data, a 1 in 4 risk for Huntington's disease because of an affected grandparent, demonstrating that he has the gene inevitably indicates that the linking parent also has the gene. The parent may not wish to have this information – yet his or her adult offspring knows. It is a secret that will be very difficult, if not impossible to keep. For this reason most clinics are reluctant to undertake testing under these circumstances.

All these problems arise because genetic information belongs not to one individual but to a family. To add to the difficulties, the clinical geneticist has divided loyalties. He has some responsibility to the whole family, and perhaps to society as well, in addition to the individual(s) who initially came for advice. The key questions are: to whom does the genetic information belong, and how far does the responsibility of the clinical geneticist extend?

Beyond even the wider family, the question arises whether there is a legitimate public concern in genetic disease. This may relate to a particular disease in a particular community (such as thalassaemia in Thailand) or in relation to specific individuals or occupations. Although instances of the latter are not common, they do occur. Let us take a purely hypothetical case: a commercial airline pilot might have a grandparent with Huntington's disease and therefore he has a 1 in 4 risk of carrying the gene. It is possible that the earliest stages of the development of the disease might compromise his competence as a pilot. Ought he to be tested for the gene? Note all the consequences for his career and for his family. Only one screening programme exists in the UK: here applicants for certain specific occupations in HM Forces undergo sickle-cell screening. These are individuals who would be exposed to low oxygen concentrations in the atmosphere, when sickling of the red cells could occur in those with the sickling gene. There would appear to be no other UK situation in which tests for genetic disease are justified at the present time (Nuffield Report).

Insurance

The principle of insurance is that of sharing a risk among a large number of people (for instance, that a car accident will happen to $x\%$ of car owners each year). The same applies to illness and death. In order to keep premiums low, insurance companies seek to identify high-risk individuals and either exclude them or charge them an extra premium ('loading'). Insurance companies have for years included standard questions on their medical forms asking about all illnesses and relevant family history. Now they can ask about genetic tests.

These are carried out in two situations. The first is where there is a family history. Here the test will show that the person does or does not carry the gene. If the latter, then the proposer should benefit and so should the company. The second involves testing carried out as part of a screening programme where the discovery of a previously unsuspected abnormality may adversely affect the proposer's acceptability. There are particular difficulties with multifactorial disorders where the severity depends on other factors, partly genetic but mainly environmental. Predicting the outcome would be little more than guesswork in the present state of knowledge. The Nuffield Report on genetic screening recommended that British insurance companies should not require genetic testing to be performed, thus continuing present practice, and that discussion should take place between the Government and the industry about the future use of genetic data, with a moratorium on their use meanwhile. Two provisos were included, one excluding large policies. The second allows disclosure of the results of genetic tests when a positive family history had already been obtained through a conventional questionnaire.

DNA data banks

In the UK, regional genetic centres commonly store samples of DNA from families whom they have investigated either through a clinic referral or as part of a research project. If a family in a research study becomes a clinic family, it is sound practice at the very least, if not essential, to obtain wherever possible a further blood sample for DNA extraction. This is for at least two reasons, the first being to ensure that there has been no error at any stage in labelling the specimen. More important is the opportunity that can then be taken to give further counselling. The aims of counselling for a research project may differ from those for a clinical situation. It has also happened that a family member may be willing for his DNA sample to be used for research or for the benefit of other members, but he specifies that he himself does not wish to be informed of his own test result.

Given the accuracy and reliability of DNA fingerprinting, police forces in the UK are setting up DNA banks. The most meticulous care will be required to ensure that errors of labelling, breaches of security, and so on, do not occur. Checking of the fingerprinting on a fresh blood sample will be essential before use in court. With such safeguards as these, there can be no objection to their development. Whether there is any foundation for the fears expressed about misuse of these data is doubtful in the UK. There must, however, be total separation of police and medical DNA banks. Whether only the DNA from those convicted should be retained is more debatable.

Genetic registers

Considerable use is made by regional genetic centres of genetic registers. They are often utilized as 'at risk' registers because such individuals are included as well as those already affected by the disorder. The consent of the index cases and of those relatives seen should be obtained before inclusion on the register. However, it is more difficult for other members of the extended family. The main reason is that there is not necessarily any communication between these scattered members and the clinical genetics service or even the original family. Secondly, the data available (*e.g.* name and area of domicile) may be quite inadequate to make any contact, yet it may prove important information and should not be discarded. For example, at a later date further identification may become possible through providing a link into another family or assisting in a diagnosis.

Such registers contain much highly sensitive information and their storage has to be secure. Access requires strict control, and it should be the responsibility of a designated senior clinical geneticist. As a register is likely to be on a computer, it will be subject to the provisions of the Data Protection Act.

When the register is used for research, the data should be rendered anonymous. The exception would be where individuals require to be identified for the purpose of the research. Extra safeguards should include referral of the research proposal to the local research ethics committee, even if it is to utilize only their clinical records.

The Human Fertilization and Embryology Authority

The HFEA was established as a result of the Human Fertilization and Embryology Act of 1990. Its membership has to represent a broad range of views and experience – medical, scientific, social, legal, lay and religious – and the chairman and deputy chairman, as well as at least half of the twenty-one members, may not be involved in medical or scientific practice. Its 'principal task is to regulate by means of a licensing system any research or treatment which involves the creation, keeping and using of human embryos outside the body or the storage or donation of human eggs or sperm'. The objective of its code of practice is wider than merely the clinical and scientific aspects, since it also includes the maintenance of respect for human life at all stages in its development, as well as a concern for the welfare of any children who result and whose interests may not be adequately protected by the safeguards provided for the adults involved. Its initial code of practice was soon modified, particularly in the light of the Human Fertilization and Embryology (Disclosure of Information) Act (1992). The Authority intends to review and, where necessary, amend this code in the light of experience, and to take account of new developments and public concerns. In its annual reports, current research projects are listed as well as the centres at which they are being carried out. They include pre-implantation biopsy and mechanisms of trisomy formation.

It has already issued two public consultation documents. The first was on sex selection.[20] Its decision in the light of the representations received was to allow sex selection only where the mother is known to be the carrier of a life-threatening X-linked disease, but not for social reasons. Nor, on the evidence currently available, would the HFEA support sperm-sorting into X and Y sperm.

The second document, entitled *Donated Ovarian Tissue in Embryo Research and Assisted Conception*,[21] covered a much more controversial field, even though answers to quite specific questions were requested. The background is that the shortage of donated eggs is a constraint on medical and scientific research. Over 9,000 responses were received, indicating the huge interest aroused. The Authority reached three conclusions. First, in the treatment of infertility, it would be acceptable to use tissue from live donors only – though they had no objection in principle to cadaver tissue from consenting adult women. Secondly, the HFEA rejected the use for treatment of eggs from fetuses because of concern over the safety of the procedures, and the possible effect on the children so produced of learning about their origins. Thirdly, the Authority considered on balance that the use of ovarian tissue and eggs from live donors, adult cadavers and fetuses was acceptable for embryo research. Such research could enable greater understanding of the causes of infertility and of congenital abnormalities. Since the issuing of the consultation document, Parliament has in fact taken action to make use of fetal eggs for treatment illegal (13 April 1994).

From the Christian angle, it is worth noting that the first form of interference with the normal reproductive process was in the use of donated sperm (artificial insemination by donor). That Rubicon has been crossed, and it has been accepted by western society at large but not by all Christians, though the precedent of levirate marriage should be noted. Egg donation is in principle no different, though the technology is considerably more complicated. However, there is a distinction between the use of donated gametes for treatment and for research. Spare embryos from the former (which are mainly inevitable) and all embryos from the latter would be allowed to perish in due course. Some Christian doctors are satisfied that gamete donation is acceptable both for treatment and for research. This is one reason the debate on the status of the fertilized egg is so important (see pp.136 ff.).

Even with the restrictions to be applied by the HFEA, the importance of consent which is truly informed cannot be overstated. Details of the extent of the necessary counselling for both donors and recipients is given in its code of practice.

Childlessness appears to be occurring more frequently, probably associated with the increase in infection with Chlamydia, other forms of tubal disease and the frequency of abortion. The key question is whether it is a fundamental right that every couple should, if they so wish, have children, by any means and at any cost (including financial). In the Bible, children are seen as a gift from God, and the agony of the infertile is recorded (for instance, by Hannah). Sometimes a child was given beyond all expectation, as in the case of Sarah and Abraham.

Scripture further teaches the central importance of the family. The welfare of any child born through gamete donation is of such paramount importance that donation should be undertaken only in the context of at least a stable long-term heterosexual relationship and preferably of a family. It should also be mandatory for the donated gametes to be from the same ethnic group, which is accepted by the HFEA as good clinical practice.

In 1994 the HFEA also decided not to license either the use of cloning by splitting embryos for treatment, or research to this end. Cloning by replacing a nucleus is illegal under the Human Fertilization and Embryology Act (1990). Fears that have been expressed, sometimes in dramatic terms, about the misuse of cloning should be allayed by their stance. However, it must be noted that in the USA one form of cloning has been successful up to a point. Hall and Stillman[22] had quite deliberately chosen human embryos that were abnormal because they were derived from eggs that had been fertilized by more than one sperm. None of these abnormal clones grew for more than six days, but the technique has the potential for clinical use, for instance to obtain two or three identical embryos, and then by IVF technology to produce identical twins or triplets, who would possibly be born a year or more apart.

The use of cloning in animal husbandry, whether by embryo splitting or nucleus transfer, is well recognized. However, because the techniques are expensive, they seem unlikely at present to be introduced into farming.

Allocation of resources

Funding for health services is limited in even the richest countries, so that hard decisions have to be taken regarding their allocation. In the Third World, even harder decisions have to be made. Priority is likely to be given to measures for the control of infection and malnutrition. For genetic disease, education and screening could have a significant effect, as has happened in Cyprus with the falling incidence of thalassaemia. On a world view, these measures would be the most effective in terms of preventing suffering and ill health – rather than the expediency which controls so many decisions (the 'fire brigade' approach!). In the developed countries there will be increasing pressure for treatment, as this becomes available, of genetic or part-genetic disease, leading to difficult decisions. In the field of assisted reproduction, we must ask whether every woman has the right to have a baby, regardless of the cause or the costs, financial and otherwise, especially in a world that is rapidly becoming overpopulated. All such financial decisions should be taken after open discussion rather than by default or expediency.

Some genetic tests are relatively cheap when compared with other investigations, but their volume may make them costly, as may the need for further sequential testing. Such tests are commonly more complicated (and therefore more expensive), but essential in the establishing of a precise diagnosis. Similarly, because of the time-consuming nature of tracing family trees and counselling family members, clinical contacts are expensive, even when carried out by suitably trained and experienced associate staff. However, much of this work will become part and parcel of many specialties, which will require appropriately trained staff.

The value of a person cannot be measured in financial terms, yet inevitably some key decisions have to be taken at this level.

Conclusions

The discoveries in modern genetics have provided an insight into the marvellous mechanisms that control both the transfer of information from one generation to the next and its translation into an adult human being. That human beings are capable of understanding these things and of responding to the reconciling love of God in Christ is equally marvellous. We are indeed wonderfully made (Ps. 139:14).

Our responsibility as stewards has been greatly increased by these discoveries revealed in the Book of Nature. Our ability to identify abnormal embryos and fetuses must make us reassess the extent of that responsibility, including asking whether terminating or retaining is the appropriate response – remembering that 70% or more of conceptuses are naturally discarded because of abnormality. The information from clinical genetics seems to me to support the view that, valuable though the fertilized egg is because of its potential, only with development does it become a human person.

That responsibility also extends to gene therapy. Providing safeguards for gamete donation, whether for treatment or for research, is another area of responsibility, even though many Christians consider such donation as essentially wrong. Yet there are Christians working in the field who are prepared to accept such donations, given stringent safeguards.

The use and misuse of information constitute yet another area where the highest standards must be upheld.

For the Christian working in clinical genetics, there are difficult, even painful, decisions to be made. Perhaps we should be prepared to be agnostic and accept that our understanding of both science and Scripture is inevitably incomplete, yet seek in every way, whatever we do, to work at it with all our heart as to the Lord (Col. 3:23).

Further reading

D. W. Vere, 'When is a person?' *JCMF* 1988/34:3, pp. 18–23.

Glossary

Abortion: intervention by medical or surgical means to produce loss of the fetus and so termination of pregnancy. Usually refers to therapeutic abortion.

Amniocentesis: aspiration of the amniotic fluid surrounding the baby, usually carried out at about 16–17 weeks.

Chorion(ic) villus biopsy or sampling: biopsy at the edge of the developing placenta, usually carried out at 9–10 weeks.

Chromosome: the structures which carry the genes arranged as 22 pairs of autosomes and two sex chromosomes (XX in the female and XY in the male).

Clone: another cell line or organism with identical genetic composition.

Conceptus: the fertilized egg and earliest stages of development.

DNA: desoxyribonucleic acid, the molecule which carries the four bases whose sequence determines the genetic information required for development of each individual.

Embryo: from approximately 2 weeks after fertilization to the eighth week.

Fetus: from 8 weeks post-conception onwards.

Gene: a section of DNA of varying size which carries specific information for the synthesis of a protein.

Miscarriage: usually used to distinguish spontaneous abortion from therapeutic abortion.

Oncogene: genes which may induce cancer but which have a normal function, *e.g.* in the control of growth of a cell.

RNA: ribonucleic acid, complementary to DNA, and involved in the transmission of information for protein synthesis.

Ultrasonography: examination of the fetus (and organs of the body) by means of high-frequency sound waves to determine structure.

Zygote: the fertilized egg formed by union of egg and sperm.

12 SEXUALITY

VIRGINITY

Trevor Stammers

In his review article 'The sexual renaissance',[1] Reiss comments: 'There does not seem to be any society, anywhere in the world, at any time in the past or present, that was able to bring up the majority of even one generation of males to adulthood as virgins. ' He goes on to point out that whereas religion had been viewed as a bulwark against premarital sexual permissiveness, this was now changing, particularly in the Protestant church. One theologian is quoted as saying that 'there is nothing necessarily wrong with premarital coitus'.

All this was written in the swinging sixties and typified the spirit of the age. In the more sobering context of the AIDS nineties, perhaps society has good reason to think again. The threat of extinction concentrates the mind wonderfully.

Why virginity makes sense

In his book *Why Wait?*[2] Josh McDowell lists twenty-six reasons – physical, spiritual, emotional and sociological – why waiting until marriage for sexual intercourse makes sense. Many of his reasons have an obvious application in medicine, not least in preventing the spread of sexually transmitted diseases. One particularly well-researched area, however, is so frequently overlooked, and yet has such wide implications for preventive medicine, that I would like to consider it here in some detail. It is the statistical link between premarital chastity and postmarital success.[3]

I have recently had the opportunity to discuss this link with a wide variety of secular audiences – psychiatrists, sex therapists, psychologists, general practitioners, social workers and marriage guidance counsellors – and all have expressed previous ignorance of it, and have been unable to offer any conflicting data. All researchers, from Terman[4] in 1938 to Bancroft[5] in 1983, have come to the conclusion that premarital chastity leads to a lower incidence of separation and divorce, and to higher scores on a variety of questionnaires to determine the level of marital happiness.

Without exception, however, these researchers react to their own conclusions in one of two ways. Either they are dismissed or diminished (Athanasiou: 'We view the findings with regard to rating of marital happiness as heuristic . . . These data may not be an indication of the dysfunctional character of premarital sexual behaviour'; Terman: 'The relatively small prediction weights warranted by our data on sex experience prior to marriage are in striking contrast to the importance attached by moralists to premarital chastity'), or they are regarded as invalid (Ellis: These findings are 'exceptionally dubious in that individuals who are afraid and ashamed to have premarital affairs are precisely the same kind of individuals who would be afraid and ashamed to admit even to themselves that their marriages are unhappy'). Such comments reveal far more about the integrity of the authors than about that of the data!

Why virginity is spiritually important

The Bible teaches that there is no such thing as casual sex. In 1 Corinthians 6:15–20, a key passage in understanding the nature of the sex act, Paul makes this quite clear. He takes what might be regarded as the most casual and fleeting of sexual relationships – that between a prostitute and her client – and states that even in this transitory sexual encounter, a union takes place which, from heaven's perspective, makes the client one body with the prostitute. The word used to describe this union, *kollōmenos* ('joined' in RSV) literally means 'glued together', so strong is the bonding in spiritual terms. The formation of this spiritual bond explains why any sexual act outside marriage is wrong. As Professor Smedes succinctly put it: 'It is wrong because it violates the inner meaning of the act. It is wrong because unmarried people thereby engage in a life-uniting act without a life-united intent. Whenever two people copulate without a commitment to life-union they commit fornication.'[6]

This also explains why sexual sin, though not branded worse than other categories of sin, is specified as a particularly distinctive type of sin in its effect on the perpetrator. What is glued together in one moment and yet torn apart in the next is sure to be damaged in the process. This is why Paul says that the sexually immoral person sins against his or her own body, and he pleads with his readers to flee immorality (verse 18). 'Drunkenness and gluttony involve the use of that which comes from without the body. The sexual appetite arises from within. They can serve other purposes, e.g. conviviality. This has no other purpose than the gratification of lust. They are sinful in excess. This is sinful in itself.'[7]

Paul then furthers his appeal with a reminder that the Christian's body is the temple of the Holy Spirit. Surely, then, the Jesus who was stirred with holy anger at the desecration of the earthly temple (Jn. 2:15) must also be moved with righteous indignation against those who encourage the sexual defilement of his spiritual temple.

Why the virginity ethic is important to Christian doctors

Paul's concepts are totally alien to our sex-mad culture, and many Christians are sadly unaware of his teaching or, more dangerously, ignore it. Much concern has been expressed recently in the Christian Medical Fellowship about the 'falling away' of Christian medical students and junior doctors. I am convinced that many of them do so as a direct consequence of capitulation in their sexual lives. Satan goes straight for the jugular, and he knows that if Christians are compromised in their sexual standards, their whole spiritual walk will suffer as a result. The Christian houseman cannot sleep with the staff nurse at night, and witness on the ward by day.

Compromise also characterizes the attitude of many Christian doctors in dealing with sexual issues with patients in the consultation. How many of us take the line that 'young people will do it anyway, so there is no point in saying anything'? Are we really so ineffective as doctors in influencing patient behaviour? By all means we must make our communication of the message sensitive and relevant to our patients, but if we blandly acquiesce to every un-married person's request for contraception without ever attempting to communicate the damaging implications of premarital sex, we surely grieve the heart of God and need to repent.

In another generation, when divinely appointed boundaries were being blurred even by those who claimed to know him, God cried out: 'I looked for a man among them who would build up the wall and stand before me in the gap . . . but I found none' (Ezk. 22:30). Will God find among our Fellowship those who will take a vocal stand against the destructive tide of extramarital sex?

Postscript

I am only too aware that for many the message of the precious-ness of virginity will come too late, but there is another message of eternal relevance: 'the blood of Jesus . . . purifies us from all sin' (I Jn. 1:7).

McDowell concludes his book *Why Wait?* with the story of Tracey, who, after a long experience in the sexual wilderness, found that cleansing for herself. 'I began to see my infinite worth and value to God. God didn't need me, but because of his love he wanted me. And because he wanted me, he provided for me a way to repent – to confess not only my sin, but also to confess that it is forgiven.'[8]

HOMOSEXUALITY

Peter Saunders

Homosexuality is rising up the political, medical and social agenda. The deaths of well-known gay athletes, actors and entertainers from AIDS and the 'outing' of other public figures less candid about their sexual preferences, have made sure of this. It is impossible for today's Christian health professional to avoid confronting the issue, whether through treating gay patients, working alongside gay colleagues or helping others in the church to be truly Christian in the way they react.

Homosexuality is one issue on which the thinking of church and world are increasingly 'poles apart'. Christians do not have a good track record in their dealings with homosexuals, so it is essential that we think the matter through well. Our reactions should be grounded in compassion and love, not fear and prejudice.

Orientation and behaviour

Homosexual orientation can be defined as preferential erotic attraction to the same sex. However, not all people have exclusive sexual inclinations. There is a spectrum of sexual orientation, ranging from those who have never had a homosexual thought in their lives, to those who experience nothing else.

Sexual orientation usually determines sexual expression, but not always. Homosexual feelings might not result in homosexual behaviour. Alternatively, under extreme circumstances (such as in prisons or during wartime), those of heterosexual orientation may participate in homosexual acts.

Nature or nurture

While there is no clear consensus on what causes a homosexual orientation to develop, the weight of opinion favours environment rather than heredity. Hormonal mechanisms, brain structure or genotype are unlikely explanations; but it is worth being aware of the arguments for each.

Hormonal mechanisms

There is little scientific support for a hormonal cause. Animal studies have shown that castrated male rats and androgen-treated female rats can exhibit atypical sexual behaviour.[1] However, unlike animals, human beings do not have a reflexly governed sexual response.

Boys with testicular feminization do tend to develop a sexual preference for men, but caution is called for. These genetically male children are phenotypically female and are usually brought up with a female gender identity. The effects could equally be environmental. There is no real evidence for same-sex erotic feelings in girls suffering from congenital adrenal hyperplasia. Nor has extensive research revealed hormonal differences in homosexuals.

Brain Structure

Correlations between brain structure and sexual orientation have been reported in some small studies. There is some evidence to suggest that homosexual men and women have an increased level of left-handedness. Also, a recent study of the post-mortem brains of homosexual males revealed an area in the hypothalamus equivalent in size to that of heterosexual females.[2]

There are reasons to be cautious. First, the numbers involved are small. Secondly, most of the homosexual men with abnormal hypothalamuses died of AIDS. Thirdly, it is not apparent how the anatomical area involved could have a bearing on sexual behaviour. Finally, even if it could, it would remain to be proven that the structural change was the cause rather than the result of the altered sexual orientation. There are simply too many confounding variables.

A gay gene?

There was much media interest in the recent claim that a region on the X chromosome (Xq28) created a predilection for male homosexual orientation.[3] However, the results of this small sample of identical twins have been viewed in the medical press as less than convincing.[4] Whereas it is clear that genes do have some bearing on behaviour, in the case of homosexuality such genetic influence is small, if indeed it exists at all. At most, there may be a genetic predisposition, with a pattern of inheritance similar to alcoholism or schizophrenia.

Environmental influences

Most researchers point to a variety of early environmental influences. They argue that male homosexuals are more likely to emerge from families where the father is remote, weak or overly hostile and the mother is the dominant disciplinarian or overly protective. This can lead to a lack of confidence and fear of failure in heterosexual contacts.

Elizabeth Moberly, a psychologist, has put forward the view that homosexual orientation develops in response to a deficit in early bonding with the same-sex parent.[5] If the child feels unaccepted in the pre-adolescent phase, he or she may later look for affirmation in relationships with the same sex. Clearly, not all individuals from such backgrounds develop a homosexual orientation. Equally, some from different backgrounds do.

It is difficult on scientific grounds to avoid the conclusion that the cause of sexual orientation is multifactorial, but with psychosocial factors outweighing biological ones. Hidden moral and political agendas mean that this is an area of research where scientific objectivity can be difficult to maintain. There is a temptation to over-interpret findings which favour one's own personal prejudices.

Changing perceptions

Public and medical reaction has changed dramatically over the past few decades. As recently as 1967 in the UK, homosexual behaviour between consenting male adults in private was a criminal offence at any age. At the time of writing it is illegal only for people aged under eighteen, and the British Medical Association Council supported this recent change in the law. In 1973 the American Psychiatric Association removed homosexuality from its list of diagnostic categories in mental illness (*The Diagnostic and Statistical Manual of Mental Disorders* (DSM II)).

This change in perception has occurred at least in part in response to a sustained campaign by the gay rights lobby for people to view homosexual orientation as biologically determined, unchangeable and one of many normal variants. The overall strategy, as outlined in books by gay authors such as *The Homosexualization of America* and *After the Ball*, is as follows: divert attention from what homosexuals do, make homosexuality a topic of everyday conversation, portray homosexuals as 'normal' in every other way, and depict those who disapprove of homosexual behaviour as motivated by fear, ignorance and hatred.[6] The thrust of the gay lobby's emphasis is that homosexual orientation is as natural as handedness or skin colour. They therefore seek minority status for homosexuals and the abolition of all forms of perceived discrimination. Practising homosexuals, they argue, should be given equality in the workforce, in social welfare and in being able to marry and raise (adopted or artificially conceived) children.

This ideology prevents objective evaluation of the evidence, but many Christians are afraid to express any opinion for fear of engendering the outrage of the 'new' establishment.

Medical misinformation

Secular media support has been solidly behind those who wish to present homosexuality as normal. Medical misinformation abounds, and unpalatable facts which may damage the gay cause do not enjoy wide circulation.

For instance, the true incidence of homosexuality is much lower than generally believed. The commonly quoted figure of 10% had its origin in the Kinsey Report.[7] This was based on a poorly designed study of a non-randomly selected sample population, 25% of whom were (or had been) prison inmates. The finding in a recent British sex survey,[8] that only 1 in 90 people had had a homosexual partner in the previous year, is much more in keeping with the figure of 1%–2% quoted in most contemporary research.

Sexually active homosexuals differ from heterosexuals in sexual promiscuity, sexual technique and frequency of substance abuse. This behaviour can adversely affect their mental and physical health.

Sexual promiscuity

Despite the popular media image of homosexual monogamy, long-term faithfulness is virtually non-existent in the gay community. Several large studies have confirmed that the vast majority of homosexual activity, among males in particular, falls outside the context of a stable co-habiting relationship. In fact, less than 10% of homosexual men or women ever experience a relationship of more than ten years' duration. In one large study, 75% of male homosexuals reported having more than 100 partners in a lifetime. A similar proportion admitted that over 50% of their partners were strangers. The figures for female homosexuals are substantially lower, but still sigificantly higher than those for married heterosexuals.[9]

Sexual techniques

Sexual practices regarded as high-risk for sexually transmitted disease occur with consistently greater frequency among homosexual men. A recent review noted that 'from the most recent studies back to those in the pre-AIDS era, the numbers are very consistent for activities regularly practised by male homosexuals: oral-genital contact (90–98%), mutual masturbation of the penis and anus (80–90%), anal intercourse (40–70%). . .[10]

Substance abuse

Recreational drug use is also more frequent in this group. A 1989 San Francisco study showed that homosexual men were three times more likely to use marijuana and barbiturates, eight times more likely to use cocaine and sixteen times more likely to use LSD than age-matched heterosexual controls.[11] Homosexuals are also seven times more likely than heterosexuals to use alcohol with sex.[12]

Psychiatric illness

Certain psychiatric disorders occur more commonly among homosexuals. Three times as many homosexuals (both male and female) are problem drinkers than members of the general population. Male homosexuals are also three times more likely to have seriously contemplated or attempted suicide, and twelve times more likely to have had a major depressive disorder than their heterosexual counterparts.[13]

It is commonly retorted by the gay community that these differences in substance abuse and psychiatric illness are simply a reflection of the discrimination homosexuals face, but in communities where homosexual behaviour is most accepted, the differential is even greater.

Somatic disease

The mechanical trauma of anal intercourse can lead to mucosal ulceration, proctitis, fissure, sphincter disruption and incontinence. The stratified squamous epithelium of the vagina and the muscular architecture of the female pelvis are well-designed for sexual intercourse. Not so the columnar epithelium and sphincters of the ano-rectum. This damage in turn increases the risk of ano-rectal infection which can be transmitted through a variety of oral-genital, genital-anal and oral-anal routes. The most common diseases are amoebiasis (25–40% of homosexual men), giardiasis (10–30%), chlamydia (5–15%), gonorrhea, shigella, salmonella, campylobacter, syphilis, pubic lice and scabies. Viral infections common among homosexual men include condylomata (30%–40%), herpes

(10%–20%), hepatitis A and B, and of course HIV/AIDS.[14]

Condoms do not protect against anal trauma, and limit rather than eradicate the risk of infection. Ironically, those at greatest risk through promiscuity or dangerous practices are the ones least likely to use them.

Multiple partners, unsafe sex practices and substance abuse in turn predispose homosexuals as a group to higher levels of mental and physical ill health than heterosexuals. This clearly does not mean that all homosexuals suffer in this way, or that heterosexuals do not. Many people feel that they have fulfilled and happy lives as practising homosexuals, and Christians, especially those working in the AIDS field, have often been surprised by the quality of some gay relationships.

Biblical principles

Over the last two decades, there has been an increasing acceptance in certain Christian circles of homosexual acts between consenting adults. In particular, the Gay Christian Movement has stated that 'it is entirely compatible with the Christian faith not only to love a person of the same sex but also to express that love fully in a personal sexual relationship'.[15] Space precludes an extensive evaluation of the often complex arguments for this position, and interested readers are referred to excellent reviews elsewhere.[16] My intention is briefly to outline the relevant biblical principles. Our supreme authority in all matters of faith and conduct must be God's Word, and the Old and New Testaments were respectively approved and commissioned by Jesus Christ himself.

Throughout Scripture, sexual intercourse is seen as a gift from God to be enjoyed, but only in the context of heterosexual marriage. All sexual behaviour which does not conform to this pattern is roundly condemned. Two Old Testament verses give specific directives about homosexual behaviour. Leviticus 18:22 states: 'Do not lie with a man as with a woman; that is detestable' and Leviticus 20:13 says: 'If a man lies with a man as with a woman, both of them have done what is detestable. They must be put to death.'

Two other Old Testament passages deserve mention. The intention to commit homosexual acts is described in connection with the men of Sodom (hence the term 'sodomy') and Gibeah. Both towns came under God's judgment for what followed (Gn. 19:1–29; Jdg. 19:1–30). According to Old Testament teaching, homosexual acts are wrong, even if the partners are consenting adults. However, homosexual behaviour cannot be singled out from other sins. Other sins (such as adultery) shared equal punishment, and Sodom in particular also came under judgment for its neglect of the poor (Ezk. 16:49–50).

New Testament teaching is even more exacting, because it shows us the true spirit of Old Testament law. Not only is sexual intercourse outside the marriage bond wrong, but even lust is counted as sin (Mt. 5:27–28). Homosexual acts are specifically mentioned on three occasions (Rom. 1:24–27; 1 Cor. 6:9–11; 1 Tim. 1:8–11). Both action and attitude must be pure, and all that is not in keeping with our new natures is to be 'put to death'. Instead, we are to 'walk in the spirit', to live out the life of Christ.

Richard Lovelace sees the growing acceptance of homosexual practice within the church as due to a 'false religion' opposed to biblical revelation and the authority of Scripture, an 'antinomian ethic' that undercuts the balance between law and gospel, a 'cheap grace' that ignores repentance and a 'powerless grace' that denies the possibility of change.[17] I agree with this assessment.

Handling the practicalities

How do we handle the practicalities as Christians? If we recognize that we have a homosexual (or bisexual) orientation ourselves, it follows that we will be more susceptible to temptation in this area than others are. This means that we need more of God's grace in order to stand. There is a difference between temptation and sin. The way of escape is to recognize that Jesus, who was 'tempted in every way, just as we are' (Heb. 4:15) lives in us by his Spirit. We are promised his strength to endure temptation. All temptation can be resisted (1 Cor. 10:13), and if we do fall we have the confidence that if we confess our sin he will forgive us and cleanse us (1 Jn. 1:9). This cannot, of course, be used as an excuse for continuing in sin.

If we have an exclusively heterosexual orientation and are not thereby exposed to this kind of temptation, we need to be patient, forbearing and understanding towards those who are. While having an obligation to urge them to repent if they continue in sin, we need also to be gracious and forgiving (Lk. 17:3). We also need to watch ourselves. God views any sexual sin (even lust) as equally wrong, and sometimes a person who has been exclusively hetero-sexual may experience homosexual thoughts for the first time.

With regard to unbelievers who are practising homosexuals, we need to repent of any wrong, judgmental attitude in ourselves and pray that they may come to know the grace and forgiveness of Jesus Christ. This may be the only means by which they will have the power necessary to change their lifestyles.

God's authoritative word in Scripture is unaltered by the passage of time. The Bible heartily endorses same-sex friendships and the strong emotional bond which accompanies them. We are told that Jonathan's love for David was 'more wonderful than that of women' (2 Sa. 1:26). Ruth and Naomi shared similar deep feelings for one another, and we see this human affection most beautifully expressed in Jesus Christ himself. The apostle John is called 'the disciple whom Jesus loved' (Jn. 21:20). However, in these relationships there is no suggestion of anything sexual.

Every homosexual act is wrong, regardless of the sexual orientation of the participants or the depth of affection they feel for one another. The gay rights lobby regard it as hypocritical behaviour when a Christian of homosexual orientation resists the temptation to take part in a homosexual act. But from God's perspective it is self-control, the fruit of the Holy Spirit (Gal. 5:22–23).

Can homosexuals change?

Many believe that sexual orientation is as unchangeable as eye colour or handedness. This is simply not true. Masters and Johnson, in a five-year follow-up of 67 exclusively homosexual men and women, reported that 65% achieved successful changes in their sexual orientation after behaviour therapy.[18] Change can and does occur, but will happen most readily when there is a desire to change, a belief that change is possible and an environment of love and acceptance. It is less likely when these factors are absent or when habits have been established over a long period of time.

A Christian has the power of the Holy Spirit working in his or her life, so that the possibility of change is greater. However, this does not mean that change will always occur. Ongoing temptation may have to be lived with, and celibacy may be the only reasonable option. It is not necessary to have sexual intercourse in order to be fully human. Jesus lived the most fully human life ever, yet never married. Paul commends the single life as one of high calling for a Christian, freeing him or her to serve God in a special way (1 Cor. 7:25–35).

A Christian response

How should we respond as Christians to patients who are practising homosexuals, or are in fact involved in any sexual sin? There is no better model for us than the response of Jesus to the woman caught in adultery (Jn. 8:2–11). We must first beware of hypocrisy. All of us are subject to sexual temptation of one kind or another. Indeed, many of us have sinned sexually, at least in our minds, if not in action. We must not judge or condemn. Rather, our concern must be for our patient's good. This will mean that we want graciously to point out the specific dangers of certain lifestyles, and offer support and encouragement to change. We will tell the truth about the aetiology of sexual orientation. Furthermore, we will be prepared to carry the cross in providing unconditional compassionate care, even if this involves personal risk to ourselves.

Christian initiatives in this area, such as The True Freedom Trust (TFT), which ministers to those struggling with homosexual orientation, or AIDS Care Education and Training (ACET), which provides compassionate care for AIDS sufferers, are good examples of what can be done. Our response must be to walk in the footsteps of Christ, who offered forgiveness and grace, even if our best efforts are rejected.

Postscript

Homosexuality throws down a gauntlet to the church. It invites us to understand people who are often misunderstood and to reflect on the integrity of our own sexuality. It requires us to be informed in an atmosphere of ignorance and misinformation. It bids us speak the truth at the cost of incurring the wrath of the politically correct, and it challenges us to offer unconditional love and care to those who suffer.

CONTRACEPTION

David Cook

Condemning or condoning the condom culture

Contraception is so commonplace in our modern world that we forget that it is a comparatively recent phenomenon. Women were all too often 'pregnant, barefoot and in the kitchen' until modern science and medicine combined to produce the contraceptive pill. There had always been a wide variety of contraceptives, but their 'reliability' and 'success' were legendary because of the high failure rate.

At the end of the Second World War, there was a tremendous boost in contraceptive research, enabling women to continue as a valuable part of the work force, following their contribution to the war effort. The pill, various coils, improved caps and sheaths have made contraception part and parcel of modern life. But with the threat of AIDS and the increasing lurch to the political Right, there has been a proper concern to ask hard questions about contraceptives. When the issue of contraception is raised, medical students (who have a wide variety of moral views, or what they claim as no moral view at all) are far more concerned about the physical risks of taking the pill, and about the high failure rate of the other forms of contraception, than about the moral dilemmas. They would often counsel young people to avoid sexual activity, even when using contraceptives, on the ground that early sexual behaviour can lead to serious physical and psychological problems, especially for young women. The students are all too conscious that the claimed failure of the contraceptive is often the main reason offered for requesting termination of pregnancy.

One sad feature of such concentration on the risks of sexual behaviour is that the approach fails to ask hard questions about the nature, role and context of sexual activity. One blessing of the women's movement has been that such questions have been raised, and that some women have refused to accept many of the assumed prejudices which underlie the nature and level of sexual activity in our society.

Christians have so concentrated on the issue of abortion in recent times that we may have been guilty of failing to pay sufficient attention to the more basic issues of sexual behaviour. The area of contraception allows us an opportunity to look at some key questions at that basic level.

The biblical view of sexuality

The Bible is quite clear that sex is good and is God's gracious gift to humanity. It is a joy and meant for our good. It is God's means of procreation and of binding human beings together in the most intimate of human relationships, marriage. The picture of becoming one flesh symbolizes the physical reality of two people in such close harmony and intimacy that they become one. This has led many to view marriage as an indissoluble bond. Others regard the marriage relationship as a covenant which may be broken by extreme behaviour. Both views repeat the biblical stress that marriage is created by God and is intended to be life-long.

Sexual expression is an integral part of that marriage relationship. The Bible recognizes that sexual behaviour can and does take place outside the marriage relationship. It is quite clear that this is sin and that it goes against God's standards and demands. This is shown by the condemnation of fornication (sexual expression outside marriage) and adultery (sexual expression with someone other than the married partner). This means that sexual abstinence is the norm expected of all Christians unless they are married. Faithfulness to one's marriage partner is the norm for all those who are married.

Such standards seem very far removed from the modern sexual climate, whose attitudes and behaviour as well as appearing to be quite normal in the rest of society, have infiltrated the church. The church has failed to help Christians understand and practise Christian sexual behaviour, and there is an increasing urgency about a return to such standards if we are light in our world.

The Christian and contraception

On some moral issues, the Bible is silent, leaving it to us to apply its general principles and rules to matters which are not specifically treated in its pages. The problem is that this can lead to varying stresses on different aspects of God's Word, and to differing views. This should neither surprise nor upset us, for we find such disagreement in the New Testament church. Paul's recipe for coping with such problems is in Romans 14–15. (See also my book *The Moral Maze* (SPCK, 1983).)

On the question of contraception, the traditional Catholic view has emphasized that sexual behaviour has a natural outcome:

children. We ought not to interfere with God's pattern embedded in the natural order. We ought not to interrupt God's natural law. If too many children and too much childbirth, with its effect on women, create practical consequences which genuinely concern us, then we should exercise self-denial and follow the natural rhythm of God's order.

The Protestant response to this view has been to criticize it on the grounds that it is highly risky and does not work, that it assumes that we do indeed know what is natural, and that it ignores the fact that we do not regard everything that happens as natural and to be accepted. When we have a headache we take something to alleviate the pain. Medicine functions on the assumption that what happens is often to be resisted and put right.

Furthermore, a positive argument is put forward for the use of contraceptives. God has given humanity the capacity to understand our bodies and to control what happens to them. This means that the benefits of modern science ought to be used if they are needed. The argument then suggests that contraception is indeed needed. We live in a world where there are too many people consuming too much of the world's resources too quickly. Malnutrition and disease result. Family planning is one key factor in solving the world's problems of hunger and disease. It is also clear that the bearing of too many children radically affects women, and a husband's proper love for his wife and a woman's proper regard for herself, mean that control of child-bearing is appropriate. Both arguments rest on the biblical theme of stewardship. God gives humanity responsibility for the world and creation. One aspect of this is to care for it and not to abuse that responsibility. Planned parenthood is part of such stewardship.

Both sides in this debate focus on sexual activity within marriage. The various forms of contraceptive may or may not be used within the context of marriage alone. The problem is that control over fertility and conception is possible for any man or woman, married or not.

Contraception and the single person

As sexual behaviour takes place within and outside of marriage, so contraception can be used within and outside of marriage. What may be seen as a right expression of responsibility for a married couple can also be a means of sexual freedom for single people and for adulterous relationships. Society seems to say that sexual behaviour is a purely personal matter; each individual must decide for him or herself whether or not to be sexually active and whether or not to use some form of contraception. This is fine if one is willing to ignore God's standards and the unpleasant physical, psychological and spiritual effects of unfettered sexual activity. But it also ignores the fact that sexual behaviour involves another person, and that contraception may involve a third party – the doctor or clinic. This is the point at which the Christian doctor is confronted by a series of dilemmas. If I hold a Catholic position as a doctor, ought I then to prescribe contraceptives for anyone, married or single? If I believe that God's will for sexual behaviour is always and only in the context of marriage, can I then prescribe contraceptives for a single person?

Part of the problem here is not merely the issue of the morality of contraception itself, but the impact of contraception on others. Am I condoning sexual behaviour outside marriage by so prescribing? Is such prescribing likely to lead to promiscuity? This in turn raises hard questions about the right of the doctor to affect a patient because of his or her personal moral views. On the other hand, the doctor has a conscience and must be free to act on the basis of it, and cannot be required to act against what he or she believes. Doctors adopt any of a cluster of attitudes to try to deal with these questions. We shall examine some of them in turn.

'I'm sorry, but . . .'

Some Christian doctors will feel unable to prescribe contraceptives for single people. As far as they are concerned, it is clear that the aim of having contraceptives is to participate in sexual activity. Such sexual activity outside the marriage relationship is wrong. It breaks God's law and the Christian cannot help another to do that. The Christian doctor may also feel that prescribing under these circumstances is to become an accessory before the fact and therefore part of an activity which is wrong. It may even encourage and facilitate promiscuity.

Some would argue that if a doctor refuses to prescribe, it enables the woman (and almost always it is the woman) to have a genuine reason for saying 'no' to sexual activity. Indeed, the woman may be looking to the doctor to give her just such an escape mechanism. The doctor is quite clear that he or she will continue to support the person no matter what happens, but has to recognize that the patient has the right to another medical view. The problem then arises of whether or not the doctor should send the patient on to a family planning clinic, or to a doctor who is sympathetic to such a situation and will prescribe, or to a colleague who shares the no-contraception view. Is referral to a doctor who will prescribe really any different from prescribing oneself?

'I will prescribe, but . . .'

Some doctors will prescribe on the ground that they are paid by the National Health Service and part of their duty is to prescribe what the patient needs. A person who intends to engage in sexual activity outside the context of marriage needs contraceptive precautions. To help the person is part of a responsible attitude to such sexual activity.

Others feel that it is much more a case of having an opportunity to present a Christian case for alternative behaviour. They see their role as doctor to advise a patient as to what is best. They will then proclaim both the practical and spiritual problems involved in such sexual behaviour, but, in earning the right to present such a view, they recognize that they will be asked to prescribe if their advice is refused. Behind this view is the idea of the autonomy and freedom of the patient. Adult patients (the prescribing of contraceptives for minors is another crucial issue) have the right to refuse to follow medical advice and to have their requests granted. In practice, there must be some limit to such requests, but contraception is not often regarded as such a limit. Patients have the ultimate responsibility for their sexual behaviour. The doctor's responsibility is to present the full facts and to try to prevail on the patient to behave differently. It is the patient's own fault if good advice is rejected.

The crucial argument which persuades many physicians to prescribe is that by so doing they are preventing a worse situation developing. This is the 'lesser of two evils' view. We live in a world where we often face choices and situations in which, no matter what we do, harm results. Sexual immorality is wrong, but so too is unwanted pregnancy which might end up with the call for termination. To fail to prevent a child being born in such circumstance, and to allow a situation where an abortion may take place, is wrong. Prescribing a contraceptive is a justified means of avoiding the greater evil of single parenthood, shotgun weddings, abortion and the like. The doctor who does prescribe does not celebrate the fact, but does so with a heavy heart. At least the lines of communication with the patient have been kept open, and there will be further opportunity to help and to change their behaviour.

Both views are committed to marriage and to God's pattern for human sexuality. They disagree not about the seriousness of sin, but about how we should respond to those who are caught in the web of sin. Both recognize that the real solution to such situations lies in showing men and women how to behave properly and convincing them to keep God's laws. Our emphasis must surely be on living and proclaiming God's standards in such a winsome way that others are drawn to follow that pattern. But the Christian doctor will still have to face hard decisions. By God's grace and with the leading of his Holy Spirit, each of us must act as we believe that God in Christ would act in each situation.

13 AIDS, MORALITY AND GOD

David Field

Some maintain that AIDS is not a moral issue, and certainly not a religious one. The churches, they say, should mind their own spiritual business and allow medical technicians to progress towards the solution of a problem which is essentially medical, not ethical, in nature.

Simply to state that view is to expose its weaknesses. Debate about the origins of HIV certainly does lie outside the scope of ethics. But the most urgent issue facing us today concerns the spread of the virus and its related syndrome. Once that distinction is perceived, the moral dimension becomes inescapably clear. AIDS spreads through well-defined behaviour patterns, rooted in chosen lifestyles. Ethics and morality are, by definition, to do with the choices people make in setting the direction of their lives and with their day-to-day behaviour. It is therefore incredibly shortsighted to see no link between the need to control this particular disease and the corresponding need to mount a critique of the behaviour which spreads it.

To rule out religious considerations is an equally blinkered approach to AIDS. The Christian gospel does not address disembodied souls. Concepts such as sin and salvation have clear physical dimensions. The God of the Bible is creator as well as redeemer. Both New and Old Testaments set out ideals for human behaviour as well as guidelines for committed Christian living. If an atheist says, 'These ideals are irrelevant to me, because I do not believe in the existence of a creator,' the Bible replies, 'You are wrong. Those ideals are inescapably relevant, because you are made in the image of the God you do not believe in.'

Such dogmatism may leave a pluralist society seething with indignation, but the claim that some behaviour patterns lead to human health and happiness while others do not – simply because of the way people are made – surely merits a hearing from a generation which faces the global threat of AIDS. Perhaps this lay behind the embarrassment of an anonymous psychologist who cares for many AIDS patients, when he was asked by a journalist, 'If we had played by New Testament rules on sexual behaviour, would we ever have had an epidemic?'

'Of course not,' he replied, 'but, for God's sake, don't quote me on that!'[1]

The approach to AIDS as a religious, ethical issue is often obscured by false dichotomies. In the interests of clarity it will help to identify and expose three of them.

Rules and results

Anyone who criticizes the kind of behaviour which maximizes the spread of HIV is liable to be charged with 'moralizing'. This is used as a pejorative term, with overtones of legalism and unjustified interference in the lives of others. Alternative approaches which major on preventive measures ('safe sex') are exempt from this charge, because they do not appear to make moral judgments on what other people do.

This is a superficial distinction. On either side of the argument there is an attempt to show that some practices (unprotected anal intercourse, for example, and the sharing of hypodermic needles) are wrong. Those who refuse to label anything as wrong in itself are still drawing moral distinctions and making moral judgments when they discourage the kind of behaviour which results in more people getting AIDS now. They are still doing their best to persuade others that 'you ought not to behave in this or that particular way at the present time'.

The difference, of course, lies in the routes taken to arrive at the common conclusion. Opponents of 'moralizing' insist that sexual conduct is value-free. A particular practice becomes wrong, they say, only when its results are overwhelmingly bad. It is wrong, therefore, to have anal intercourse so long as that practice carries a high risk of spreading a lethal disease. If, at some time in the future, the risk is nullified, anal intercourse may become right once again in certain circumstances.

The 'moralizer' takes a different route. Following his ethical code, with its principles and rules for behaviour, he insists that anal intercourse (for example) is wrong in itself, whatever the consequences that follow.

In the debate about AIDS it is often assumed that Christians and other religious people follow the rules route, while everybody else makes moral judgments on the basis of results. That, however, is not quite true. Christians certainly have principles and rules (God-given, they believe) to direct their behaviour. Among them are the biblical vetos on homosexual acts and promiscuity. But the Bible also encourages believers to modify the way they behave by thinking about the long-term consequences of certain life-styles. Paul put it in a nutshell when he wrote that 'a man reaps what he sows' (Gal. 6:7).

'Long-term' is the operative phrase. People who make their judgments between right and wrong by measuring consequences can take into account only the results they foresee. Inevitably, their horizons are limited. Who foresaw AIDS in the 1960s? The Bible, by contrast, declares the eventual results of certain behaviour patterns. The authority of its predictions rests (Christians believe) on the reputation of the best Long-Range Forecaster in the business. God sees over all human horizons. So when the New Testament declares that all extramarital intercourse leads to human disaster, the Christian takes the forecast seriously, even when the exact shape of the consequences is lost in the mists of the future.

The arrival of AIDS fills Christians with intense sadness, but it does not take them by surprise. The relationship of rules to results is that of signpost to destination. The warning signals along the road have been there for centuries. It is only those who refuse to read the writing who are shocked by the appearance of cosmic disaster round the next bend. And, Christians want to add, even when the medical solution to AIDS is found (and may it be soon), the road will only lead on to further human unhappiness of a different, unforeseen kind. Why not join the 'moralizers' now, they ask, and pay sensible attention to the signposts?

Public and private

Ten years before the Sexual Offences Act (which legitimizes homosexual acts between consenting adults in private) became effective, the Wolfenden Committee had paved the way by drawing a sharp distinction between public and private behaviour. Wolfenden argued that it was not 'proper for the law to concern itself with what a man does in private unless it can be shown to be so contrary to the public good that the law ought to intervene in its function as the guardian of that public good'.

The distinction itself was not all new. John Stuart Mill had articulated it very powerfully in his famous tract *On Liberty* in 1859. 'The only purpose for which power can be rightfully exercised over any member of a civilized community, against his will,' he wrote, 'is to prevent harm to others.'

This plea for personal liberty swayed Members of Parliament in 1967. Men over twenty-one who wished to practise anal intercourse in private, they concluded, should no longer have to do so with the threat of the law hanging over their heads.

The arrival of AIDS has set large question marks beside that conclusion. The boundary between private and public has been blurred – AIDS is very much a personal and a public concern. What one person does by way of risking the spread of HIV has far-reaching consequences for others unknown to him or her. Society as a whole, therefore, must take on the responsibility for influencing individual behaviour.

Carrots are probably more effective than sticks. The provision, at public expense, of free condoms for those who insist on putting themselves at risk sexually, and of clean needles for those who cannot or will not break free from drug abuse, is the price society must pay for safeguarding the health of the majority. So is a Government-sponsored advertising campaign which is openly aimed at persuading individuals to change their freely chosen habits.

If this erosion of personal liberty makes us uneasy, we should remember how readily we accept such controls in other areas of life. We limit freedom of speech by laws against libel, and no-one complains. We curb acts of racial discrimination, and all fair-minded people applaud. Such laws actually promote freedom by restricting it. We censor the atmosphere by creating smokeless zones so that the majority can breathe more freely. We even have laws to limit noises and smells in the interests of public health. It is only an extension of this principle to seek the prevention or control of anal intercourse and drug abuse in order to safeguard the well-being of the majority.

Christians would want to add that genuine liberty is to be found only when the individual's will is submitted to God's law. The Bible's vetos on homosexual behaviour and promiscuity have the effect of maximizing human freedom, not destroying it. Released from behaviour patterns which dehumanize their victims, men and women experience the refreshing liberty of relating to others as their maker always intended.

Condemnation and compassion

AIDS is not God's judgment on those who catch HIV. To say that it is would be to caricature him as a capricious creator who aims the thunderbolts of his punishment with a careless disregard for justice. Why do haemophiliacs become infected? Why do wives of unfaithful husbands die of the disease, along with their babies? Why do male homosexuals run such dreadful risks, while most lesbians escape? Those who imply that every individual who contracts AIDS is being directly punished by God for his or her personal sins has no acceptable answers to these questions.

Christians do, however, see the hand of God's judgment on a corrupt society in the AIDS epidemic. The New Testament warns very plainly that people who tear up the creator's blueprint must live and die with the consequences. Those who give up God and his values inevitably experience the results of losing the social protection of his norms. We live in a society which encourages behaviour that leads directly to the spread of AIDS. It follows that those who catch HIV are the victims not only of a lethal virus but of a society which dresses up unhealthy patterns of behaviour as normal.

Even this limited relationship of God's judgment to AIDS, however, makes some people very angry. Surely, they protest, Jesus would want us to treat AIDS sufferers with bold compassion, not wag a judgmental finger in their faces! There is, of course, an important half-truth here. With biting humour, Jesus exposed the hypocrisy of religious people who were so preoccupied with picking splinters out of other people's eyes that they completely failed to notice the huge planks of wood in their own. Time and time again, the gospel writers tell us how he was 'moved with compassion' by human need, whether or not the sufferers had brought their fate on themselves. He would undoubtedly have beaten the Minister of Health to the first handshake in an AIDS ward. And Christians have indeed been the first to open an AIDS hospice in the UK.

But the other half of the truth is equally important. Jesus exposed sin with such candour that his life was soon at risk. He saw no contradiction at all between warm compassion and piercing criticism. When a woman was brought to him after being caught in the act of adultery, he told her to change her lifestyle with the same simple frankness as made her judgmental accusers creep away with shame on their faces. It is not, in fact, at all compassionate to withhold criticism in the name of love. Men and women who get caught up with drug abuse or sexual promiscuity (and thus run an above-average risk of catching and spreading HIV) face temptations which become increasingly difficult to fight off. Their only hope of change lies in being convinced that change is essential. The battles will never be won unless they are sure the war is worth fighting.

The Christian would want to add the tailpiece that habits can be broken and deeply ingrained lifestyles altered. The most important thing the Christian gospel has to offer anyone in need of a change is the promise of fresh, effective, supernatural resources to achieve it.[2]

14 ETHICS AND PAEDIATRICS

John Wyatt

One of the most remarkable features of the Old Testament law is that it contains special regulations relating to certain under-privileged groups in society. Three social groups were singled out as requiring extra protection and provision, and they are frequently mentioned together. They are orphans, widows and aliens.

What were the characteristics that united these disparate social groups? Most commentators have agreed that it was that they were *defenceless* or *powerless* in ancient Israelite society. The orphan had no father to defend him or her from abuse, the widow had no husband, and the alien or immigrant had no racial or cultural status and was therefore open to exploitation. These were the groups who had no natural defender in society. They were intrinsically weak and therefore at continual risk of abuse by the strong. And these are the groups that God singles out for his special concern.

In Deuteronomy 10:17–18 Moses describes the character of God illustrated in the law. 'For the LORD your God is God of gods and Lord of lords, the great God, mighty and awesome, who shows no partiality and accepts no bribes. He defends the cause of the fatherless and the widow, and loves the alien, giving him food and clothing.'

I am struck by the extraordinary contrast in these verses between the awesome power and might of God and his special concern for the weak in society. It seems that precisely because God is so powerful he is especially concerned for the powerless. God is the defender of the defenceless. It is as if God is saying, 'No-one else is on their side, so I will be!' Because God is concerned for the defenceless he commands his special people, who are called to be his imitators, to be concerned as well. Numerous regulations were given to the people of Israel to ensure that these vulnerable social groups were protected from abuse, and that special provision was made for them (see Ex. 22:21–22; Dt. 14:28–29, 16:11, 24:17–19).

As God's people in the modern world, the questions we need to ask ourselves are these. What social groups in modern twentieth-century society correspond to the orphans, widows and aliens of ancient Israel? Who are the defenceless, the vulnerable and the powerless in our society? These are the individuals whom God is specially concerned to defend, and these are the individuals with whom the people of God should be specially concerned too.

Many medical specialties are involved in the care of the vulnerable in society, but I see paediatrics as being particularly in this sphere. The essence of paediatrics is that our patients are vulnerable. Every time I am involved with a child who has been abused by his parents, a fragile and tiny pre-term baby, or a multiply-handicapped infant with cerebral palsy, I need to remind myself that even if society thinks these children worthless, God is on their side; he is their defender and he calls me to be on their side as well. When we tackle the difficult, complex ethical issues in modern paediatric practice, this is the spiritual perspective we must retain at all cost.

I shall mention five areas of clinical paediatrics in which ethical dilemmas arise.

The unborn child

Although issues concerning the unborn child and abortion are primarily the province of the obstetrician and gynaecologist, the paediatrician may be directly involved as well, particularly in cases involving prenatal diagnosis of fetal disease or malformation.

Is it ethical to recommend screening procedures for fetal abnormality or disease if the only 'treatment' that is available is termination? The abortion of fetuses with, for example, a chromosomal abnormality is often put forward as an example of preventive medicine and therefore worthy of our wholehearted support. I have to say that the selective killing of patients with a particular disease or abnormality would not normally be thought of as a shining example of preventive medicine! This kind of euphemistic terminology can easily become a subtle form of self-deception for doctors and parents alike.

Other paediatric issues raised by the availability of medical abortion include the questions: should abortion be allowed for minor fetal abnormalities? Do all parents have the right to be supplied with a perfect child by the medical experts? Should parents be allowed to determine the sex of their baby?

The issues of experimentation on and disposal of human embryos are also of major concern at present. It seems that major therapeutic advances may become possible if extensive research on human embryos is allowed. But is the manipulation and destruction of human life, however microscopic, justified for the benefit of future generations? Can the ends justify the means?

The major theological and ethical issue at stake here is obviously the personal and spiritual status of the unborn child or human embryo. If the unborn child is to be regarded as a fully human person, made in the image of God, then the deliberate destruction of that life, except in the most extreme circumstance, can never be justified. My own conviction, shared incidentally with the vast majority of evangelical biblical scholars, is that Scripture does teach God's intimate knowledge of and personal relationship with the unborn child (seen very clearly in Ps. 139, for example), and that this seems to extend right back to the beginning of life itself. Although the biblical writers were obviously not concerned with the technical biological processes implicated in the development of the fetus, I think that their description of God's involvement with the unborn child implies an extension right back to conception. There is no suggestion of a discontinuity or a point in time during pregnancy when a 'blob of jelly' becomes a human person. Rather, the continuity of the entire process is stressed. I have no doubt, then, that the unborn child is a prime example of the defenceless individual in our society with whom God is especially concerned.

Our responsibility as Christian clinicians is not to abuse, manipulate or destroy that vulnerable life, but rather to protect it against the exploitation of the strong. If we would not contemplate the deliberate infanticide of a child with Down's syndrome after birth, it seems impossible to defend the 'therapeutic' abortion of the same child before birth. The development of fetal medicine to treat disease in the unborn child seems appropriate, but when 'treatment' becomes deliberate destruction we have changed our role from doctor to executioner.

The extremely pre-term baby

The dramatic advances in neonatal intensive care over the last twenty years (one of the great success stories of modern medicine) have brought new dilemmas for paediatricians. Should we try to use all the currently available resources of hi-tech medicine to ensure survival if there is an increased risk of long-term handicap?

The pre-term baby has often been seen by society as one of 'nature's duds'. The implication is that the premature infant should be allowed to die, or even actively killed, as he or she is of little value to society and likely to be a drain on resources. In ancient Greek and Roman culture, babies who were premature or seemed weak or sickly were often killed after delivery by the attending midwife or left to die of exposure to prevent them becoming a 'burden to the state'. Interestingly, when Christianity became a favoured religion in the time of Constantine, this practice was discouraged. This was because of the ethical teaching of the Christian church, which taught that every human individual, however insignificant, was of infinite value. I see the development of neonatal intensive care, dedicated to the increased healthy survival of pre-term infants, as a direct outworking of the Christian view of the value of every human life, however weak and vulnerable. Obviously this does not mean that hi-tech medicine should be applied thoughtlessly and irresponsibly. If death becomes inevitable, it is surely inappropriate to use intensive care simply to prolong the act of dying. It seems fitting to withdraw intensive care support in individual cases where the outcome seems hopeless. Our high view of the value of each life should make us strive to allow the terminally ill baby to die with peace and dignity, rather than with a tube in every orifice.

Neonatal intensive care is not cheap, and questions about the efficient use of resources are inevitable. In the context of severely limited medical resources, as in most developing countries, neonatal intensive care may be inappropriate. In such circumstances, money and manpower should be concentrated in areas of primary prevention, such as immunization and health education. In the developed countries, on the other hand, where economic wealth is so much greater, hi-tech medicine may be a genuine expression of practical Christlike compassion for the vulnerable. If our society is wealthy, should we not apply pressure for more recources to be released, for the care of the vulnerable, rather than spending the excess wealth on consumer durables or armaments? Incidentally, we should also be applying pressure for increased aid to developing countries. In countries crippled by the international debt burden, infant mortality has risen over the last few years. Children are paying for the international debt with their lives.

The severely abnormal baby

The problems that frequently cause ethical dilemmas are either major congenital malformations, such as spina bifida, or severe brain injury, caused by birth asphyxia, for example. Is it right to preserve life at all costs, with all the resources of modern medicine, or should some abnormal babies be allowed to die? Who should make this kind of decision – the medics, the parents or the courts? Is it ever right to practise deliberate euthanasia on a hopelessly damaged baby?

225

All babies deserve the highest standard of nursing and medical care, but the exact nature of the care that is appropriate may be different for each individual. The fact that sophisticated intensive care techniques are now available does not mean that they should be used thoughtlessly in every case. Where severe brain injury has occurred, and survival without continuous intensive care support is impossible, then withdrawal of mechanical support after full discussion with the parents seems appropriate. The decision on what level of care is right for each individual may be a desperately difficult one, and it seems hard to formulate theoretical rules which would apply in every case. Here are some suggested guidelines.

1. Determine the prognosis as accurately as possible. Modern techniques for non-invasive assessment of brain injury, including cranial ultrasound, have an important contribution here.

2. Recognize the limitations of medical knowledge and our inability to predict the future outcome with complete certainty. If there is significant doubt about the long-term prognosis, it is essential to give the baby the benefit of the doubt and continue full intensive support until the outcome becomes clearer.

3. Discuss the issues fully with medical and nursing colleagues and with the infant's parents. I believe that it is the responsibility of the paediatrician in charge of the case to make the final decision, but that this must be done in open discussion with all those involved. If the parents insist that full support should continue even though the outlook is hopeless, I think the clinician in charge should respect their wishes except in the most extreme circumstances.

4. If a decision is made to withdraw intensive support, every baby still deserves adequate nursing and medical care to allow him or her to die with dignity. This should include fluids, nutrition and adequate analgesia as an absolute minimum. I believe that the deliberate killing of infants with an overdose of a sedative or other drug is always immoral as well as completely illegal.

Paediatrics in society

Following the Cleveland sex abuse controversy, the ethical dilemmas confronted by paediatricians have suddenly become front-page news. Under the circumstances, is it appropriate forcibly to remove a child from his or her parents? Who should decide? What if a serious abuse is suspected but cannot be proved? Are bad parents better than no parents at all? Should the power of the law be applied to force parents to protect their children, for example by immunization? Is it ethical to test a baby or child for HIV infection without the parents' knowledge or consent, given the implications of a positive result? Whom should we inform if the result is positive?

The realization that many children are physically abused by their parents is a comparatively recent one in the history of medicine. Prior to the 1950s and 1960s, doctors could not accept that child abuse ever happened, though we now realize that it has probably been a sad reality for thousands of years. The recognition of the sexual abuse of children is an even more recent development. The secret physical, sexual and emotional abuse of children is another classic example of the exploitation of the defenceless by the strong. There is no doubt that paediatricians, social workers and others concerned with the welfare of children must intervene when abuse comes to light. But exactly what intervention is appropriate is often very unclear. The forceable removal of children from their parents should be contemplated only if there is a major risk of serious physical harm. In most cases, help and support within the family structure is the best approach. As Christians we see that the family is a God-given environment for the nurture and protection of children. On the other hand, we cannot be naïve about the capacity for evil in the human heart. Our first responsibility must be for the protection and welfare of those who cannot protect themselves. The role of the law in forcing parents to take care of their children is a very controversial issue. If parents are grossly negligent or actively abusing, the law must step in. In the case of prophylactic measures such as immunization, education and persuasion seem preferable to the force of law.

The dilemmas raised by the current worldwide HIV pandemic are obviously not limited to paediatrics, but tragically they are bound to become increasingly frequent in clinical practice. The early diagnosis of HIV infection in a child is of more than academic significance, as it has important implications for treatment and medical care. As new therapies for HIV become available, early diagnosis will become even more important. I believe that it is therefore in the child's best interest to be tested for HIV if there is any degree of risk, even though a positive diagnosis will have catastrophic implications for the child's mother and the rest of the family. In general, parents should be informed and counselled if an HIV test is to be performed, and their permission should be requested. I think, however, that there may be extreme circumstances where HIV testing should be carried out even without parental permission, if it is clearly in the best interests of the child himself.

Paediatric and medical research

The major advances over the last two decades in the medical care of children, especially the spectacular advances in neonatal intensive care, could not have occurred without a great deal of medical research. Much of that research has been carried out on children and babies undergoing medical treatment. But medical research has great potential for abuse, as the appalling experiments carried out by Nazi doctors on Jewish prisoners during the Second World War demonstrate. Following this shameful episode in medical history, it has become an accepted tenet among medical investigators that no research should ever be performed on children below the age of sixteen. If this principle had been applied rigorously in the past, a great many more children would have died or suffered pain and permanent disability.

I believe that certain types of research are justified in infants and children if they will contribute to the saving of life. Paradoxically, research on humans is justified precisely because, as Christians, we believe in the supreme value of human life. However, the limitations and regulations on paediatric research need to be even more stringent than those for adults. Some guidelines that have been widely accepted by researchers are as follows.

1. No research can be carried out that carries any significant risk, or causes significant discomfort to the child.

2. Informed parental consent should be obtained in every case.

3. There must be no open or implied pressure on parents to consent to research. The treatment offered to children must be of the same standard whether parents give consent to research or not.

4. The research study must have a realistic prospect of advancing the care given to children and must make a significant contribution to medical knowledge.

Conclusion

The essence of paediatrics is that our patients are especially vulnerable. The responsibilities of paediatricians are therefore correspondingly greater. However, in caring for the vulnerable and wrestling with the ethical dilemmas that are inevitably raised we have an incredible privilege. For among our patients are the twentieth-century equivalents of the orphan, the widow and the alien. In the paediatric ward, the infant clinic or the neonatal intensive care unit, we are putting into practice the compassion of the mighty God, the Lord of lords, defender of the defenceless.

15 HOPE, HEALING AND THE CHARISMATIC MOVEMENT

Peter Lewis

The charismatic phenomenon is now worldwide and so is the controversy that surrounds it. It inspires and repels, challenges and cautions, appears courageous and naïve – and all these reactions may be experienced not only by different people but also by one individual. Its genuine spirituality and fundamental orthodoxy ought to be as obvious as its theological naïveté and fringe follies. Its massive effectiveness among people long untouched by the gospel should leave critics humbled, though not, I think, silenced. It faces forgotten scriptures and touches neglected needs, it walks in faith and works by love, and it dares us to take all scripture with all seriousness as our standard for personal belief and church practice.

Its diet of wonders and daily talk of miracles, however, threatens to flood the engine and discredit the drivers. What is needed now is as much self-criticism on the part of charismatic leaders as self-distrust on the part of its too-confident opponents. Nowhere is this more true than in the areas of healing, where great claims and great contempt meet head-on, giving the evangelical world at large a considerable headache. This chapter attempts to untangle some of the wreckage so that we can get on with the journey.

Natural laws and divine intervention

We live in a God-created, God-sustained world where the natural order is his active, on-going work of wisdom, power and faithfulness. Into that world sin has come, bringing with it disorder, wrath and the curse (Gn. 3:17–20). Yet even in the world of the fall, God made a covenant with Noah that he would continue to uphold the fundamental order of creation, including what we term the reliability and even predictability of natural laws (see Gn. 8:20–22). These observable, reliable, predictable mechanisms of physical life form the basis of much of our lives: of daily work, of national economics, of medical and scientific progress. Without them life would be a nightmare of insecurity.

We do not live in the open universe of the animist, where natural laws are nothing and spiritual forces (divine and demonic) are everything – maturing or blighting harvests, healing or destroying people, capriciously sending success or failure. Rather, we live in a world of natural order, of cause and effect, of in-built laws of creation.

However, God's created order has been disturbed, and fallen humanity now falls victim to its crushing regularity. Mankind is now not only lord of creation but victim to its forces – not only because they are out of place but also because we are. We are rebels running amok in creation and away from our creator. We are out of the will of God, under the wrath of God, 'free' from the protection and guidance of God (Eph. 2:1–3). We are trapped in a world of danger, disease and death. Now the very laws which were meant to preserve us frequently threaten to destroy us.

Notwithstanding all this, ours is not a closed universe where created laws are everything and a creator God is nothing. Nor is this world order final and for ever. God did not abandon mankind at the fall (Gn. 3:15), and in time he came personally as he promised, to our race – the king of peace with his kingdom of reconciliation, healing and deliverance from evil. The kingdom of God came in and with and by Jesus Christ, his only Son. At his coming, a new order entered our world in its disorder; first to rescue us in our old world and then to prepare us for God's new world. At first the kingdom of God came secretly with the birth of Jesus at Bethlehem. In time, it was openly announced and demonstrated in his ministry with words, works and wonders (Mt. 11:1–12; Lk. 11:20; *etc.*). Then it came to the church at large at Pentecost (Acts 2:1–4, 17–21, 38–41) and characterized the church thereafter in her evangelism and her gifts (1 Cor. 12:7–11; 2 Cor. 2:14–4:6; Eph. 4:7–13). Whenever this kingdom was announced, it counteracted sin and its effects in the world, spiritual, physical and social.

The kingdom: now and not yet

The arrival of the kingdom of God, however, was always partial and provisional. It is already here, but not yet here in its fullness. It was, and is, and is yet to come (Mt. 6:10; Lk. 22:30; 1 Thes. 2:12; 2 Tim. 4:1; Heb. 12:28; Jas. 2:5; 2 Pet. 1:11; Rev. 12:10). Until the second coming of Christ with his kingdom in its fullness (Rev. 12:10, 21:1–4), the church on earth would live in two worlds; it is a world in process of passing away (Heb. 12:26–28; 1 Jn. 2:15–17) and a world in process of becoming (Jn. 14:3; Rom. 13:11; Rev. 12:10). Only at the coming of Christ will the kingdom of God, which has entered the world, fill up the world. Only then will the people of God be entirely free of the penalties of living in the world of the fall (see 2 Cor. 5:2 and Rom. 8:23) for then they will be undyingly alive in 'a new heaven and a new earth' (Rev. 21:1).

Until then, we are touched with both the glory of the world to come and the corruption of the world that is. We are justified children of God and sinful creatures; we are kept under the shadow of his wings and led into times of suffering like others; we have eternal life and dying bodies; we are healed and we sicken again. This is our glorious hope which does not disappoint us, and these are the grim realities it lives alongside. In theological terms we must now be careful to walk between an under-realized eschatology and an over-realized eschatology. Even the early Christians found that difficult at times (1 Cor. 1:7, 4:8; 1 Thes. 5:19–22).

That is why, even in the New Testament, miracles are never ordinary. What is ordinary is reliable conformity to wise and good natural laws. Nevertheless, in a disturbed creation, God in grace does interrupt his usual way of working, his natural order, for a greater good. He is not the prisoner of his own laws. But his kingdom-related activity is always extraordinary in the world as we know it. It is the partial and periodic invasion of one order by another. Miracles as the suspension or contradiction of natural laws are extraordinary signs of the kingdom which is coming; they are powers of an age to come breaking through.

The chief purpose of healing miracles is declaratory and revelatory rather than therapeutic. Even as healings, they are not so much a local response as a public statement, a promise that God in Christ will one day break the stranglehold of sin, sickness and death. The statement made in isolated instances points to the certainty that one day God will renew the face of the whole earth.

For all these reasons we can see, I think, that miracles must be both *real* and *rare*. We live neither in the open universe of animism nor the closed universe of scientism, but the controlled universe of 'our God and his Christ' (Rev. 11:15), a God who is fulfilling in his own time and way his sovereign plan for the salvation of the world.[1]

Miracles today?

There is not, I believe, a single datum in the New Testament writings to warrant the dogma that miracles ceased or that various gifts were withdrawn with the end of the apostolic age. Such dispensationalism depends on extra-scriptural arguments and hermeneutics (the science of interpretation). The gifts were given to the church, not just to the apostles, and as signs of the kingdom, not only as signs of the apostles' authority. Indeed, the apostles themselves and all apostolic ministries were said to be gifts for the church as a whole. There are better arguments for the diminution or disuse of certain gifts of the Holy Spirit, arguments which, as Calvin thought, have more to do with the poor spirituality in the churches than with the sovereignty of God. But certainly God in his sovereignty can restore such gifts to the church and work miracles in her midst as and when he wills.

I find it increasingly hard to define a miracle, both biblically and scientifically. Biblically, the words most often used are 'signs' and 'wonders', which range from God's use of natural laws (as with most of the plagues of Pharaoh's Egypt in Exodus) to God's suspension of natural laws (as with our Lord's walking on water or his resurrection from the dead). Scientifically, so much now seems to be on a continuum so that, like matter and energy, the physical and the spiritual are widely perceived to be related. The phrase 'signs and wonders' in the Bible, is therefore usefully elastic.

John's word for Jesus' miracles is 'signs'. He uses this word to make us look beyond the miracle to its meaning, its significance; why God did that particular thing in that particular situation. In the Bible generally, signs relate to the significant more than to the impossible. They reveal something about God – not only his power, but his kingdom and saving plan. As Donald Bridge puts it in his helpful and balanced book:[2] 'The question is not: How on earth did he do *that*? It is rather, what can I see of the power and grace of God in this? How must I react? What does he want of me?'

This is the true and first response of faith. If faith is absent, then the miraculous will not be properly significant, only fascinating and even irritating. For instance, Jesus' miracles did no good at all to his critics: 'Christ could produce no credential so conclusive but that the Jews would demand one more conclusive still.'[3] An appetite for the miraculous (1 Cor. 1:22) which leaves us no wiser, no humbler, no more believing, and no better, is the religious equivalent of having worms. Without faith there will always be an explanation somewhere and a true understanding nowhere.

Jesus' miracles

Jesus' miracles must always be seen against the background of his person and his work. The greatest sign and wonder is Jesus Christ himself incarnate and crucified; the greatest miracle of all, on which

232

our faith is founded, is his resurrection; the greatest demonstration of power will be at his second coming to summon the dead to resurrection and to judgment. Moreover, the preaching of this in power, with its evident effects in the hearts and lives of sinners, is still the most widespread, permanent and profound work of God in his kingdom-power. As one leading British charismatic puts it: 'We must insist that the message which we preach has more to do with sins than headaches, with guilt and forgiveness more than rheumatism.'[4]

Jesus' own healing ministry was, for all its power, always dependent and even selective (see Jn. 5:19 and *e.g.* Jn. 5:3–6). He waited for the Father and worked by the Spirit. His healings were often many, sometimes few, sometimes absent. It was, even for our Lord in the days of his lowliness, never a case of power on tap and independently used. Similarly, in Acts the miraculous is selective, spasmodic and meaningful. In *Signs and Wonders Today*, Donald Bridge points out that 'eight times in Acts, powerful, effective evangelism is directly related to miraculous signs. But on twenty-two other occasions there is no such link . . . the common feature of all apostolic evangelism is the spoken message . . . by which the gospel is presented in power.'[5] It is a well-known fact that miraculous signs occur in 'spates' in both Old and New Testament histories, and this too confirms my earlier point that a statement is being made of general import rather than simply local significance. Miraculous healings are commentaries upon the word proclaimed and not a staple kind of emergency treatment.

Healing today

Charismatic healings today, I think, rarely involve the suspension of natural laws. They are not miracles in that sense. Yet they are truly a ministry of the Holy Spirit of God in the churches. Where healings occur they do so at many levels and in many settings. We ought to recognize that in God's kindness and mercy there is much healing built into life. All healing is divine healing, and divine healing comes by various means and in varying degrees. Much disease is stress-related and much disease can be stress-relieved. Rex Gardner writes: 'We know something of the bodily mechanisms involved: both the hormonal and immunological defence mechanisms are eventually controlled by the fore-brain which is the seat of the emotions . . . so there will inevitably be beneficial effects mediated through the psycho-endocrine pathways.'[6] These too, he points out, are divine healings in divine care and love.

Obviously, not all such healing is kingdom-related in the way charismatic gifts may be. It is interesting, however, that the distinguished Roman Catholic theologian Heribert Muhlen[7] not only includes nature's self-healing but sees the possibilities of spontaneous cures, rooted in creation, as 'the basis of charismatic healing', adding that the latter is 'not essentially supernatural but only the way it takes place'. Such an overlap of the natural and supernatural is obvious in some of the gifts of the Spirit (*e.g.* Rom. 12:6–8) and may well be true in most of the 'gifts of healings' in 1 Corinthians 12:9. There, miracles, including presumably healing miracles, are in a category of their own (1 Cor. 12:10).

Divine healing comes through many channels, external and internal, obvious and mysterious, surgical and psychological and spiritual. God gives us skills to conquer disease by medicine and surgery. Christ walks along the psycho-endocrine pathways as surely as he walked the Galilean road. But the Christ who did walk on earth now reigns in heaven, preparing a kingdom and calling a people. His power is no less than the power of God in every sphere (Mt. 28:18), and he authority to speak to disease and death now as then, when and how he wills. His gifts of healings are given to his church, including that rarest but also most revealing of gifts, the true healing miracle. No-one, I believe, can claim or predict it, and certainly no-one has it on tap. I am deeply shocked when I read of the proviso 'If it be thy will' being dismissed as a 'faith-defeating prayer'. This is bad theology. Faith does not create its own reality by 'willing' something into existence; it is the gift of God which listens, waits and works according to his will. It is the mark of the shaman in other religions that he tries to harness the powers and manipulate the deities. In contrast to that, it should be the mark of the Christian healer or sufferer, that he or she places every prayer and every attempt towards healing at the feet of a sovereign Father.

The place of suffering

If healing is in the will of God in any of its many forms, so is victorious suffering. As to Paul, so to very many who know and trust his Lord, the revelation comes: 'My grace is sufficient for you, for my power is made perfect in weakness' (2 Cor. 12:9). For some, sickness *is* in the will (purpose, decree, providence) of God for a while; but so is final healing and full redemption. He who allows us to suffer, and who suffers with us in many circumstances, knows what ultimate plans he has for us (Je. 29:10–11).

Even suffering shall subserve his good purpose (Jb. 23:10). By it some are kept from a greater evil (*e.g.* 2 Cor. 12:7, 'to keep me from becoming conceited because of these surpassingly great revelations'). By it some are given a ministry beyond price (*e.g.* Joni Eareckson Tada). By it some show, with quiet triumph, that 'his glory' is more than 'my healing'.

I should like to close with the words of the Manila Manifesto produced at the end of the Lausanne II Congress on World Evangelism:

> We reject both the scepticism which denies miracles and the presumption which demands them, both the timidity which shrinks from the fulness of the Spirit and the triumphalism which shrinks from the weakness in which Christ's power is made perfect. We repent of all self-confident attempts to evangelise in our own strength or to dictate to the Holy Spirit.

This chapter is based upon a section of an address given at the CMF conference at Swanwick in 1990, which formed part of a series by Peter Lewis on the theme of hope.

16 ALTERNATIVE MEDICINE

Andrew Fergusson

Between September 1985 and December 1986 the London-based
Medical Study Group of the Christian Medical Fellowship spent
seven meetings discussing alternative medicine. There was a great
deal of preparatory reading, from A for acupuncture to Y for yoga,
if not to Z for Zen Buddhism's influence. The review which follows
attempts to distil the main conclusions from discussions, especially
seeking to establish *principles* which Christians might apply in
assessing therapies.

A few alternative medicines were examined in more detail, but the
value of discussion here was perhaps more in illuminating principles
than in defining details. The group acknowledges that much remains
to be done in understanding medical treatments, orthodox or
otherwise, and that all should approach these subjects humbly, yet
using the twin tools of science and Scripture wherever possible.

What is alternative medicine?

The name encompasses those therapies which are not based on the
same principles as conventional (or orthodox or allopathic) western
scientific medicine. By definition, the word 'alternative' implies an
'either/or' and some prefer the title 'complementary medicines' to
emphasize that they can work with orthodox treatments in a 'both/
and' way. Sometimes the therapies are also called 'wholistic' or
'holistic' to underline their claimed whole-person view.

Whatever the name, there is no doubt of the public's increasing
interest in them. In its very first leading article of the new decade,
the *British Medical Journal* of 5 January 1980 discussed the 'Flight
from science'; and correctly predicted the rise in interest that has
taken place throughout the 1980s and 1990s.

Why so popular?

Before examining the disenchantments with orthodox medicine, it
must be remembered that the public's concern is with curative
medicine. The public conveniently forgets the huge contribution to
world health of preventive medicine which is based on rational

scientific principles (and often on Scripture). Alternative medicine may be a rival in the field of curative medicine but not of preventive, and with a few exceptions it has little to say about community health and prevention of disease.

However, orthodox medicine is nowadays criticized, often rightly, for the following reasons.

Failure

Orthodox medicine sometimes fails to deliver the goods. Over the last fifty years there has been notable success from increasingly interventionist hi-tech procedures focusing on one organ or system. Medicine now manipulates the very genes themselves. Orthodox medicine at one time seemed to offer a cure for everything, a 'pill for every ill'; but untreatable diseases remain, and death is inevitable for all of us, and so an understandable disillusionment has arisen. Interestingly, many turn to alternative medicine only when conventional treatments can offer no more hope of a cure, as, for instance, when dying of cancer.

Arrogance

Linked with the increasing successes of technology, orthodox medicine has, perhaps, assumed an arrogant face, hiding shortcomings and uncertainties behind a veneer of sophistication. As leaders within medicine, doctors are probably most guilty of ignoring failure, and refusing to come to terms with the limitations of medical treatment.

Iatrogenic disease

Iatrogenic disease has become more common, as increasingly powerful treatments have more side-effects. The public is now suspicious of drug therapies, and many medical practitioners have become disillusioned too. There is obviously justifiable concern here, while by and large alternative medicines are physically harmless.

Neglect of the whole person

As doctors have become increasingly involved in technology, they have lost sight of their previous commitment to the whole person. Patients respond to treatments psychologically, socially and spiritually as well as physiologically, pharmacologically and pathologically. This loss of the holistic approach is seen specifically in time, touch and trust.

Time. Conventional practitioners – at least within the National Health Service – are seen as being in too much of a hurry. Short general practitioner consultations and the brisk 'in-out' of out-patients, if not of in-patients, are perceived as not allowing time to get to grips with the real problems. Most alternative practitioners give a lot of time to every consultation – one non-medically qualified homoeopath gives 1¾ hours to every new patient and 45 minutes to every follow-up.

Touch. The old-fashioned commodity of physical touch – the handshake, the ritual pulse-taking, the arm round the shoulder – seems to be disappearing, and this is probably to the detriment of the therapeutic relationship. Without perhaps exerting any specific effect on pathology, touch expresses involvement and can make people 'feel better' and that is what most patients want. Many alternative medicines specifically involve touch, and more time and more touching are probably two of the factors leading to the next aspect.

Trust. Almost certainly, patients trust their doctors less than they did. To some extent this may be healthy, but trust in the therapist is one of the main factors involved in 'getting better', or at least 'feeling better', and so orthodox medicine is seen by some as failing them.

To sum up, doctors have gained in the *science* of medicine at the expense of losing its *art*. Many alternative practitioners have rediscovered the art.

Cost

The problems which follow from the cost to the National Health Service of high technology medicine are clear. Most alternative medicines are very cheap, requiring mainly the therapist's time. This simple fact adds to their popularity with politicians.

Health on demand

In western culture, health is now assumed to be the right of all, and the present cult of high consumer expectation encourages the growth of systems providing what people want. The public is now better informed, the media highlighting not only curative treatments available, but also featuring both techniques and standards of reasonable care. In this context, Christians will realize that physical health is not the only, or main, goal in life. The devil would be content if all striving for improvement were confined to biological excellence. What may be an overemphasis by some areas of the church on physical healing may be going along with the Satanic strategy to divert attention and energy from spiritual issues.

Thus the prevailing view is that alternative medicines are cheap and mostly harmless, and may do some good. It is likely that they will become even more in demand.

What is the Christian view?

Curiously, Christians seem polarized. One group accepts all alternative medicines on the above grounds, rejoicing that they are 'natural' (a word which needs a lot of examination). The other extreme rejects them all as being rooted in the occult. The first group tends to see God in all the gaps in their understanding, the second to see the devil in the same gaps.

The study group attempted to examine the whole subject in its context, and to develop a framework within which Christian professionals might be able to assess any particular alternative medicine for themselves.

A framework for assessment: preliminary considerations

The relation of truth to efficacy

All medical practice should be within a scientific framework where the criterion of validity is efficacy: does it work? However, the problem with this familiar concept lies in the question: what do we mean by 'work'? This introduces the problem of language. All too often, conventional and alternative practitioners (especially ones who are not medically qualified) are talking about different things when using the same words, or using words the other does not understand. Assessments of efficacy depend on the baseline used for a comparative study, and it may not be possible to agree on baselines. Thus, for example, comparability studies such as the definitive, double-blind, placebo-controlled trial are not usually possible with alternative medicine.

It is therefore important to be on the alert for 'pseudo-science', where proponents have written papers to establish theories already born of an ideology. This is, of course, the reverse of the normal scientific process. In assessing an alternative medicine, principles such as these should be examined first, but details must be examined too, as they can often obviously discredit the whole.

All members of the group agreed on the importance of *truth*. G. K Chesterton remarked that when people stop believing in God, they don't believe in nothing, they believe in anything. The present post-

Christian culture has little interest in truth, and while any serious student of medical matters (orthodox or alternative) must say from time to time, 'We cannot yet know', truth should still be central in all assessment. It is, after all, a divine characteristic; Jesus said: 'I am the truth' (Jn. 14:6), whereas Satan 'is a liar and the father of lies' (Jn. 8:44).

Wherever possible, Christians will want to apply the judgment of Scripture. It has already been said that the criterion of validity is efficacy – does it work? If an alternative therapy does not work on objective testing it cannot be true. However, some of the group also felt that even if a therapy seemed to work, it might not necessarily be true in the sense of being factually correct or *ethically right*, because Satan can 'perform great signs and miracles to deceive even the elect' (Mt. 24:24).

The problem of the 'Is it true?' approach is that truth cannot always be known at the desired time. Open minds and humble hearts to which God can speak are essential.

The therapist

Many practitioners of alternative medicine have no medical qualifications. This can make dialogue difficult, and can mean that there are no professional bodies with regulatory powers controlling their activities. It was felt that there is little evidence of frank charlatanism, and that most unqualified practitioners have the same sincere motives as most orthodox doctors have.

Lack of training in diagnosis, however, gives more cause for alarm. Many alternative practitioners are little concerned with a specific medical diagnosis, and it may be that serious organic pathology, treatable if detected early, is being missed. Examples were quoted. At the moment, most patients in Britain consult alternative practitioners only after the doctor has failed, but it may be that this balance will alter, as has occurred in parts of the United States.

Many therapists also avoid any responsibility for continuing care of patients and in this sense are actually less than holistic. Some are also more obviously technicians than are most orthodox doctors!

The spiritual status of the therapist is, of course, important. The Ayurvedic therapist will spend 2–3 hours daily in spiritual preparation of himself before starting treatments – a challenge to the spiritual preparation of the Christian doctor.

The spiritual dimension in alternative therapy

Some alternative medicines openly relate to the spirit world, spiritualist 'healing' being the most obvious example. In others, involvement may be more subtle. Some practitioners introduce an occult element of their own into an otherwise acceptable practice, or, more commonly, an alternative practitioner will use a number of different therapies, most but not all of which are spiritually harmless.

It may be that some groups vocal in the church today see too much of the devil in alternative medicine; it may be that as scientifically trained CMF members, some are less perspicacious and tend to under-estimate the work of the devil.

The questions whether there is always a spiritual component to a therapy and if so, whether this component can remain neutral, were left unanswered.

A specific checklist for Christian assessment of any alternative therapy

The group is indebted to Christian Szurko for suggesting the first five points of this checklist.

Do the claims made for it fit the facts?

So far as an alternative therapy can be tested, is it true? The most elementary examination of a therapy may suffice to show that it is a lie. Christians would presumably not want to be involved any further themselves or for their patients.

Is there a rational scientific basis for the therapy?

Medical science is based on a (limited) understanding of God's orderly creation. Scientific research has been described as 'thinking God's thoughts after him'. If a therapy does not seem to fit in any way into that understanding, Christians should be suspicious.

Is it the methodology or is it the principle which is the effective element?

If an alternative therapy works, whence does the truth originate? An example will illustrate the value of this check. Transcendental Meditation can claim with scientific justification to produce benefits such as lowered blood pressure or reduced arousal, but it is not the principle of meditation (a specifically spiritual activity) which is effective but the methodology of the technique. Anything equally relaxing would produce the same physiological benefits.

What are the assumptions of the worldview behind the therapy?

Many alternative medicines are based on eastern, mystical, Hindu concepts. Words like 'energy' or 'life-force' occur frequently in many variations. Christians will be suspicious of this spiritual stable, but sound horses may emerge.

Does the therapy involve the occult?

Is it one of the practices specifically forbidden in Scripture, or like one of them? It should be emphasized again that some therapists add their own occult elements to techniques which might otherwise be harmless. Christians have the Bible to help in examining alternative medicine.

Has the therapy stood the test of time?

(This is a test added by the study group.) Fads and fashions will be eliminated by this test, but there may be some time-honoured techniques which should cause Christians concern.

This checklist does not give definitive answers in every case. It should be used for sounding alarm bells. Clear failure to measure up to any of these tests should make Christians think again.

Placebo

Three meetings were spent on specific types of alternative medicines, and a final meeting on placebo summed up much of the entire course, including the uncertainties about cultural context, the ignorance the profession has about why people 'get better', some of the ethical difficulties about treatments which most orthodox practitioners use regularly, and perhaps the need for an explanation for most, if not all, of the apparent successes of alternative medicine.

Professor Duncan Vere introduced the subject by correcting the common but unsatisfactory definition of placebo as 'inactive treatment', which he rephrased as 'any components of a therapy which are without specific activity for the condition being treated or evaluated'. In other words, placebo is not inactive, but it is not active specifically.

Thus the homoeopathic physician handing out pills is not handing out pills alone, he is giving a large dose of himself also. The same is true of the allopathic physician, and no orthodox general practitioner pretends otherwise – although in conventional medicine the double-blind placebo-controlled trial can at least get truthful answers in research.

It is this non-specific effect – often too naïvely called placebo – which makes assessment of efficacy in alternative medicine so difficult. However, there are very few reported comparative trials of placebo and alternative medicine, and all alternative systems cannot be categorically dismissed as being wholly dependent on the placebo response, though it may be operative in up to 35% of cases.

People fall ill for many reasons, and no allopathic clinician can unravel all legitimate components of the presenting symptoms. It may be that alternative practitioners have touched on areas lost to the more scientific doctors.

Placebo is another huge and fascinating area which cannot be covered here, but one ethical dilemma should be mentioned. If a placebo is given, knowing it has no specific bearing on the patient's condition, is it not a deception? The group concluded that, if beneficial results follow (wherever they come from), that represents a responsible treatment, not least without the possible side-effects of a pharmacologically active drug. To use placebos to fob off patients is morally wrong; to use them to bring relief without harming the patient is surely legitimate.

Perhaps much of what doctors have always done – and still do – is to use that powerful placebo, themselves, in every contact with a patient. Balint called this the 'doctor-drug', and Christians above all will recognize the importance of the integrity of the physician.

Conclusion

Consideration of this last section must convince the honest enquirer that there are many mysteries still. Openness of mind and humility of heart are needed, but Christians will want to check any alternative medicine with the twin instruments of science and Scripture.

There is in fact huge potential for the gospel in all this confusion. Many are becoming increasingly aware of the supernatural, and, indeed, feel the need of a power outside themselves to enable them to cope with life. Satan has as usual overstepped himself, and in all the willingness of patients to believe in anything, some are prepared to believe in God again. May members of the CMF examine themselves, increase their integrity, and reveal Christ to their patients more and more.

17 PSYCHIATRY

STARTING PSYCHIATRY: SOME DIFFICULTIES FOR CHRISTIAN STUDENTS

Monty Barker

Many medical students find psychiatry a disturbing subject within the curriculum. Sometimes Christian students find it particularly so. The purpose of this section is to explore some of the reasons for this.

Difficulties for medical students in general

New concepts

Hitherto our training and our concepts of illness have been based upon the natural sciences. Our teachers have spoken with a fair degree of unanimity and authority. We have learned to diagnose illness by such means as sight and touch, backed up by a plethora of sophisticated laboratory tests. We have learned to treat illness with drugs specific to the particular condition, or by means of an operation for the removal of diseased tissue.

In psychiatry, much of the teaching is based upon the new behavioural sciences. Aetiology is now discussed frequently in terms of the effect of his or her environment upon the patient, and the difficulties he or she may have in interpersonal relationships. The clinical features noted are disordered behaviour, anomalies of mood and disturbed thinking and perception. Physical methods of treatment are used; but treatment frequently consists of psychotherapy, the verbal interchange between therapist and patient, which to some may seem to be mere chat. Another new factor is that there seem to be so many schools of thought among psychiatrists, ranging from those who take an organic approach to mental illness to those who take a Freudian psycho-analytical approach. Others unashamedly combine both extremes. This new understanding of illness, its causes and treatment, coupled with the lack of unanimity among their teachers, may create in students a feeling of unease. This may result in their rejecting the subject completely.

Personal involvement

Previously, in our study of medicine, we have progressed from the study of matter and the basic sciences to the study of lower forms of life, which was followed by the study of the human body, and finally the study of diseased function in the living body. This materialistic approach to illness has always been combined in the good physician with a real concern for the patient as a person. However, when dealing with physical illnesses it is much easier to ignore the person who is ill and concentrate upon her lesions and pathology.

In dealing with a patient who is mentally ill, this detachment is much more difficult. This is partly because psychiatric case-history-taking is much more detailed than the case-history-taking with which we have been familiar so far. For instance, we have to record the patient's response to his parents, his marital relationships, his response to crisis and stress, and his feelings and attitudes towards a wide variety of situations. Inevitably, as we look more closely at how the patient deals with life and those around him, we ourselves become involved and compare our own attitudes with his. We certainly react in some way. We may sympathize with the patient so much that we become unduly involved, or we may find ourselves becoming critical and so we reject the patient.

In addition to this we learn about the way in which the mind works, we gain insight into the way in which we habitually cope with stress in our own lives. For some this is disturbing. Also, as we hear about the nature of psychiatric symptoms, we would not be medical students if we did not introspect a little and do a symptom inventory upon ourselves. The discovery of similarities between ourselves and our patients does not of course indicate illness, any more than a pain in the chest indicates a heart attack. However, the fear that we share some of the symptoms of our patients may cause us to protect ourselves – either by rejecting psychiatry and those who suffer from mental illness, or by becoming over-involved with our patients, hoping thereby to solve our own problems. This is why part of the training in psychiatry is directed towards enabling us to recognize and use our own personality, in order that we may avoid the pitfalls of rejection or over-involvement in dealing with patients. The result is that we are able to become more objective in our assessment and treatment.

Further difficulties for the Christian

For the Christian, there are further difficulties. Failure to identify these can lead to greater tension than is necessary.

Attitudes

The picture of the traditional atheistic psychiatrist is largely derived from Sigmund Freud and his followers. It is really just as false as the idea of the atheistic scientist of a generation ago. The latter was due to the presence of a few well-known scientists in the late nineteenth century, who were good writers for a popular readership and who spread their own radical atheism along with their discussion of current scientific findings.

Sigmund Freud was undoubtedly a genius who helped to make real progress in psychiatry. But he was first a materialist and an atheist. He expanded his psychological observations into a philosophy, and subsequently integrated his preconceived religious views within this philosophy. His views on religion and God have been expounded in his book *The Future of an Illusion*. In this he sees God as a projected father-image in the skies. This view has been frequently discussed and answered by psychiatrists who otherwise owe much to Freud and his teaching, but who have also seen very clearly the connection between Freud's problems with religion and those which he had with his own father. Carl Gustav Jung, one of Freud's early disciples, states in his autobiography *Memories, Dreams and Reflections* that, following a disagreement with Freud, he 'observed in Freud the eruption of unconscious religious factors'. He continues: 'Evidently he wanted my aid in erecting a barrier against these threatening unconscious contents.'

Many psychiatrists beside Freud have been interested in the immaterial part of human nature, and have examined the belief and practices of their patients, including Christian and religious belief. As they seek to understand the psychological and sociological factors associated with these, they may be able to give helpful insights into the way in which certain techniques or persuasion or cultural pressures may influence a person or operate within different Christian groups. This does not mean that they can pass comment on the validity of the claims of Christianity. Here the psychiatrist is no more competent than any other specialist. Unfortunately, in our contemporary deference to the expert, whatever his or her subject, we do not always stop to examine the person's credentials.

Aims

It is because the aims of psychiatric treatment seem so close to those of the Christian gospel that conflict arises.

We can see that medicine generally shares with the Christian gospel the aims of helping, healing and restoring. Where healing a limb is concerned, however, we can see this clearly as the province of medicine. Healing a mind, giving new purpose and strength to a person may, on the other hand, seem very close to the province of the Christian church.

Therefore the question in the minds of many Christians starting psychiatry is: what relevance does psychiatry have for the Christian, who believes that he has the fullest answer to a person's need in the gospel of Jesus Christ? The question may be posed in other ways, such as: will not conversion be the answer to this person's problems? Or: Should not the Christian psychiatrist seek the conversion of his or her patients, as only thus can they be really helped?

Perhaps the best way to deal with these questions is to regard the psychiatrist as dealing with the mechanisms of the mind and seeking to adjust them as far as possible. The patient is one in whom the mental mechanisms have become distorted and whose mental functioning is impaired. The programme of life is going on around her, but she is picking it up with distortions. The patient's reaction to this may show itself in varying degrees, ranging from acute anxiety to madness, but her first need is for the distortions to be dealt with and eliminated. In her suffering she requires the help of a clinician, who has been trained in the special skills and techniques appropriate to mental illness.

Physical methods of treatment such as electro-convulsive therapy (ECT), phenothiazines and antidepressant drugs have, over the past forty years, transformed the treatment of many patients. For some they have been life-saving, while in others they have shortened the course of illness, and many patients suffering from chronic mental illnesses have been enabled by them to lead much more dignified and useful lives. Psychotherapy may be used alone, or in conjunction with these physical methods of treatment, to enable the patient to come to terms with the problems in his life and to deal more effectively with stresses and crises which occur.

In the pastoral ministry it is increasingly being recognized that many people, who never reach a psychiatrist, require careful and skilled counselling before and in addition to more direct spiritual help. The psychiatrist is increasingly being used in the training of clergy in the techniques of counselling. How much greater, then, is the need for skilled exploration and help for the person whose mind is sufficiently distressed to require referral to a psychiatrist, or admission to a psychiatric hospital. This is not to say that these people have no need of Christ; but the reason they have rightly come to a psychiatrist is that he or she has the training and skills to help to restore their mental function.

It must be emphasized that all of us as doctors enter into a professional contract with our patient. The essence of this is that certain things are guaranteed to him. First, he comes to us as doctors, for our medical skill, not for our evangelism. Secondly, he trusts us to view his case with complete objectivity, unclouded by our own personal views. This professional restraint has the added advantage that the patient with a sordid life is enabled to talk about it with freedom, and also the hidden resentments and hostilities of the Christian patient, which may be responsible for his present illness, are more readily explored.

Apart from these ethical considerations (that doctors should not use their professional position to impose their own views or beliefs on their patients), the psychiatrist must be additionally cautious. The success of the therapeutic relationship depends upon the psychiatrist's avoiding the temptation to offer solutions, but rather helping patients to make their own decisions. Christian psychiatrists (as well as humanist psychiatrists) may explore, where relevant, their patients' religious views or lack of them; this does not give them the right to alter those beliefs.

Frames of reference

The Christian and the psychiatrist are both interested in human beings and their behaviour. But, in studying this, they may describe the same phenomena and behaviour from different frames of reference. The Christian is concerned with sin and guilt in the setting of a theistic universe. The physician specializing in psychological medicine is dealing with the experience of the sufferer in relation to his environment, and his disturbed behaviour or guilt feelings may, or may not, have underlying causes comparable to those seen by the Christian.

For the Christian, therefore, behaviour can be either 'good' or 'bad' according to how it relates to the laws of God. Strong moral feelings are expressed, and 'bad' behaviour is seen as an offence against God, a violation of what his glory demands, and is called 'sin'. When David sinned, he said, 'Against thee, thee only have I sinned and done what displeases thee' (Ps. 51:4 NEB). For the psychiatrist, however, behaviour is often spoken of as being 'socially acceptable' or 'unacceptable', 'stable' or 'unstable'. The terms 'good' and 'bad', if used at all, are used within the context of what society permits or tolerates. As society is constantly changing in its attitudes, and at present moving away from the biblical view of humanity and sin, the divergence between the Christian's frame of reference and that of the psychiatrist is increasing.

An example may be given of the way in which the Bible and society may view behaviour differently. Homosexuality is condemned in the Bible, and yet it is praised in certain great traditions. In our own culture it is tolerated now among the middle classes, though despised by the working classes. We may take also a situation where behaviour may be viewed differently by the psychiatrist because of his frame of reference. A young mother is referred to a psychiatrist because of her feelings of rejection of her child. Discussion may show her to have committed adultery, desertion, child neglect, lying and theft. Theologically all this is sin, but if the psychiatrist finds that she is illegitimate, comes from a disturbed home, and has had no adequate father figure or consistent affection from her mother, he may consider that he had adequate grounds for seeing this as the cause of her disturbed behaviour. He may ask what background, instruction or model she has had from which to form acceptable behaviour, what pattern she has for becoming an adequate mother or model citizen. Accordingly, it can be seen how her behaviour may be described as 'sinful' in the Christian context, and as 'unstable' from the point of view of the psychiatrist.

It is here that tension and anxiety arise because many Christians feel that sinful behaviour is being explained away. In fact, only the thoroughgoing determinist would agree that it was. Even though psychiatrists may describe the background and motivation of behaviour, they still hold out the possibility and hope of change. Unstable behaviour is not inevitable, although why people should respond differently to the same backgrounds and stresses is not clear. Certainly the psychiatrist's treatment is aimed at helping the person to change and achieve more stable behaviour. At the same time, it is not the psychiatrist's task to condemn or condone a person's behaviour.

Language and terminology

A further problem contributing to communication difficulties is the use of the same words, but with different meanings. 'Guilt' is an example here. When used by the lawyer it is something absolute and decreed, declared by jury and judge on account of proven law-breaking. The feelings of the guilty party are immaterial. Theological guilt is not exactly the same, because not all sins in the biblical sense have been declared crimes by the law of the country (for example, adultery and lying). Bigamy and slander, on the other hand, have been declared to be against the law. In addition, in theological guilt there is also the awareness of a broken relationship and separation from God. So the person is guilty before God, having broken his law. He is also aware that his sin has come between him and God, and separates him from God, so that he can say with David: 'Turn away thy face from my sins' (Ps. 51:9, NEB). Only the assurance of God's mercy and forgiveness can relieve this guilt.

Psychiatrists also use the word 'guilt', but they are almost exclusively concerned with *feelings of guilt*. This is a sense of shame, failure or need of punishment, often unrelated to whether the person has done wrong at all. It may be quite unreasonable, and out of all proportion to the supposed offence, and, although resisted or confessed, it remains dominant and distressing, unrelieved by spiritual counselling or psychological treatment. People suffering from such feelings of guilt are frequently mentally ill, and some have had to be referred to a psychiatrist by priests or ministers. Spiritual counselling, and allowing them to dwell upon their supposed wrongs and sins, may only make them worse. Some can be dramatically and permanently relieved by modern psychiatric treatment, without losing their faith. Perhaps if William Cowper, the hymn-writer, had lived today his periods of profound depression and intense feelings of guilt and rejection by God would have been relieved. His friend John Newton, the evangelical vicar, was unable to help lift his guilty feelings.

The problem today is that, because of the very real success which psychiatrists have had in relieving some of these states of morbid guilt, there is a tendency to feel that all guilt feelings are morbid and have a pathological basis, and either require treatment or should be ignored. But most psychiatrists would admit that for many who are referred for treatment for their 'guilt feelings', their 'symptoms' and 'feelings' are directly related to an unsolved problem or impaired relationship, which the patient refuses or is unable to accept or resolve.

Responsibility

Lastly, the psychiatrist and the Christian appear to come into conflict on questions of responsibility and punishment. Again the Bible seems clear in its statement that we are responsible for our actions before God. David said: 'I have sinned . . . so that thou mayest be proved right in thy charge and just in passing sentence' (Ps. 51:4, NEB) – acknowledging human freedom and a degree of self-determination. It is on this basis that the punishment of God is expressed and the pardon of God is offered to the person who seeks it.

Today, however, punishment is often equated in people's minds with revenge, which produces revulsion. Accordingly, there is increased pressure on the legal system to abolish the idea of retributive punishment and to substitute treatment programmes for the reformation of the offender. Psychiatrists have been drawn into this debate because they found themselves in conflict with the law in certain cases. The law, in its duty to protect society, was using punishment both as a retribution and as a deterrent. Psychiatrists, however, recognized that for some offenders their law-breaking was the result of mental illness, and only treatment of their illness would prevent their committing further crime. Over the years, the law has conceded the case for the brain-damaged, the insane, and the mentally handicapped. But the problem remains with those whose intelligence is normal, whose mood is stable, but whose will seems defective. They repeatedly offend, and punishment seems of little help. Or again, there are those whose offence seems to arise out of unconscious or only partly conscious emotional factors, such as the middle-aged woman with no previous convictions, who shop-lifts while depressed or in emotional turmoil. She may be deeply shocked and ashamed at her behaviour. Are such people not also ill and requiring treatment?

It is because of situations like these that some people wish to reject altogether the concept of responsibility and punishment in dealing with offenders. They prefer to speak of social deviation and the need for treatment. They would base their views on the belief that we cannot rightly apportion degrees of responsibility, and that punishment is not an effective way of dealing with deviants. They would say that in any case none of us is entirely responsible for our actions. There may be considerable force behind these views. It must be emphasized, however, that concepts of responsibility and punishment safeguard the freedom of the person by guaranteeing to her the dignity of free will, and protect her from the whim of society, which after all determines the deviation. Another sound reason for retaining the idea of punishment is that it is prescribed for each offence; 'treatment' may be indefinitely prolonged until the desired result is produced. It has been rightly said that the divine punishment safeguards the individual freedom of the human being as a responsible person; anything less makes us less human. Maybe the same is true of human punishment.

Undoubtedly there are issues here which pose considerable problems, to which there seem to be no clear answer. It can be seen, however, that the Christian and psychological observations of human behaviour are not so different or incompatible, if it can be realized that they are couched in different language and described from different frames of reference.

The remedies for a person's behaviour and condition may, on the other hand, show much less in common. This may arise from the conflict between the Christian view of humanity and the view held by certain psychiatrists. But even the Christian is only too well aware of the difficulties encountered by some in overcoming their problems of background, personality and motivation. Perhaps these issues are nowhere better illustrated than in the biography *George Burton: A Study in Contradictions*, where a man, prominent as a Christian and evangelist in the East End of London is shown battling with these problems in himself.

The Christian in psychiatry

It is a pity that some Christian doctors and medical students have tended to show suspicion and even hostility to the practice of psychiatry. In so doing, not only have they deprived the specialty of their specific contribution, but also they have left to others one of the most needy and neglected areas of patient care, especially in the field of mental handicap. Here, I would suggest, is an area of medicine which should commend itself strongly to the Christian student and physician. For the most important skill of the psychiatrist is psychotherapy, and it has been shown repeatedly that it is the personality of the therapist which is more effective than the particular approach or school of psychotherapy. As a Christian therapist establishes a relationship with the patient, this relationship must surely be influenced by the Holy Spirit, who is himself dealing with the life and personality of the therapist.

Certain things, however, need to be said here. First, compassion and concern are no substitute for training and gathering experience. This process involves years of apprenticeship, supervision, and the study of associated disciplines such as psychology and neurology. It also involves higher postgraduate examinations. Second, all of us have our own personality problems, foibles and ways of dealing with stress. If we are to help others who are unable to cope with these, we must gain some insight into ourselves. Most psychiatrists gain this as they undertake psychotherapy of selected patients and discuss their progress with senior colleagues. A preparedness to examine and work through our own problems is an essential part of our training, and Christians should not expect to be exempt from this personal scrutiny and facing up to ourselves. Indeed, it should be beneficial for Christians to take stock of ourselves spiritually, and in every way, from time to time. We should be well prepared for this, knowing that 'the heart is the most deceitful of all things' (Je. 17:9, NEB). Third, it must be emphasized again that the psychiatrist is not an evangelist or a clergyman. Although there may be considerable overlapping of roles, he or she should spend time working out the difference between them.

Having said this, here is a specialty in medicine which requires the physician to explore the whole life of the patient. It frequently extends his interest, involvement and healing beyond the person to his family, work and social unit. In addition, in psychiatry there is a great need to develop competence in other related disciplines, in order to enrich the original and primary sphere. Are not such aims those which should appeal to the Christian, who has a special understanding of the family, humanity and society?

It is well, too, to remember that it was Christian initiative which pioneered some of the great reforms in the nineteenth century in the care of psychiatric patients. William Tuke, who founded the Retreat in York, where the spiritual and moral aspects were to play as important a part as the medical in patient care, brought his Christian mind and conscience to bear upon the conditions and care of the mentally sick. It was prominent evangelicals such as Lord Shaftesbury in England and Lord Kinnaird in Scotland who championed the cause of the insane by setting up 'commissioners in lunacy'. They sought to preserve the rights and dignity of mental patients as persons. It was due to people like these that British psychiatry has led the world in concern for the care of the mentally sick.

Conclusion

To sum up, then, we may say that the difficulties in the minds of many as they start psychiatry are due partly to the novelty of the subject and partly to apparent conflicts between the Christian and psychiatric approaches to people. The difficulties due to the novelty of the subject will be largely overcome as the student becomes more familiar with the language of the speciality, sees more patients, and understands himself or herself better. The course in psychiatry should help us to approach people in a more mature way, and make our study and practice of medicine a deeper and more satisfying art.

Those issues which seem to point to an inherent conflict between the Christian faith and psychiatry are often due to misconceptions concerning the authority that the psychiatrist has on specific topics, or to thinking that he means the same thing when in fact he is using the same words for a different concept. Further, many people expect a complete synthesis between the Christian view of humanity and psychological concepts. Such a synthesis does not exist. The Christian psychiatrist must use the tools at his disposal, fully realizing their inadequacies. At the same time he recognizes that there is an area where two very different worldview outlooks and disciplines meet and overlap. While interested in the same people, they have only some aims in common. Mental health and spiritual life, though perhaps related, are certainly not synonymous or necessarily dependent on each other. Consequently, we still require both approaches. At the same time, we must always strive to examine and solve the problems associated with the tension points.

THE PROBLEM PATIENT

Woody Caan

In any branch of healthcare, a patient may present as 'a problem', if the doctor feels unable to address the challenge of his illness ('he's incurable, I'm inadequate') or if the patient is unwilling to cooperate in the doctor's treatment regime ('he's a stupid, self-destructive, waste of time'). We can all imagine situations which straddle our notions of specialization (like attempting to explain to a psychotic patient that he has a terminal illness), but how good is the care we give to patients whose condition includes medical, social and criminal dimensions? For example, does a victim of recurring domestic violence evoke in us the distasteful label 'problem patient'?

I work in the field of substance abuse, and a major part of my job is the evaluation of services for drug dependency and training courses for doctors hoping to engage their patients with drug problems in treatment. I am unusually fortunate to work in a multidisciplinary team of psychiatrists, psychologists, nurses and social workers, and many of our patients have long histories (ten or more years) of substance abuse, while we are faced with a many-headed Hydra of psychiatric and medical complications, of which spreading HIV infection appears the most distressing.

The root of the problem

Collectively, drug abusers often appear as problem patients. Research in America and Britain suggests that health professionals are prejudiced against working with substance abusers, and this attitude tends to harden as their clinical training progresses. In my own hospital, this outcast status seems to be reinforced by our patients' entrance being as far removed as possible from the rest of the hospital. Merely being a 'demanding' group of patients does not confer 'problem' status; compare the attitudes in your own hospital to its drug dependency unit and its neonatal intensive care unit.

Individually, patients with drug problems present challenges to doctors which are likely to result in 'counter-transference', in which we involuntarily express against the patient hostile feelings that he is disgusting, threatening or intimidating. Not only is there the unique patient-doctor relationship in which the patient (almost) inevitably argues about any therapeutic drugs and doses, but all known addictive substances distort the machinery in the brain which gives an emotional and motivational colouring to one's experiences, so that even in routine patient-doctor interaction the doctor may be upset by what manifests itself as inappropriate or frustrating patient contributions. In particular, the physician is hurt by patients who 'do not want to get better'!

This is the root of the real problem, and lies in our whole attitude to humanity, because, to the physician, the state of 'not wanting to get better' is like the state of sin to our Father in heaven. However, Jesus said, 'It is not the healthy who need a doctor, but the sick. I have not come to call the righteous, but sinners' (Mk. 2:17).

Christian response

Individual by individual, how should Christians respond to problem patients? I have recently been thinking of several challenges of the older embittered in-patient who is aggressively undermining the other patients' progress by venting his despair in trying to discourage them too: the psychotic, relapsed, out-patient with a history of assaulting the female staff, who returns to disrupt the clinic and, even after ejection by Security, sits down in the street outside shouting threats and exposing himself with demoralizing animosity; or the patient discharged against medical advice who returns to the unit only when seeking an alibi for her latest criminal charges.

Three avenues are commonly followed after this hostility to the problem patient has appeared: *abdication* (she is somebody else's problem), *analysis* (I hate him, but I know I hate him) or *authoritarianism* (I am going to dominate him, whatever it costs in terms of his dignity or mine, till one of us cracks). As Christians, however, a good starting point is humility: 'Brothers, if someone is caught in a sin, you who are spiritual should restore him gently. But watch yourself, or you also may be tempted' (Gal. 6:1). This should be coupled with faith in the saving power of Jesus, 'who, by the power that enables him to bring everything under his control, will transform our lowly bodies so that they will be like his glorious body' (Phil. 3:21).

When Jesus was faced with the paralysed man, he first recognized the latter's deep need for forgiveness. With a self-hating problem patient, we have a duty to share this mission of forgiveness: 'If you forgive anyone his sins, they are forgiven; if you do not forgive them, they are not forgiven' (Jn. 20:23).

Some patients present particular emotional challenges. Take our drug cases in prison, perhaps Rule 43 prisoners identifiable as child-killers, sex offenders, HIV-positive rent boys, and the like. Here we can witness as Christians by our commitment: 'Let us, then, go to him outside the camp, bearing the disgrace he bore' (Heb. 13:13).

Sometimes it is a very small thing that gives a new perspective on problem patients. Our in-patients had the wonderful treat of a royal visit by a princess who has set a worldwide example of meekness and commitment in caring. During rehearsals, in the frantic preparations for the royal visit, the staff, representing every rank in the Health Service, treated the patients as if they were invisible, or at best messy bits of furniture to be shifted around in assembling the scenery and props for the big show. Perhaps foolishly, I broke ranks to speak to the patients: 'Remember, you are the real VIPs here!'

All of us are some time going to face the ultimate Royal Visit. In the parable of the sheep and goats, Jesus said: 'The King will reply, "I tell you the truth, whatever you did for one of the least of these brothers of mine, you did for me"' (Mt. 25:40).

DEMONS

Roger Moss

Belief in demons and demonic possession has occurred throughout the world since early in recorded history. Moses and the prophets repeatedly warned against practices such as divination, sorcery and idol worship – practices rooted in the demonic. Yet Jesus and the New Testament writers do not ascribe all physical and mental illness to demonic causes; they distinguish illnesses brought about by demonic influence from those that are not. The church has mostly continued to maintain that demons are real, and that they may be responsible for physical and mental illness, but that not all illness has this origin.

Levels of demonic involvement

Four levels of demonic involvement have been distinguished,[1] on a continuum ranging from simple temptation to significant possession.

First, Scripture is clear that temptation may arise from our sinful human nature, without demonic interference. Jesus said that 'from within, out of men's hearts, come evil thoughts and actions' (Mk. 7:21). Quite how this concept would be dealt with in modern psychological terms is not clear, because it has not been tackled with any thoroughness. Nevertheless, it is striking how behaviourists in recent years have strongly reaffirmed concepts of personal responsibility; the implication is that unsociable or harmful actions are governed at least in part by personal choice, however that arises.

Secondly, Scripture sees some temptations as originating from demonic agents. Christ was tempted by Satan. Satan filled the heart of Ananias so that he lied to the Holy Spirit (Acts 5:3). Furthermore, it is clear that opening one's life to sinful practices provides a portal of entry for demonic temptation (Jn. 8:34; 1 Pet. 5:8.).

Thirdly, a more intense level of demonic influence in human life is known as 'oppression', or perhaps subjection or obsession. A biblical summary of manifestations at this level includes blindness and hardness of heart to the gospel (2 Cor. 4:4), abandoning the faith, and doctrinal corruption (1 Tim. 4:1), and indulging in shameful, disreputable behaviour (2 Pet. 2:1–2). People seem to become oppressed in two main ways: either by continual involvement in sin and courting occult and demonic influence, or through family involvement in the occult. Oppression occurs more commonly than the next, and most serious, category.

Fourthly, there is demon possession. Typical symptoms include supernatural strength; going about naked; being unable to speak, hear or see; experiencing self-destructive convulsions; and saying things that indicate a supernatural knowledge. The problem is that all of these symptoms may be seen on a psychiatric ward in the context of psychosis and perhaps personality disorder. Demon possession may result from idol worship, occult involvement, spells cast by others, and by healing administered through sorcery; all of these practices actively lay a person open to demonic entry.

Theologians in recent years have helpfully pointed out that we gain a much better understanding of the healing miracles and exorcisms of Jesus when we see his work in the setting of the kingdom of God. Hans Küng wrote:

> Jesus himself, living in the very midst of this period of solid belief in devils . . . preaches the joyful message of God's rule and not the threatening message of Satan's rule . . . he does not develop any doctrine of devils . . . Jesus' exorcisms and expulsions of devils are a sign that God' s rule is at hand and that an end is being prepared for the devil's rule . . . God's kingdom is creation healed. Jesus liberates the possessed from psychical constraints and breaks through the vicious circle of mental disturbance, devil religion and social ostracism.[2]

This is well demonstrated in the familiar story of the demon-possessed man in the Gerasene tombs (Mk. 5). The effects of the possession are described. Jesus deals with the evil spirits without showy drama, and lets everyone see where the spirits have gone by transferring them to the herd of swine. The man's sanity is returned to him, and he uses it to tell how much Jesus has done for him. Signs of God's kingdom are being revealed: 'If I drive out demons by the Spirit of God,' Jesus said, 'then the kingdom of God has come upon you' (Mt. 12 :28).

Luke 11 contains discussion of the process, more than description. The diversity of explanations for spiritual wonders like this is illustrated. Jesus is keen to attribute his power in driving out demons to the 'finger of God', and to declare that this means that the kingdom of God has come among the people. And he warns that the process involves more than the chucking out (the literal sense of the Greek) of demons; the vacated house has to be filled with a new spirit.

The psychiatrist's role

A proper diagnosis is important. Many people suffering from a brief reactive psychosis or severe depressive state have been harmed by being told inadvisedly that they are demon-possessed. As always, a careful history is most helpful, and an absence of contact with occult practices or practitioners makes the diagnosis much less likely. An assessment of the presenting symptoms, an evaluation of the dynamics of the individual's social system, and consideration of their responses to treatment, all play a part. It is also thought important to investigate family involvement in the occult back as far as three or four generations.[3] A Christian who has an acknowledged gift of spiritual discernment may help with diagnosis, but 1 John 4:1 suggests that this task is within the remit of all mature Christians.

During the writing of this article, a Christian patient with a previous history of depressive illness came to me, troubled that she had been through a period when, she firmly believed, she was possessed by the devil. She had many symptoms of severe depression, and prior to believing she was possessed she had been briefly manic and deluded. She sought help from an experienced clergyman who practises faith healing, and he brought up the possibility of demonic causation, probably in order to eliminate it. But his well-intended action had been enough to disturb her while in the suggestible state of depression.

This anecdote illustrates the way consideration of the demonic most often presents to the psychiatrist, that is, as a fear or even delusion in the setting of mental illness. The distinction is by no means always easy. Most Christians faced with the task of diagnosis will not be experienced in both the theological-pastoral and the psychiatric-psychological spheres, and will lean towards the approach with which they are most familiar. Those with little relevant training may resort to a diagnosis of demonization simply because they find the person's behaviour odd.

It is very rarely necessary to rush the diagnostic process, and it is always wise to have the opinion of someone experienced in the field. The Church of England strongly recommends psychiatric evaluation before exorcism is considered, and doctors could more often call on pastoral expertise.

Difficulties of differential diagnosis, because of overlapping symptomatology, are particularly liable to occur in schizophrenia, and in the much rarer disorder of multiple personality. Other patterns of mental illness which may give rise to doubt include depression (especially when psychotic), obsessive-compulsive disorder, mania with religious content, hallucinations from whatever cause, paroxysmal states such as epilepsy, and people with marked inferiority feelings.

Symptom patterns

Some of the features of demonic oppression which have been listed by Koch[4] as mimicking mental illness include a sense of being controlled, mental heaviness or oppression, nightmares, abnormal personalities (hard, uncongenial, 'dark'), abnormal sexuality, violent temper, a tendency to addictions, meanness or kleptomania, compulsive thoughts, melancholia, suicidal thoughts, destructive urges, blasphemous thoughts, religious delusions and simulated piety.

Symptoms associated with the rare state of demon possession may be divided for convenience into three categories.[5]

Physical manifestations

These include preternatural (greater than natural) strength; change in facial demeanour to one of intense hatred or evil; changes in voice tone and pitch, becoming deeper, harsher and perhaps mocking; epileptiform convulsions; and anaesthesia.

Psychological features

Such features include clairvoyance; telepathy; ability to predict the future; speaking in unknown languages; clouding of consciousness while in a trance state; and amnesia for things which happened while in a trance state.

Spiritual signs

The signs include a significant change in moral character; becoming verbally or physically aggressive or falling into a trance if someone prays; and an inability to say Jesus' name reverently or to affirm that he is God's Son in the flesh (1 Jn. 4:1–2).

The importance of accurate diagnosis becomes clear when the differences in management are compared. It is rather like the difference between attending to a hurt child (in the case of mental illness), and ejecting a marauder (in the case of demonic manifestations). Mental illness requires safety, the healing of deep emotional hurts, love and care and help with relationships, acceptance and understanding of what cannot be changed, and perhaps medical and psychological treatments. Demonic oppression, by contrast, needs the authority of Christ in deliverance, the spoken word and prayer, and a life protected by spiritual disciplines thereafter. In many respects, deliverance is much simpler than the relief of mental illness, and this is why it tends to appeal to those who want to see dramatic spiritual cures for all manner of personal problems.

Caution for enthusiasts

Richard Lovelace[6] has pointed out that 'some deliverance ministries identify any deep-rooted compulsive pattern of sin as an effect of "demon possession"'. He says that 'it is important to understand that indiscriminate exorcism for every behavioural problem which does not yield to the immediate exercise of will-power may actually *induce* symptoms of an alternate personality which are hypnotic or psychological in origin'. He wisely comments that 'both charismatic and ordinary Evangelical ministries need to recognise that deep spiritual problems cannot always be cured by one or two "magic wand" experiences of the infusion of grace. It takes time, and the penetration of truth, to make a mature saint'.[7] I know that I am not the only Christian psychiatrist who has been called upon to pick up the pieces after short-sighted enthusiasts like the above have been at work.

A psychiatrist's experience

In the course of psychiatric work, I have occasionally encountered patients who possess psychic powers, though very often they have no wish to exercise them, and may even be frightened of such powers. But in my experience a direct encounter with the demonic has proved rare, and I do not think that this is because I have had a low index of suspicion.

I well remember one young woman who recognized that her marriage was going to fail as she walked up the aisle at her wedding. When it proved a disaster within a short time, she reacted so strongly that she went in for everything evil she could lay her hands on, including witchcraft. She described herself as 'giving herself to the devil', much as a Christian gives himself to the Lord (and she had subsequently done the latter). She needed skilled exorcism and then psychological help to recover from the damage that was inflicted on her life and personality. But I believe that some form of abandonment to evil, albeit often less dramatically, is at the heart of demonization.

I think that oppressed or possessed individuals usually retain a sense that they have a spiritual problem which requires spiritual help should they wish to seek it, and they therefore tend not to take their problem to a psychiatrist. Even if they do, they may well conceal the spiritual cause.

I also hold the view that psychiatric hospitals inevitably tend to become repositories for much of the evil that generations of patients have entertained in their lives. This does not mean that demonic problems are obvious and rife, but the spiritually discerning may sense a quality of oppression and confusion in psychiatric hospitals which seems to exceed the ordinary sociological problems of institutions. Christians need to pray for the chaplains working in psychiatric hospitals, as well as for the patients, and to recognize the battleground of spiritual warfare that may rage around vulnerable people. At the same time, Christian psychiatrists need to stick to their last, and to provide appropriate assessment and help for the far greater numbers of people whose mental health problems are not demonic in origin.

We need to exercise humility in areas like these, where cross-disciplinary thinking is still required which will sort out the problems and complexities in this field. We will approach with sensitivity and care those vulnerable individuals who may be further damaged by inept handling. And we should be ready to call on those with greater experience in these matters, so that we may learn to be useful agents of our Lord in dark places.

Further reading

J. Richards, *But Deliver Us from Evil* (Darton Longman and Todd, 1974) remains an authoritative and useful introduction to the demonic dimension in pastoral care.

THE CHRISTIAN DOCTOR AND ALCOHOL

Dorothy Lowe

We have a wonder drug on our hands. It is hidden in many attractive elixirs, and there is hardly a time of day when it cannot be obtained somewhere. Hospitality is considered mean and odd if it is not included. The market is continually bringing new products to our attention to boost consumption, just as in Solomon's day people were 'always trying some new spiced liquor' (Pr. 23:30, NEB). The substance, of course, is alcohol.

It is an amazing substance. It is used in happiness and celebration and also in sadness and suffering. It is served on many social occasions, helping talk to flow more freely. It makes people feel they belong together, relaxed and confident and warmed. In times of distress it may be turned to for relief. Its relaxant effect eases anxiety and tension. It can soothe pain and dull the memory of hurt and rejection and loneliness. It shortens those long sleepless nights. And for the serious and hard-working person who has left no time or place for play and fun, alcohol can offer a temporary mood change. It may also be the pattern in bout drinking, where the serious times with abstinence alternate with chaotic heavy drinking. Social settings are often associated with alcohol, and a habit of regular drinking is easy to acquire. Meeting friends for a drink is for many an acceptable and normal social life. But for others, the regular habit and a gradual increase of quantity lead to trouble.

'I don't drink as much as my friend Harry'

It is always important to note that you are not dealing with 'Harry' but with the patient before you. He or she is a special and unique person made in the image of God and worthy of respect. Look behind the outward appearance, which may be red-faced, liver-palmed, shaky and sweaty and perhaps unkempt (or, on the other hand, smooth, defensive and denying the problem), and there is a person created and loved by God. Your patient and 'Harry' have their own unique tolerance levels. It may not be useful to question the quantity, as after the first few drinks it is hard to keep count. It is much more useful to look carefully with him at ways in which his drinking is affecting his life or making things worse for him, and to find out if he has become dependent on alcohol.

To relate to others in a warm and loving way is one of God's richest gifts. 'What', I ask, 'is happening to the people you love, what do they say about your drinking? And how is your life going? Tell me about your job, your finances, your efforts to get money for drink. Have you had any problems with the law, any drink-driving offences? What are your interests and hobbies?' (When drinking has become a full-time occupation, there is often little time for anything else.) 'Then there is your body – any stomach trouble, memory difficulties, blackouts, suicide attempts?' Liver-function tests can give a useful clue to the doctor and hard evidence to help the patient to diagnose himself. These are the areas of harm and need to be looked straight in the face. It is wise to see the patient and spouse together whenever possible.

'It's my stomach, not my drinking'

Mrs S. was very angry. Her occupational health doctor had referred her, whereas she considered her drinking was no problem. In fact, alcohol helped her severe stomach pain and calmed her down. It was X-rays and perhaps an operation she needed, not drying out. She was a most reluctant patient and, but for her job being at risk, she would not have stayed. But she was an intelligent person and, when she had been helped to list the ways alcohol was affecting her life, she settled down. She was not chemically dependent on alcohol, but her liver-function tests provided evidence which she found convincing. She decided alcohol was not for her. She made a good recovery, and her stomach and nerves do not trouble her now. She, like many people whose harm is initially to their bodies, was able to stop drinking without too much difficulty, once she saw the connection. If dependency has not developed and the evidence is clearly presented, patients like Mrs S. can and do stop drinking. Here the doctor is still an authority figure.

Detoxification at home and in hospital

Dependency is a different matter altogether. In patients who have become dependent, the brain has become used to a level of sedation provided by regular alcohol. Without this sedation, it becomes irritable and withdrawal symptoms occur. The aim of detoxification is to prevent the more serious symptoms such as fits or delirium. This is achieved by re-intoxicating the brain with a drug which is cross-tolerant with alcohol, and then gradually reducing this drug over the course of one week. A dependent patient knows that when he stops drinking, he suffers from symptoms which can be very unpleasant. He has learned that a further drink will settle him. In fact, he may have been drinking to get going in the morning for some time. For him, to stop without medical help is difficult and frightening. Detoxification ('drying out') is the first step in treatment. When motivation is strong and there is good family support, this can be carried out in the patient's own home in much the same way as in hospital or a detox centre. Drugs in common use for detoxification include chlormethiazole (Heminevrin) and diazepam (Valium). They should be used only for the week of detoxification and never for maintenance.

Mr B. came with his wife. He was concerned that I should not think of him as an alcoholic. He certainly would not want anyone to think that was what he was. Yes, he did need to drink every evening, but it wasn't really a problem. He had a job, his wife still loved him and he was able to pay his way. He didn't have the shakes in the morning, so he didn't need to drink then. He was, in fact, drinking so much in the evenings that his level of alcohol remained high enough to avoid withdrawal symptoms until next evening. But he wasn't feeling or looking well. He was very anxious and sweaty, and a lot of the time he was afraid of losing his driving licence. And he was annoyed with himself for spending so much money on drink. His wife was very worried about him. A home detox with his wife's help went well. He was very proud of himself for managing it.

Staying 'dry'

For the dependent alcoholic *abstinence* is the right decision. But just stopping drinking is never enough. The man who threw out the devils, and swept and garnished his house and left it empty, soon had many worse devils instead. When we recognize the positive things alcohol provides, we soon realize that these must be found in some other way, or the pull to return to alcohol will be hard to resist.

Repeat prescriptions

A few weeks ago a bank manager patient said to me, 'It is impossible for me to do my job if I don't drink.' He was full of self-confidence, but agreed with me that it is a strange world where it is considered more normal to use alcohol – a mind altering substance – than to refuse it. He still drinks. So do a great many people in the course of their work and leisure. Against this compulsion, it is part of our social and Christian responsibility to change public opinion. Start where you are and be positive: create a situation where people have choices.

Why do they never learn?

Most people learn when they have had enough. They are in control of their occasional drinking. But others have somehow gone on drinking excessively until their drinking is a real problem. They have managed not to hear any negative comment on their behaviour long before becoming dependent. They have turned a deaf ear, or they have been amusing and entertaining or potentially violent and so comment has been withheld. When they are drunk, it is no use talking to them, and if you talk to them next day, they say your nagging drives them to drink. It is remarkable how whole families can be found to have adapted to the needs of the drinker and how they shield him from the real consequences.

Mr R. has a pleasant personality and an impish sense of humour. At work he was a genius. He was sensitive and kind and generous. He liked a drink – but then he worked hard and was entitled to a bit of fun. His drinking increased – at business lunches, then in his office. His work deteriorated. He had time off work. For two years, because of his good days, his firm indulged him, but finally he lost his job. His wife stood by him. When she found that she could get work more easily than he could, she took a job to support the family. The children kept out of the way when he was drunk, but when he was sober, they enjoyed his company and his indulgence of them (prompted by guilt). Money was short. Mrs R.'s earnings were not enough. Mr R.'s GP was sympathetic, and the sickness benefit helped to pay for drink, which was now a priority. Debts mounted up. The children were ashamed and stopped bringing their friends home. Social life was at an end. Since nobody in the family could trust Mr R. not be to drunk, all invitations and plans were abandoned. The whole family was by now 'sick'. Life for each member was an adaptation to the needs of dad's drinking. Only an external intervention would change things. When Mrs R. at last could take no more, but still had energy enough to do something, she went to a solicitor for a separation order. That external event led to Mr R. coming for help. He is now painfully rebuilding his life and, so far, is abstinent. He could not have gone on drinking so long if his employers, his family and his doctor had not enabled him to do so. Almost every problem drinker has his enablers.

Enabling for good

Am I my brother's keeper? It seems like a huge burden to take on. After all, my brother needs to take responsibility for himself and I have myself to look after. But when I think of this, I realize how dependent I am on the way my family, my friends and my patients relate to me. I look out for appreciation of some at least of the things I do, and in a deeper way I am strengthened and encouraged when, by a look or comment, someone seems to affirm who I am. This enables me to go on. A good brother's keeper gives honest, caring and loving comment. We can develop the habit of enabling for good.

Joyful service

There are days of disappointment and sadness, when some struggling patients seem to have given up and gone back to drinking and chaos. But there are days of rejoicing as well, and there are reunions packed with patients whose lives have been changed for the better because they have stopped drinking. I find it important to make sure I balance my books. Output and input need to match, or I get into the red and become disheartened, exhausted and useless. But I do not have to do all the loving and caring. The good news is that God is never off duty.

Summary points

● No doctor should fail to take a drinking history. Liver-function tests can provide a clue.
● Patients need help and honest comment so that they can diagnose themselves and be motivated for change.
● Detoxification – at home or in hospital.
● Understand what alcohol offers the patient and help him to find other resources.
● Make a habit of affirming people.

Practical measures we can all adopt

● When serving alcohol, we could serve attractive non-alcoholic drinks at the same time, on the same tray.
● Those who take alcohol could plan to abstain voluntarily at several social events each month or year. This will make it easier for others to abstain, and those adopting this practice will feel for themselves how much pressure is put on people to drink.
● When a relative or friend is drinking too much, we should not

cover up for him or accept his excuses, but do something about it. We should try to overcome our own fear, anger, disgust, and embarrassment. Our silence and acceptance of his behaviour enable the drinker to go on drinking. We should help him to stop before harm and dependency develop.

18 WHY DOES GOD ALLOW SUFFERING?

Peter May

The problem stated

It is unlikely that we will ever have a good discussion about the gospel with anyone without questions being raised about why God allows evil to persist and 'innocent' people to suffer. Only this week in my surgery I had an angry, tearful patient crying out against God for the unfairness of it all, and turning to me to answer her indignant questions.

The problem of suffering vexes the mind of the greatest thinkers, but also the simplest and least-educated folk. The problem confronts all mankind in some shape or form, in that all suffer to some degree and see others suffer also. For our generation it is especially acute as the pains of the world are beamed into our homes.

Even the complacent secularist has to wonder why his life should be so free of trials while so many struggle to survive. Last week a perfectly healthy nineteen-year-old student was working for finals. She developed a headache and vomiting. The next morning she walked into my surgery. The briefest of examinations confirmed the diagnosis of meningococcal meningitis. She was probably within hours of death, were it not for her clear clinical signs and the ready availability of parenteral penicillin.

The problem, of course, is especially acute for Christians who have reason through Christ to believe not only that God exists, but that he is good and loving. Furthermore, we understand him to be the all-powerful creator and sustainer of the universe. So the logic of it would seem, at least to a non-believer, that either he is not good, remaining unmoved by the cries of human pain, or he is not powerful enough to do anything about it. He cannot be good and all-powerful. The force of the argument against the Christian case seems irresistible.

Now the problem can be posed at that level – an intellectual and logical one – or it can come with a hidden agenda. People are often loathe to talk about their deepest agonies, if only because they know they cannot keep the lid on their emotions. Perhaps the only clue that this is not purely an academic issue will be the underlying anger with which the question is asked. In attempting to formulate any response, it is always worth bearing in mind that there may be a personal land-mine lying just beneath the surface. This may be the untimely death of a close relative. It may be a tragedy for which the person carries a deep sense of his or her own involvement and guilt. It follows from this that our answers need to be carefully phrased in terms of their argument and sensitively delivered in terms of their humanity. We may convey more of an answer by our personal caring than by our theodicy.

Towards our answer

What then can we say? Well, we should admit at the outset that we cannot say everything that we would like to be able to say. Much remains a mystery on a general level, and most of it is shrouded in difficulty at an acute personal level. Having said that, we actually have a lot to contribute. Let us take courage; the point of suffering is for many people the point at which the cross of Christ speaks to them.

Let us start at the point at which the accusation is levelled against God. The Bible teaches clearly that God is good, loving and just. If Christianity is true and has anything to say to our difficult world, it concerns the 'righteousness' and compassion of this world's owner and rightful ruler. Furthermore, his goodness is on a completely different level from ours, so that Jesus could say that 'no-one is good – except God alone' (Mk. 10:18).

We are created by God

The opening chapter of the Bible launches straight into an account, not of the goodness of God, but of his creation of the universe. The point is repeated throughout the different stages of creation to the climax at the end of the chapter, which tells us that God surveyed everything that he had made and concluded that it was 'very good' (Gn. 1:31).

That account of creation introduces the idea that when God made humankind he made us in his own likeness (Gn. 1:26–27). Whatever might be implied in that phrase – and it has wide implications, covering all the things that mark us out from the rest of the animal kingdom, and including all the attributes that we inherit from our Father in heaven – it is generally agreed that it includes our moral characters.

But our inherent goodness was not like that of a competent machine, which has a lifetime guarantee provided it is used correctly. No, God has made us as responsible moral beings, not only with consciences to distinguish right from wrong, but with the capacity to make moral choices with the freedom to get it wrong. Of course he need not have done it like that, if he had wanted robots for the purpose of play. However, it seems clear from the major themes of Scripture that he wanted persons to love and enter into relationship with him. When we are told that 'God is love' (1 Jn. 4:8), this is not some incidental aspect of his character. It is rather the essence of his being; and, because we are made in his image, relationships are the central significance of our lives.

Now it should not come as a surprise to anyone who has experienced the genuine love of another to know that such love cannot be coerced. The freedom to respond or not to respond is intrinsic to love's nature. We have been made with the capacity to love God and our fellows, but the exercise of such love is optional. It cannot be mandatory, or it ceases to be love. We are wooed by God and invited to love him, but the freedom is ours.

We need to be guarded when we affirm that God is all-powerful. Actually he is not. He cannot make a contradiction in terms. He cannot make a square circle. Neither can he make love a programmed response.

We refused to love him

The fact that we chose to love ourselves rather than God, and that we fell out of relationship with our Maker, is what the biblical story from Genesis 3 onwards is all about. The repercussions were endless, affecting the whole of humanity, and somehow (though it is not at all clear how) affecting the whole of creation (which groans in tribulation, according to Paul in Romans chapter 8). The original goodness of humanity continues to be evident even in the most depraved, while the deceitfulness of sin is to be found even in the finest of people. Furthermore, the sins of the parents have lasting implications for their children, and hardly a sin can be committed without someone else being diminished by it.

The effects of sin are to be found everywhere and no part of our being retains its former glory. When the Reformers spoke of 'total depravity', they did not mean that man is as bad as he could possibly be. Rather, they meant that no area of our being is unaffected by the fallenness of our natures. Our minds are corrupted so that we are blinded in perceiving the truth and need to be enlightened by the Holy Spirit to see the glory of God in the face of Jesus Christ. Our emotions lead us astray in every direction and our consciences no longer give us an accurate read-out. Our moral sensitivities can be blunted in the extreme, or even become over-sensitive so that we get everything out of proportion.

Who is to blame?

It is with these thoughts in mind that I put the word 'innocent' in quotation marks in the opening sentence of this article. Jesus makes it quite clear that there are no innocent people; we are all caught up in the iniquity that is set loose in the world, and all deserve the just judgment of God. This point needs to be clearly grasped if we are to be able to answer the question, 'Why doesn't God intervene?' It should be clear from what I have said that if God were to break into our world and bring in just judgment, none of us would be spared. The mercy of God and the justice of God appear to be at odds, and the Bible tells us that God delays judgment out of mercy (2 Pet. 3: 9).

With a little thought we should be able to demonstrate that the bulk of the world's suffering has been induced by humankind itself. Alienation and violence are easily seen in these terms. Many apparently 'natural' disasters are also man-made, whether the Ethiopian famine resulting from civil war, flooding in Bangladesh resulting from deforestation, or destruction in the Armenian earthquake resulting from jerry-building. We might go on to point out how many of the world's diseases result from poverty, smoking, obesity, alcohol, neglect or sexual immorality.

However, some suffering cannot be explained in these terms. It seems to have to do with the way the world is. For instance, if you step out of a third-floor window you can expect to come crashing down . If you go to sea in a boat with a hole in it, you will probably drown. The world would be in a fine old pickle if the laws of nature were not constant. We rely on the force of gravity and the nature of water. They are part of God's good provision in providing us with such a splendid environment in which to live. It can be used or abused. To live well in this world we need to take due note not only of the moral laws but also of the laws of nature. Living at the foot of an active volcano, or beneath sea level in an area prone to flooding, would be a risky endeavour, and one should be hesitant in blaming God for the resulting tragedy. Viruses and other causes of disease may have no purpose that is evident to us, and thus remain part of life's undisclosed mysteries. How such things relate to the fall, and to what extent they existed before the fall, are areas for speculation.

That we do not know all we would like to know should not surprise us. Our thoughts are not God's thoughts. There is much that we – frail creatures that we are – do not understand. We would like to be like God, knowing all mysteries, but that is patently not the case. A little intellectual humility would not go amiss. Being the impure vessels that we are, we should be hesitant to put the blame on God when we are clearly responsible for so much that is wrong with the world. The Bible does not set out to flatter our intellects and puff up our proud minds. Rather, it is concerned to tell us what we need to know about the mysteries of the universe. It is a practical book giving us enough information to live by, without satisfying our endless, idle curiosity. (If we understood exactly what life was like before the fall, would it alter the way we live?)

God's response

When we have considered our responsibility for the mess that we are in, we need to take the focus back to God and consider his response. The gospel is that God has not sat idly by, laughing at us in our plight. Rather he is portrayed as being deeply moved, to the extent of a most costly rescue mission: 'For God so loved the world that he gave his one and only Son . . .' (Jn. 3:16).

The incarnation of God in Christ is a mystery beyond our grasp, that leaves us basking in wonder. That he should actually come and join us and enter our suffering so profoundly, from his illegitimate birth in an out-house to his death by crucifixion at the hands of an occupying army, is more than we can take in. Here is no distant God who stays uncaringly on the touchlines. Rather his love compels him to suffer for us. Neither is the cross just a statement about God's compassion, though it certainly is that. In ways which defy analysis, it was God's chosen way of handling the conflicting interests of his justice and his mercy. Here on the cross, the justice of God was fulfilled. The judge himself paid the penalty that our wickedness deserved, that we might be forgiven. And final judgment is delayed out of mercy, so that the good news of the gospel might be taken to every corner of the world, and that men and women might be restored to that relationship with God for which we were made and through which all other relationships find their fulfilment. Here the love of God is declared, the offer of forgiveness pronounced and the hope of glory laid bare. In the light of this hope, all our suffering is transformed.

Our part

But that is not all. Those who come to the cross to find God's forgiveness and acceptance are not brought into an inner world of personal fulfilment that removes us from the scene. Rather we are turned round, to face the world's pain and be sent into it to convey the love and compassion of God. We are called not merely to identify with people, empathizing with their predicament. Rather, we are called to exercise compassion, to roll up our sleeves and be their servants. As the Father sent the Son into the world, so we are sent into the world, following his example, taking up our crosses, entering into their pain and being light in a dark place. That is why I suggested that the way we answer this question may say more than the verbal content of our answer. We are ourselves to be caught up with the love of God and be part of the answer to the problem of suffering.

It will not be possible to remove all mysteries. They include 'the secret things' which 'belong to the LORD our God' (Dt. 29:29). However, in answering these questions it should be possible to focus attention on the central themes of the gospel. Many people are pre-occupied in escaping from life's difficulties. The values of Jesus turn everything upside down. It is in dying that we live. It is in giving that we receive. Those who find their lives will lose them, while those who lose their lives for Christ's sake and the gospel's will find life – and find it abundantly.

19 EUTHANASIA

Andrew Fergusson

Definitions

'Euthanasia' comes from the Greek *euthanatos*, which literally translates as 'well death' or 'easy death'. Of course we would all want a good death for ourselves, our loved ones and our patients, but the word 'euthanasia' is most commonly expressed as 'mercy killing'. A more helpful definition is as follows: 'Euthanasia is the intentional killing by act or omission of a person whose life is felt to be not worth living.'

This emphasizes killing. Proponents of euthanasia object to this, but that is what the despatch of the patient is by any dictionary definition. Proponents try to draw an analogy from the difference between rape and love-making, but their emotive example is illogical; the fact in their example is that sexual intercourse has taken place, and the motive does not alter that fact. In euthanasia, the fact is that someone is dead.

The definition emphasizes the moral, ethical and legal concept of 'intent' (or 'motive'). There is a world of difference between a medical act designed to end life, such as a lethal injection, and the abandonment of treatment which is ineffective or inappropriate. One is killing, the other is good medical practice, and the profession and the law have always recognized the difference. It has been summarized as the difference between 'mercy killing' and 'mercy dying'.

The definition confirms that one can kill patients by doing things to them or by not doing things to them. Again, it is the intent that matters. (This definition does away with the unhelpful and unnecessary concepts of active and passive euthanasia, which have simply confused many, including doctors.)

The word 'person' is deliberately used rather than 'patient' because of the very reasonable fear that any permissive legislation would lead to euthanasia being performed on categories of people who would not normally be termed 'patients'. The last part of the definition teases as to who feels the person's life is not worth living. The word 'euthanasia' may be qualified to mean the following:

276

● *Voluntary euthanasia*. The person himself feels his life is not worth living. This is of course the only sort of euthanasia publicly advocated, and much is made of 'persistent and durable' requests. Privately, this would still be the only sort of euthanasia advocated by the majority of proponents, but there are exceptions.[1]

● *Non-voluntary euthanasia* is where the person is not competent to decide for himself, for example, because he is demented.

● *Involuntary euthanasia* is performed when a competent person is not consulted, and is arguably against his real will.

Spiritual considerations

Although an overwhelming case can be made against euthanasia on purely pragmatic grounds (see below), people's presuppositions will influence their thinking. Christians believe that man and woman are made 'in the image of God' (Gn. 1:26–27), that God prohibits killing outside (possibly) judicial situations and in 'just war' (Gn. 9:5–6), that 'you are not your own; you were bought at a price' (1 Cor. 6:19–20), and that, taking the analogy of something we value by what we are prepared to pay for it, 'God so loved the world that he gave his one and only Son, that whoever believes in him shall not perish but have eternal life' (Jn. 3:16). There are of course many other texts illustrating these concepts, and Christians should begin by considering these wonderful truths.

Jews and Muslims have similar absolute prohibitions, although there are obviously significant theological differences. It is not yet clear what influence the increasing New Age (Hindu) concept of reincarnation will have in this area. The secular materialistic humanism which perhaps predominates in our society sees death as the end of everything, and provides the most fertile soil for euthanasia.

Philosophical arguments

There are essentially only two arguments in favour of euthanasia. One is compassion (and we need to ask what the word really means), and the other, which will be considered at length here, is autonomy. This means 'self-determination', and to a limited extent is a concept which Christians can support in that it does recognize the value of each individual human being. However, when autonomy leads to 'my right' drowning out any sense of 'my responsibilities', caution is needed.

A patient might choose to commit suicide, which is no longer (since 1961) unlawful in Britain. (The morality of suicide is debatable, and non-Christians as well as Christians argue against it.) If a patient is prevented by disease from committing suicide, should he not have a 'right' to be killed at his free, informed and repeated request? It seems a powerful case. But the following points can be made against it.

● Exercise of the patient's autonomy infringes the autonomy of the doctor performing euthanasia. It would be argued that if the doctor freely consented, this is no problem. But what happens to the character of the healer?

● Autonomy is about the capacity to make moral choices. A request alone would not be sufficient; the doctor would have to look at the reasons for the request. Can a seriously ill, frightened patient ever be in a position to make a proper moral choice? In the very act which claims to endorse autonomy, would medicine in fact be ignoring it?

● Once it was decided that there were valid reasons for killing people because their quality of life had been estimated and found wanting, and once the law was changed accordingly, a very significant change would have taken place in that a class of people would be created who had lost their right not to have their lives taken from them. This would create a slippery slope in logic which is actually even more significant than the slippery slope in utilitarian practice, which is the one usually mentioned (see below).

Pragmatic and practical points

(It is with these that the debate will be won, but Christians should be inspired by all the above.)

Let us assume there was now legislation permitting euthanasia. In each case, how could society be sure of the following aspects?

● That the right diagnosis had been made. There are plenty of examples of wrong diagnoses from the hospice literature!

● That the right prognosis has been determined. Most doctors become wise enough not to attempt to answer the question, 'How long have I got?' Appropriate care can make a huge difference.

● That this was the right patient. This may seem far-fetched, but every year the defence-society journals recount wrong operations performed, wrong limbs removed, *etc*.

● That the patient was not depressed, *i.e.* suffering a false sense of worthlessness. (The Dutch talk confidently of a 'persistent durable request', but Dr Admiraal is known to have performed euthanasia within three days of the first request.)

● That the patient was not confused, *i.e.* that acute physical illness

278

was rendering the patient unable to make judgments. (There would of course be no autonomy here.)

● That the patient was not demented. Any euthanasia here could not be voluntary.

● That the patient was not suffering a false sense of 'burden'. While not depressed clinically, patients can feel worthless. The very existence of euthanasia legislation would send a strong signal that society deemed some to have life of insufficient value.

● That the patient was not being pressurized by relatives. It is said that 'where there's a will, there's an anxious relative', but even the most caring of relatives could be transmitting messages because of their own sense of pressure.

● That the patient was not being pressurized by other carers. Again, there could be several different motives here.

● That the patient (or attendants) were not being pressurized by a community short of resources.

Many of these points relate to the question: how could euthanasia be policed? The key witness is dead.

Other pragmatic points include the following:

● What about the effect on the doctor?

● What about the effect on the nurses and other professional carers?

● What about the effect on surviving relatives?

● Would a 'slippery slope' in practice occur here as it has in Holland? Official Dutch statistics[2] show that many hundreds if not thousands of cases of euthanasia which are not voluntary take place there. This evidence deserves studying by all CMF members, as it alone ought to prevent the legalizing of euthanasia in the UK.

The positive alternative

This account has attempted to clarify the confusion of language by pointing to a simple and genuine difference between 'killing people' and 'good medical practice'. It was the good medical practice of the (initially Christian) hospice movement which removed the drive for euthanasia in the terminal cancer situation. Good medical practice and adequate resources are needed to care for those dying with AIDS, and for the increasing numbers of the very elderly, more than 75% of whom are in no way demented. Christians are making encouraging initiatives in these areas, but more work is needed. The legalization of euthanasia must be resisted, and we must preach 'You shall not . . .', but we must also teach by example, demonstrating Christ's love for every human being.

20 OTHER ISSUES AT THE END OF LIFE

BEREAVEMENT

George Chalmers

Bereavement is an experience which is common to humanity and which is in the ultimate sense inevitable where any form of relationship is established between people. In different cultures its expression will vary, and the variety of expression may include everything from the silent vigil to the extended wake involving the whole of a community, from the silent tear to the brass band. The behaviour pattern for the bereaved is often quite stylized and established and, while it may not be specifically prescribed in detail, it may none the less be expected. For this and other reasons it may be quite difficult to assess the true feelings of bereaved individuals simply by their behaviour pattern, and these underlying feelings and reactions may take a longer time than might be appreciated to be fully worked out.

Despite this, it may well be considerably less traumatic for the bereaved to accept and follow out such expected behaviour at the appropriate time, rather than to discard it or significantly delay doing so. There is much in the accepted process of grief which becomes constructive and which facilitates the resumption of normal life patterns.

These considerations are not irrelevant to our own day and age in which urban anonymity has eroded the patterns of community, and in which grief has a lesser place as an acceptable emotion. Even in medical practice, there is still too great a tendency to sedate people rather than to permit them the natural expression of their grief. The effect is to establish a dependency upon such preparations, or to delay the person's grieving until others around them have forgotten and no longer give the support which might have been there at the appropriate time, immediately after the death.

What is bereavement?

The word itself is eloquent of its significance. The bereaved is 'bereft'; something or someone important to them has been taken from them. The fundamental emotion is a sense of loss.

One author suggests the analogy of amputation, and there are certainly some important parallels. 'I feel as if I had lost part of myself!' is a common expression in bereavement, and the frequently expressed sense of the deceased person's presence might be considered analogous to the 'phantom limb' of the amputee. I have myself known several amputees who have gone through a recognizable process of grief for the amputated limb, and there is increasing awareness of the same kind of psychological reaction and mechanism in cases of mastectomy for malignant disease. It is recognized that the analogy breaks down when the physiological considerations relating to the phantom limb, for instance, are taken into account, but I believe it is helpful in appreciating the depth of feeling which bereavement represents to many people. It is a situation of trauma, a loss which diminishes the wholeness of the person and something which will make a difference to the way life will be lived from that time forward.

It is essentially a time of adjustment and acceptance and to some extent a time of rehabilitation. If it is unduly abbreviated or prolonged, there may be problems which relate to the extent of adjustment or the continued appropriateness of the patterns of behaviour. The length of time involved will, of course, be an individual matter and in some senses may be lifelong, but a level of adjustment adequate to allow the resumption of normal life and relationships will usually prove possible in a few months to a year. The recurrence of grief, especially at the anniversary of death, or at the anniversary of significant life events such as marriage, is also to be expected, and this may not necessarily indicate any abnormal element in the adjustment.

The extent of grief is usually related to the closeness of the relationship between the deceased and the bereaved. The length of time they have been in relationship, the demands which the relationship may have made, the extent to which death was expected and the appropriateness of death to the age or previous condition of the person may all play a part. For instance the death of a child may be seen as less acceptable than that of a very old person, and the death of someone who has undergone a serious or distressing illness may be seen as a happy release, rather than as a tragedy. All of these factors are readily recognizable in attitudes to death and bereavement, whatever the beliefs or culture of the people concerned. It is my intention in this section to examine the biblical and indeed the Christian view of bereavement, and this will inevitably include some thought about the Christian view of death itself.

Death

The records of the beginnings of human history indicate that even at that early stage man was left in no doubt about the inevitability of his death. 'You must not eat from the tree of knowledge of good and evil, for when you eat of it you will surely die' (Gn. 2:17). Later in the Old Testament we become aware that death is a state or condition with an element, however ill-understood, of continued existence beyond the grave. Several Old Testament writers are quite clear that they see the earthly life of human beings as only part of their existence, in the sense that they are born with a purpose in the predeterminate counsels of God, and that that purpose is not eternally terminated with death. Perhaps the most striking example is in Job's great declaration:

> Oh, that my words were recorded,
>   that they were written on a scroll,
> that they were inscribed with an iron tool on lead,
>   or engraved in rock for ever!
> I know that my Redeemer lives,
>   and that in the end he will stand upon the earth.
> And after my skin has been destroyed,
>   yet in my flesh I will see God.
>
> (Jb. 19:23–26)

David sometimes seems to see death as final. 'What man can live and not see death, or save himself from the power of the grave?' (Ps. 89:48). But he also seems to give some intimation of immortality for the people of God's choice. 'Turn from evil and do good; then you will dwell in the land for ever . . . the just will be protected for ever, but the offspring of the wicked will be cut off' (Ps. 37:27–28). I am not presenting these as proof-texts in any didactic manner, but simply suggesting that they may indicate the sense of immortality which is in fact common to people in many places, cultures and circumstances.

When we move into the New Testament, Jesus himself stresses the reality and certainty of a life hereafter and turns physical death into the portal to a new and fuller life through his own sacrificial death. The Christian hope, then, is quite clear: death has been overcome; hope for the dying and for the bereaved is established in his resurrection, and that hope is established by faith in Jesus Christ and in his finished work of redemption. Much could be written about this as a subject in its own right, but here I should like to take it simply as the basis for our thinking about the Christian view of bereavement.

Notice, first, that Christian hope does not *exclude* physical death. The Lord of life himself passed through physical death. While he changed its nature, making the experience into a means of entering into a new phase of life, he did not remove it from human experience. Inherent in that retention of the physical event is the persistence of *separation, loss* and *bereavement* for those who have not yet passed that way. We may well sing 'Hallelujah!' when we recall that eternal life is entered by means of physical death, but we must not derive from that any notion that bereavement ceases to be part of Christians' experience, or that Christians have neither need nor right to grieve. Christians grieve in the light of the resurrection, but I believe it is wrong to expect them not to grieve at all.

Grief and bereavement

The validity of mourning. While Scripture states unequivocally the hope of the resurrection, it also acknowledges unequivocally the validity of grief. Perhaps the only instance that need be mentioned here is that eloquent two-word verse in John's gospel (Jn. 11:35): 'Jesus wept.' That really says it all.

Jesus knew the power of the resurrection, he knew that he was about to bring that power to bear upon this man's situation, and he knew that Lazarus would step forth from that tomb and be restored to those who were mourning around him. But he still wept, in sympathy with those who mourned, in grief that his friend had had to go this way in the purposes of God, in sorrow that Lazarus' sisters had had to go through the pangs of progressive deterioration and eventual death as they watched him in his terminal illness. Jesus wept for all of these reasons and possibly for others as well, but the significant point is that, like those who grieve in the full knowledge of their loved one's faith and hope in Christ, Jesus wept because he cared deeply and was sad. I believe that establishes the right and indeed the need of any parent, husband, wife, brother or sister, to weep by a graveside and to express a sense of loss.

The hope of the mourners. At the same time, the immediately subsequent raising of Lazarus, and more significantly the resurrection of the Lord Jesus himself, throw light upon that situation which the darkness of grief cannot put out. It injects hope into the situation, and hope is the essence of Christian bereavement.

The specific characteristic of Christian bereavement is not an assumed joyful exuberance, nor a mere stoical acceptance of what cannot be changed. It is a hope which cannot be extinguished, because it is based upon the finished work of Christ.

It is hope of the resurrection (1 Cor. 15); it is hope of reunion (1 Thes. 4:14), and in particular it is hope for the Christian who has died in Christ, and for those who grieve, of union with Christ and of the assumption of his likeness in a way never possible in this life. Should not such a hope, then, banish the expression of grief? Certainly it should modify the desolation of that grief and remove its hopelessness, but does that mean that there is to be no sense of loss or sadness at parting?

If, for some reason, I am seeing my wife off on a journey with a pleasant and attractive outcome expected at the end of it, while I remain at home because of my work, I do not leap around, saying, 'Isn't it great – you are going away, and the people will be so glad to see you, and they will really make you welcome!' No. Normally I should feel a little sad at the parting. It might be only a week or so until we should expect to be together again, but at the time of the parting it can seem a very long time. It is not that I begrudge her the welcome, but I know that I am going to miss her until I can go and join her. I can, at the same time, look forward to that joy and feel sadness at the separation. This Christian in bereavement has a much greater, but rather similar, hope, and equally may feel sad, bereft and lonely for the one whom he may know for certainty to have departed to be with Christ, which is, as Paul reminds us, 'better by far' (Phil. 1:23).

Christian mourning is real and sore, but it is different. If we look again at Scripture, we find the words: 'We do not want you . . . to grieve like the rest of men, who have no hope' (1 Thes. 4:13). The apostle is not so stupid as to write simply, 'We do not want you to grieve'; he realizes that his readers are human, and he points out the difference between the Christian and 'the rest' – hope. In verse 18 Paul says, 'Therefore encourage each other with these words.' If they were not to grieve at all, where would be the need for encouragement for one another? Such strengthening is clearly still necessary, and there is no suggestion that Paul is telling the Thessalonians off for grieving. The currency of faith is hope, and hope removes the sting of death through the power of the resurrection. It replaces death with 'sleep in Christ', but it does not remove the parting, the missing and the longing.

If we find ourselves in the role of the comforter, personal

testimony to the care and love of God and to the hope of eternal life can hardly be inappropriate. But a breezy 'Rejoice in the Lord, you will meet again in glory' type of 'comfort' is usually totally inappropriate, even for the staunchest of believers. It is not the fact or the message that is wrong. It is the timing and the presentation.

In Romans 12:15 we find the sound advice, 'Rejoice with those who rejoice; mourn with those who mourn', and in the book of Proverbs, we are told that 'like one who takes away a garment on a cold day, or like vinegar on soda, is one who sings songs to a heavy heart' (25:20).

Reactions to bereavement

Reaction to bereavement is individual and personal. It is important to bear this in mind when counselling or comforting someone in this experience. In the initial stages some will seem non-reactive, entering a state not dissimilar to clinical shock. Apathetic immobility, inhibition of thought and indecision (often not characteristic of the person), and a feeling of total emptiness and rejection are all quite frequently experienced. Others become restlessly active, concentration and application become difficult and a sense of blame and shame with self-doubt and futile regret are expressed. Yet others may achieve a quiet acceptance and exhibit a strength which has been previously unsuspected.

Some unexpected emotions are not infrequently found in young people who have been bereaved without having thought about the possibility. Panic, simply because they do not know what is expected of them, may be related to the breakdown of the established patterns to which I referred earlier. Guilt is frequently experienced. Guilt about things said or un-said, about things done or undone, and, now that nothing more is possible, about the seeming inadequacy of what was done – all of these may haunt the bereaved in the period immediately after the loved one's death. Many who have been under stress during the final illness are extremely distressed by a sense of guilt related to the relief which they feel now that the burden of caring has been removed. This may be even more acute if, in the heat of the pressure, they have felt or said that they wished the end would come. Someone who has even thought this way can feel that, in some way, their wish has been responsible for the outcome.

Resentment may seem to predominate. A caring relative resents those who have given less care. One who has been unable to make a valid contribution may resent those who have done so, thus handling a sense of guilt by transferring it to someone else. From time to time one also meets resentment of the person who has died, for going away and leaving so many problems to be dealt with. Bitterness and accusation are frequently directed towards others where there is a sense of guilt, and this often lies behind the highly emotionally charged complaints lodged with hospitals or homes after the death of a patient or resident.

Our own reactions

It is easy to resent these reactions, especially if we are the target of the more negative ones. But it is important to remember that bereaved people, especially those with no Christian hope, are not being rational at such a time and that they are reacting in a way which is quite different from their normal patterns, and even alien to them as they later look back on it. Perhaps the best advice here is to recall that 'a soft answer turns away wrath', otherwise such people may become confirmed in their disaffection.

Unexpected reactions

Sometimes one finds a bereaved relative who appears to have no sensation of grief, yet on closer knowledge of the situation it turns out that the person has done his or her grieving already, before the death occurred. In Scripture we have an example of this in the story of the child conceived in David's adulterous union with Bathsheba (2 Sa. 11–12). David mourns and grieves for the child and for his sin until the actual death of his son is reported to him. Then, we are told, 'David got up from the ground. After he had washed, put on lotions and changed his clothes, he went into the house of the LORD and worshipped. Then he went to his own house, and at his request they served him food, and he ate' (12:20). David's mourning was complete; he was ready to face the business of living again.

'A woman whose husband had died said to me: 'I cannot grieve for him now. My grieving was all done seven years ago when he had his stroke, lost his speech and changed his whole character. I lost my husband then and I have no grief left – only relief, because it was out of duty that I looked after what was left.' This was said, not in bitterness, but in a context of warm appreciation of the man he had been before that catastrophic event.

Some will grieve for too long, moving from the acceptable place of understandable mourning into the hinterland of depressive illness. Queen Victoria entered a state of prolonged and depressive mourning for her beloved Albert until her ministers found it essential to recall her very firmly to her public duty. David, too – a man who really did have his share of the experience of bereavement – had to be sharply reminded that his inconsolable grief for Absalom, the son who had been seeking his own very life, might well be undermining his people's morale and hindering the work of God (2 Sa. 19:1–7).

Yet others may seem to grieve too little at the right time (a situation which may well be brought on by the use of inappropriate and excessive medication with tranquillizers and sedatives for the bereaved), only to break down later under an apparently minor loss. 'To see the way she is going on about that cat's death you would think she thought more of it than she did of her husband, who passed on only six months ago.' Such a critical comment may express a total misunderstanding of delayed and transferred grief. She grieved for her husband all right, but put such a brave face on it that she had used up all her reserves of courage, and the death of poor pussy was the last straw that broke her.

Caring in bereavement

Under the stress of bereavement, people react in ways which vary according to their resilience, their personalities, their background, their faith, their doubts, their emotions and their self-respect. This is a time at which we need the grace to accept them as they are, warts and all, and to seek to bring them into contact with the healing grace of the Lord Jesus, to whom their hearts and their needs are known far better than to us. We will usually achieve this better by caring than by preaching, by listening rather than by speaking, and often by being there rather than by anything we do. There is often opportunity for prayer, the offer of which is more acceptable than we might think, even to people whose church connection is quite tenuous, and we should never venture into such a sensitive relationship without praying ourselves, however silently and briefly. Prayer is a comfort in itself to the bereaved, but simplicity rather than theological comprehensiveness should be the watchword.

The Word of God is often of much more help than our own merely human expressions of sympathy, and again simplicity is desirable, using familiar, preferably short, passages from a version to which the bereaved person can relate. Thus I would tend to use the Authorized Version with an older person who had been brought up on it, rather than a more modern translation.

From time to time all these things, including our mere presence, may be totally rejected. In that case a readiness to withdraw without offence may be a means of grace as well as an evidence of grace, and may open the door to further contact at a later opportunity.

Paradoxically, bereavement can become a time of blessing, sore though the experience may be. Some people are more open to the grace of God at such a time than at any other, and there is ample justification for prayer to this end, that they might seek eternal comfort in Christ rather than in human relationship.

The Lord has a very special care for the bereaved. The widow and the fatherless are repeatedly commended to the care of the people of Israel and to the church, and it is no empty phrase which we find embedded in the Lord's teaching: 'Blessed are those who mourn, for they will be comforted' (Mt. 5:4).

CHRISTIAN CARE IN THE HOSPICE

Dame Cicely Saunders

The word 'hospice' comes from a Latin root meaning 'host and guest' and from Roman times was applied to places that gave hospitality to pilgrims. Soon there were many such hospices, and, while much of their work was in welcoming travellers who were fit enough to continue their journey, the sick, wounded and dying were also cared for and stayed as long as they needed help. Their work was founded on two texts in Matthew's gospel; the first, the command to feed the hungry and thirsty, welcome strangers, clothe the naked, visit the sick and the prisoners; the second, the statement that 'whatever you did for one of the least of these my brothers of mine, you did it for me' (Mt. 25:35–36, 40).

To these six commands, a seventh, to bury the dead, was absorbed in the thirteenth century from a passage in *Tobit* (2:7). For a thousand years, Christian charitable institutions carried the burden of needy travellers and also of the sick and the poor. In the UK this service disappeared abruptly with the dissolution of the monasteries, causing great distress. There is a petition from the Lord Mayor and the citizens of London to Henry VIII, asking him to refound the priories of St Bartholomew and St Thomas, 'for the ayde and comfort of the poore, sikke, blynde, aged and impotent persones, beying not able to helpe themselffs, nor hauyning any place certeyn whereyn they may be lodged, cherysshed and refresshed.'

From then on the word 'hospice' appears less and less as gradually the new hospitals were founded, often with much Christian concern but no longer as specific church foundations. Apart from the dreaded Poor Law or equivalent institutions, care for dying patients seems to have largely disappeared.

The word 'hospice' was taken in 1842 by Mme Geanne Garner when she opened homes for patients dying of cancer in France. Mother Mary Aikenhead (who founded the Irish Sisters of Charity in the mid-nineteenth century) used the same word when she opened Our Lady's Hospice at Harold's Cross, Dublin, in 1879 especially for dying patients, although she included some long-stay patients. In 1905 St Joseph's Hospice was opened in Hackney by the same Sisters after they had been visiting in the poverty-stricken homes around there for several years. By then, other foundations, also with a Christian basis, had started similar work among patients dying of cancer and tuberculosis, although under different names.

Similar foundations were opened in the USA and in Australia. These early homes continued their work through the twentieth century, but when the survey *Peace at the Last* was carried out by Brigadier Glyn Hughes and published in 1960,[1] he reported that while their care was enormously dedicated and loving it was often hampered by lack of money, staff and accommodation. Care for dying patients in general wards and in their own homes was shown, in this and in other surveys of that time,[2] with few exceptions to be very inadequate.

I knew little of all this in 1948 when the first ideas of somewhere to help those with advanced cancer began to come together. I knew only of the patients I had met myself. St Christopher's received its founding gift when David Tasma, originally from the Warsaw ghetto, left me £500, saying, 'I'll be a window in your home', and the idea of openness of all kinds is built into the life of and work of the hospice. Another of his phrases also forms part of our foundation: 'I only want what is in your mind and in your heart.' As I thought of this later, I saw this phrase as a commission to bring to our patients all we could of the skill and understanding of the mind together with the friendship and caring of the heart.

Training

The years of preparation and training began. It started with experience as a volunteer nurse in St Luke's Hospital, and the experience of seeing that much better pain control could be achieved than I had seen in general wards. The regular giving of morphine by mouth had already been established there for over ten years, using the mixture first developed at the Brompton Chest Hospital and named the 'Brompton Cocktail'. I also had my first experience of working in an ecumenical Christian foundation, for 'St Luke's Home for the Dying Poor' had been founded in 1893 by the Methodist, Dr Howard Barrett, whose caring and lively spirit still seemed to fill the atmosphere.

By 1951 the surgeon with whom I was working had visited several patients with me, and when I told him I had to return somehow to nursing these patients, he firmly told me to go and read medicine. 'There is so much more to be learnt about pain and you'll only be frustrated if you don't do it properly.' So medicine it had to be. As I finished my training I was soon able to follow up an earlier contact with St Joseph's Hospice. In October 1958 began my busy and happy seven years with the nuns there, introducing and developing the regular giving of opiate drugs by mouth (in a modified Brompton Cocktail) and gradually introducing the new drugs that had been discovered during the 1950s – tranquillizers, anxiolytics, antidepressants, synthetic steroids and non-steroidal anti-inflammatory drugs. We did not test new drugs for pain and symptom control, but we exploited what was generally available to their better potential. At the same time I was able to look at the various aspects of 'total pain', with its physical, emotional, social and spiritual components, at the needs of families both to be cared for and caring, and at the possibilities for home care and better communication and therefore more control by the patients themselves.

So the hospice experience and the developing knowledge in this new field came together in the opening of St Christopher's as the first research and teaching hospice in 1967, with its beds integrated into the local National Health Service hospital and community care, and its home care and family support programmes.

Hospice development

St Christopher's has seen many initiatives stemming from this basis. There are now home care and hospital teams, and palliative or continuing care wards or units within the NHS, as well as free-standing independent hospices. The NHS gives some revenue to a few of these, but many, like St Christopher's, depend a great deal upon their local public support. Many of the founders and original members of all these groups came first to learn at St Christopher's, and we are delighted to maintain close contact with them and to see members of our staff go to work with them as they develop hospice knowledge in their own settings. The main increase occurred after 1975 when the first pioneers from the UK, USA, and Canada went out from experience at St Christopher's. Now there are some 97 units, over 100 home care teams and 20 hospital teams in the UK, and an unknown number of hospice units and teams around the world. The number is always growing.

The aims remain the same and the story goes on. Hospice, giving skilled hospitality to pilgrims, is itself a pilgrim. Just as the first ideas came from one lonely man and grew through the years as other people brought their need and their achievement of the foundation and planning, so we believe it will continue as each team interprets the basic principles.

Maximizing potential

Patients should be enabled to live until they die, at their own maximum potential, performing to the limit of their physical activity, mental capacity and social relationships, with control and independence wherever possible.

This demands full consideration both of the nature of their suffering and of the appropriateness of various possible treatments and settings in their particular circumstances. Alertness to any remission of disease should accompany the effective control of all the manifestations of an inexorable advance. Even in the terminal stages of disease, it can be true that there is a potential for new achievements or the resolution of longstanding problems.

Place of choice

Patients should end their lives in the place most appropriate to them and their families, and where possible have choices in the matter. This does not necessarily mean total 'open awareness' on the part of the patient, but some insight into the serious nature of the condition will help facilitate realistic decisions.

For many, the choice will be their own homes, for others the hospital with the staff who have carried out previous treatments, while some will need the smaller community of the separate hospice unit. These act as a *complementary* local service for particularly complex physical and social situations.

The patient and the family as the unit of care

Help may be needed to deal with guilt, depression and family discord. Emotions are intensified, and although they may seem irrational there is also the possibility of resolving old problems and finding reconciliations that greatly strengthen the family group.

If time is to be fully used, there needs to be some degree of shared awareness of the true situation. Truth needs to be available (though not pressured) so that the family can travel together. In general, sharing is more creative than deception. The often surprising potential for personal and family growth at this stage is one of the strongest objections most hospice workers feel to the legalization of a deliberately hastened death.

Bereavement follow-up

The family has to recover. A bereavement follow-up service will identify and support those in special need, working in cooperation with the family doctor and any local services which can be involved. Many doctors give such support as part of their service to the families they have known over the years. Some of the bereaved are not so fortunate, and some extra follow-up may be needed to ease the tragedy and long morbidity of some bereavements.

Competent symptom control

The patient and his family will not use the time left to them unless there is good control of pain and all the other symptoms that may arise. All doctors and nurses should be aware of the developments of these skills, and special units have a responsibility to initiate research and disseminate such knowledge. Once good symptom control is achieved it is then easier to become aware of the mental, social and spiritual aspects of each family crisis.

An experienced clinical team

The team or unit for terminal care must carry out its practice in such a way as to earn the respect and cooperation of the doctors who refer their patients. Both there and where the patient remains under his usual clinicians, a multidisciplinary medical approach is as important in the later stages of cancer management as in the earlier phases of the disease.

Supportive team nursing

The definition by Henderson and Nite describes the following unique function of nurses:

> To help people, sick or well, in the performance of those activities contributing to health or its recovery (or to a peaceful death) that they would perform unaided if they had the necessary strength, will or knowledge. It is likewise the function of nurses to help people gain independence as rapidly as possible.[3]

The character of the nursing of dying patients illustrates this definition particularly well, and we find it best carried out on a team basis. Nurses are closest to the impact of family grief and need to share the pressure.

An inter-professional team

These patients may need an inter-professional team approach. These teams are to be found in many specialized units – for example, intensive care and renal dialysis. They are particularly needed by those who are grappling with emotional as well as with practical demands. Psychiatrists and social workers have frequently been involved as support. Volunteers may have an important role both within an institution and at home, but must receive sensitive selection, training and support.

A home care programme

Any programme or plan for home care must be developed according to local circumstances and be integrated with the family practices of the area and any local beds that may be available. Skilled support and confidence in their potential may enable a family to keep a patient at home, often confounding all predictions.

Methodical recording and analysis

Effective recording makes possible the evaluation and monitoring of clinical experience and the establishment of soundly based practice. This is a challenge to those who feel that 'tender loving care' is all that is needed. Nothing can take its place, but terminal care in the 1990s is developed from and should not now be the same as, that in the 1890s or even the 1960s. 'Efficient loving care' is our aim, and every resource of clinical and social medicine has to be exploited.

Teaching in all aspects of terminal care

Though much of the future development must be more closely integrated with general teaching centres, the special units are likely to maintain their role of stimulating initial interest and organizing seminars and courses for those who will in their turn be concentrating in this field, for those in general medical practice and indeed for many of the public. This is no longer a discipline in which no past special experience need be required, but there is much that can be shared with those in related fields.

Supportive administration

Efficiency is very comforting, and competence in administrative detail gives security to patients, families and staff. It eases the liaison with outside contacts that is so essential for the small, specialized unit or team, and supports those who are managing such work among other pressures. This is particularly true for the sometimes isolated home care nurse.

The search for meaning

Many patients wrestle with feelings of failure and worthlessness, of longings to reach out to what is seen as true yet far distant, and with bewilderment or fear at the mystery of death. There may be a great need to be assured of acceptance and forgiveness, and here the authority of a minister or priest may be needed. But any member of staff may be asked that poignant question, 'Why should this happen to me – or to the one I love?' Here there is a greater need to be able to stay listening with little or nothing to say than to come forward with any attempt at explanation.

Such work will at times cause pain and bewilderment to all members of staff. If they do not have the opportunity to share their strain and their own questions, they are likely to leave this field or find a method of hiding behind a professional mask. We have to find some way of sharing the pains of parting and the often desperate anguish of family members and of supporting each other.

Hospice care is carried out under many names, and palliative or continuing care, support and Macmillan units and teams all face these demands. Not all claim the early Christian hospice commitment, though many include staff with this vocation. Those of us who try to follow this calling believe we are serving and working alongside the God who said, 'I was sick, I was in prison, I was dying.' He shares our questions and the suffering; this is still his place. At one of St Christopher's conferences, Bishop John V. Taylor asked: 'I wonder when the Church will dare to believe in the paradoxical power of helplessness and in the strange success of offering one's failure to others. It is there in the final truth of the cross of Christ, and does not answer our questions but stills them.'[4] Those of us whose hospice work is part of a continuing spiritual journey throughout our lives find it a place where our living Lord is continually present to 'make all things new'.

CARING FOR THE DYING

Derek Macallan

Dealing with dying patients and their relatives is one of the most demanding aspects of medical care. It highlights the frailty of human life and the inevitability of our own passing. The way we, as doctors, cope with this situation is primarily determined by the way we, as people, cope with the fact of our own demise: we like to think we have 'security of tenure' on the contract of life, but we do not. If we are to be honest with our patients, as I believe we must, we must first be honest with ourselves.

The problem is this. Within the humanist philosophy, now so widely prevalent, there is found no peace in death and no hope beyond death. As a consequence, many doctors find it difficult to accept the mortality of their own patients, and tend to fall into the slap-on-the-back 'It'll be all right' mould or else into a gentler, more subtle manner of providing falsely based reassurance. What a contrast is found in the Christian gospel: a purpose for living, a prospect of peace and comfort in death, a hope of eternal life beyond death! As Christians, therefore, because we can come to terms with our own mortality, we are enabled to help others cope with their own imminent death or that of a loved one. To be fair, there are many non-Christian 'humanist' doctors who have come to terms with their own mortality and who do have a valuable ministry in this sphere, and conversely there are some Christians who still cling to a worldly perspective on life and become ineffectual ministers as a consequence.

Honesty

Honesty must be the hallmark of our practice of medicine. Honesty with ourselves is the beginning; honesty with our patients is its consequence. To be dishonest is not only wrong before God but implies that we somehow 'know better' or are exempt from the frailty of the human condition. By 'honesty', I do not simply mean 'telling all', which in some situations leaves the patient hopeless and helpless. What I do mean is telling enough to give a realistic appraisal of the situation, and that everything that *is* said must be true.

Bad news

Bad news must be communicated gently and sensitively, sometimes repeatedly and sometimes in stages over a period of time. Patients and their families frequently give verbal or non-verbal cues indicating how much they wish to know. One such phrase is, 'You're the doctor, you do whatever you think best.' I have heard this used several times to terminate a discussion on prognosis or management. It is insensitive and disrespectful to plough on with unwanted information through signals like this. However, it is usually still possible to communicate a few truths about what is happening with carefully chosen words. This is important, because ignorance breeds fear and the imagination runs wild.

I recall two referrals within the same week to the radiotherapy ward where I worked. One lady had a spinal tumour causing a paraplegia; it was relatively low grade and she probably had several months, possibly a year or two, of useful, if severely disabled, life. Her diagnosis had been discussed with her, but her understanding of what she had been told was that she had an incurable cancer and would be dead within a week or two. The other referral, for post-operative radiotherapy, was a middle-aged man. He had a cerebral tumour that had been excised and shown, on histology, to be a secondary carcinoma. He thought he had been cured. These two cases, to me, highlighted the importance of honest information. Both these patients had unrealistic conceptions of their disease; one grossly pessimistic, the other over-optimistic. We were able to reassure the lady and gently had to introduce to the man the concept of palliation as opposed to cure. Some might have left him to carry on in blissful ignorance until further problems developed, but personally I think that such an approach would have been wrong.

Information packaging

The way we package information is vitally important: it is better to communicate an understanding of the situation than to concentrate on medical facts. The words we choose must be designed to do this. Information must be intelligible: some folk have a very limited understanding of human biology, and we can falsely assume words to be meaningful or understood in a specific way when they are not. It is a revealing and helpful practice to ask the patient or relative, 'What do you understand by what I have just told you?'

'Information by instalments' is a useful technique and one to which medicine easily lends itself: for example, a radiological 'shadow on the lung' can become 'a small lump' on bronchoscopy and 'a tumour' on subsequent histology. In this way bad news can be broken over several days. There are, however, no hard and fast rules, and it may be more appropriate to come straight to the point and say at the outset, 'Your X-ray looks as if you may have a lung tumour', explaining what this means and thus dispelling anxiety based on ignorance.

The positive aspects must be stressed as much as possible: relief of pain, control of breathlessness, possible palliative measures, maintenance of dignity, and so on, should be highlighted, though not to the extent of unrealism, for when the promises fail to come true, confidence will be lost.

Family dynamics

Whom to tell first? Every situation is different, but I have often found it helpful to discuss things with the patient early on, either with his family, or on his own before his family have been spoken to. This avoids the question, 'What shall we tell him?' but does risk there being an 'unsupported interval' when the patient knows his diagnosis but his family are not yet there to support him; they must be involved as soon as possible.

It is important to know something of how the family relate to one another; bad news draws some families together, but in others widens pre-existing rifts or sharpens longstanding bitterness. Obviously the closest relatives must be spoken to first but it is not always clear who is closest! Appointing a family spokesman saves time, friction and confusion; it avoids repeating the same phrases fifteen times to fifteen different relatives and ending up with (more than) fifteen different interpretations. Having spoken to a family member, I personally like to go back with that relative to the bedside or wherever and summarize what has just been said, even if couching it in different words or with a less bleak 'colouring'. 'I've just been having a chat with your wife and explained about the . . .' This creates an atmosphere of openness and honesty and pre-empts the question, 'What did they tell you?'

Demanding relatives

As a junior doctor, one rapidly learns how demanding relatives can be. Inevitably, they arrive at 7 or 8pm on one's night off and, quite reasonably, expect an explanation of events while the doctor, quite reasonably, wants to go home. For the doctor it is probably one of many such patients; for them it is a loved one in a unique situation. I am afraid one has to be forbearing and look at things from their point of view, though there are a few short cuts, some of which I have already mentioned. Haste is probably not one of them.

First, try to deal with the family together; appoint a family spokesman if possible, or see them all at once. Secondly, make an appointment to see them at a mutually convenient time of day when distractions are likely to be at a minimum. Thirdly, be ready to refer on to your senior colleagues, and avoid duplication if they have already spoken to the family or arranged an appointment to speak to them. Be very careful not to disagree openly with colleagues or criticize them by what you say, even if you think they are wrong. Avoid committing yourself on facts of which you are unsure, and be ready to admit your ignorance. Do not be drawn into predicting when someone may die. I remember a friend of mine who told a family their father had two months to live: he died that same night. On the other hand it is possible to give loose guidelines: 'He would be lucky to be here at Christmas' or 'I think the end may be very near.'

Finally, remember to ask yourself what is really being asked for behind the question. We need to pray for spiritual insight to enable us to see beyond the outward question. Is it denial that provokes this repeated questioning, or a desire for reassurance? Is it difficulty accepting the truth or a misunderstanding over what they have been told? Our answers should be chosen to meet the need where possible, rather than the question.

Expression of grief

Grief expresses itself in many ways. Sorrow is obvious – we should be ready to 'mourn with those who mourn'. Denial is not uncommon, and may require repeated and patient discussion. Anger is the reaction doctors are least prepared for, especially when it is directed towards medical or nursing staff. It may be an expression of guilt on the part of the relative for past actions. This may be difficult to handle, but criticisms are probably best answered with patient explanation, and argument should be avoided at all costs.

Often the doctor is not involved after the death, but it is worth the effort to say something. A very simple expression of commiseration is usually all that is appropriate.

Spiritual opportunities

I have not so far specifically mentioned the 'Christian' input in all this. Christian love must be *implicit* in all our actions and attitudes; we must behave with the same love and grace that characterized Christ's ministry. But what opportunity is there for *explicit* expressions of Christian love? To me, this is the most difficult aspect of all. For Christians, although the sorrow of parting is no less grievous, we are able to rejoice in the knowledge of Jesus' promises that he has gone ahead 'to prepare a place' for us (Jn. 14:3), and that death is not simply the end of this existence but the gateway into the next. In this situation we can reassure the patient and his family by letting them know we share their faith, by words of support and encouragement, and possibly by praying with them, if appropriate.

How explicit can we be in dealing with those we do not share our faith? If we believe the teaching of Jesus, we must believe in a doctrine of eternal separation from God, or hell, though we can be sure that God does not wish any to perish in this way. How then do we apply this at the bedside? There are no hard and fast rules for this situation. Each of us must work this out thoughtfully and prayerfully with due regard to both our own personality and the patient's situation. It may indeed be that, at the last, we have an opportunity to lead someone to Christ, but such a death-bed conversion has never yet been my own experience.

As healthcare professionals we tend to shirk such a spiritual role, and rightly so, for we must not abuse our position as doctors. However, I sometimes wonder if we use this as an excuse for non-involvement in spiritual matters; I doubt whether God is quite as concerned as we are with professional labels. Certainly, it may be more appropriate for us to confine ourselves to the medical care of the patient and to suggest the involvement of the chaplain to deal with the spiritual aspects that arise; this option should not be forgotten. It is worth getting to know who the chaplain is before the need arises.

In terms of the family, the same considerations broadly apply. Often opportunities for spiritual discussion do not arise, because the wounds of loss or potential loss are so fresh as to be too painful.

Conclusion

Caring for dying patients highlights our own mortality. We are no less human than our patients, and we need to ask ourselves whether we are ready to meet God were we to die. Those who trust in Christ can be sure that he has paid the penalty for our wrongs and that we shall be able to appear blameless before God, not because of any righteousness of our own but because of what Jesus did for us. Recognition of our own mortality should make us humble and sensitive in the way we handle patients and their families. We must at all times be utterly honest, we must not abuse our professional position, and yet we must not forget our higher calling to be ambassadors for Christ, always ready to give a reason for the hope within us.

GROWING OLD

George Chalmers

Most people are becoming aware of the changes which have been taking place over the past fifty to eighty years in the structure of the population of the UK and other western nations. Falling birth rates have been reducing school rolls and causing some employers to wonder where tomorrow's work force is to come from, while extending expectation of life has increased the numbers of the older and more dependent members of the community. In the next thirty years we can expect to see the number of people aged over 65 increase by 1 million from the present 8.8 million, and the over-85s may be expected to double.

Not all of these, of course, will be dependent older people. The majority will be reasonably fit and active, making relatively little demand upon healthcare and social services, and, to an increasing extent, the main problem will be the care of the frail and disabled very elderly falling upon the younger and fitter elderly. These more recently retired people may well prove to be a resource, rather than a liability, and, with second employment or extension of the first, may help retain the skill base within commerce and industry, as well as in the caring sector.

The liability implied in an ageing population is a real one, however, since disability is undeniably more frequent in an older population. At present, 40% of National Health Service expenditure and 50% of personal Social Services expenditure is taken up by people aged 65 or over. Whether we see these developments as a problem or as a challenge is perhaps a matter of point of view or even of personality, but, to the Christian, both in spiritual and in social terms, there must be an element of challenge.

Challenge to society as a whole

What does caring for the elderly mean in the 1990s? I attended a conference some time ago entitled 'Meeting the Challenge in Scotland', to which personnel from politics, Health Boards, social work, medicine and other areas of healthcare had been brought together with the representatives of the private nursing home and residential care 'industry'. We discussed the maintenance of standards, the criteria for registration, the auditing of care by means of outcome indicators, and all the current jargon was on parade to reassure us of the high ethical ground of the private care providers. It became very clear, however, that the challenge of an ageing population, to some people in the caring industry, involves an increasing awareness of the elderly as a consumer group and, to some politicians, their potential as a voting group seems also to be dawning.

Only a few days later, listening to the radio as I travelled between hospitals, I heard of two instances of social workers in the Norfolk area who were offered cash inducements of around £200 in notes for each client whom they successfully recommended to specific private old people's homes. The social workers concerned reported the matter, but such pressure puts a very great strain upon the professionalism of any group. We are manifestly in the world of market forces, and it becomes clear that, to some people, the challenge of an ageing population is a commercial one, with profit as the 'bottom line'.

Age-care organizations on a charitable and voluntary basis and, to some extent, the NHS, may find it difficult to compete with such commercial pressure, and in some areas the commercial motive is being strongly introduced into the Health Service itself.

Christian compassion and caring may still have a place in our current society's plans to meet this challenge, but others have plans to cash in, and we should be aware that altruism may feature well down in their list of priorities. I believe that most people want to see a system of care for older people which transcends the merely commercial, and I think they would prefer to see this integrated and regulated from within the local authority and health service structure currently engaged in this area, through which the major advances in the field have been mediated.

Challenge to the profession

We owe a duty of care to these older people, whether personally or professionally, and, as far as we individually are concerned, they constitute the challenge to care.

When geriatric medicine began, the early pioneers insisted upon an adequate level of attention to the diagnostic, therapeutic and rehabilitative needs of the elderly ill and disabled, and brought about the revolution in the concepts of care for the elderly which we have witnessed in the past forty years. NHS and social work legislation very rightly lays emphasis upon local responsibility, with local authorities taking on an even greater caring role. General practitioners in the changed contract are required to make specific provision for the review of older patients and, at this level, healthcare provisions have a high profile.

The real future response to the clinical challenge of an ageing population in these and other respects may depend, very largely, upon the direction in which the NHS is being taken at the present time. It has been suggested that the NHS is being progressively replaced by a series of local health services, losing, perhaps, in the process, the degree of integration which currently exists.

Many have expressed legitimate concern over the extent to which decision-making in the NHS is becoming increasingly economically and fiscally, rather than clinically, orientated. Clinical audit, the system by which we seek to determine the effectiveness and cost-effectiveness of what we do, should present no threat to the Christian, to whom the concept of stewardship should be biblically familiar. But there is an increasing anxiety about the kind of financial audit which places the emphasis upon the saving of money, it almost seems, at any cost. We already hear murmurings about the problem of those who are 'an intractable burden upon the economy', and with the concept of rationing healthcare on this side of the Atlantic, there is real pressure towards solutions which might not involve continuing support and care.

The debate on euthanasia continues here and in other countries, while in Holland doctors are not only freely admitting to killing patients, but are writing papers about the matter, and seeking to encourage others to do likewise. At the recent 8th World Conference of the World Federation of the Right to Die Societies, Dr Peter Admiraal, who has practised euthanasia in the major cancer hospital unit at the Reiner de Graaf Hospital in Delft, stated that he had never previously campaigned for a change in the law to permit euthanasia, but that he had now changed his mind. When asked why, he gave this reply. 'The circumstances we have today, described by Josephus Jitta, will soon spread to all districts in Holland, so I thought I could live without a change in legislation but after talking to Jitta, I realize it is not so. *Euthanasia must be legalized because there is more work to do. We are speaking about the handicapped newborn, we are speaking about coma patients . . .'*

Clearly, these people to whom he refers are considered to have lives which are not worth living, and are most likely to become the targets for the euthanasiasts over the next few years. In the context of an ageing population, many of the candidates for such measures would be older people, with the exception of the HIV population and a relatively small number of sufferers from progressive genetic or neurological disorders.

Abortion has been accepted already as our society's way of handling the problem of unwanted children, and is openly and specifically recommended by doctors for those with the risk of congenital defect, let alone the condition itself. Human life already has been devalued in the interests of expediency. Why? Because the leaders of church, profession and nation did not keep faith with the unborn in the 1960s. We should not delude ourselves; our 'compassionate society' could find it equally acceptable to kill the dying and the deteriorating, as a cheaper alternative to proper support and care. All we may need to do for the same to happen again is to do what was done last time. Keep quiet!

We are also hearing the call for introduction of 'living will' legislation, a concept which, on superficial examination, may seem to have some commendable points. The patient is given the initiative in determining the extent to which intervention might be made in the terminal phase of life, and the doctor may also have a clearer idea of the attitudes and values obtaining in the specific case. There might be, indeed, a place for the opportunity to express the desire *not* to be prematurely 'terminated' in such a manner, especially if the concept of voluntary euthanasia did gain acceptance.

The potential for error and abuse, as well as the restriction of clinical judgment at a time when such judgment is essential, however, should give us pause. If such a possible easy way out were available to many doctors, more demanding symptomatic and supportive care might well seem less attractive.

All of these issues should stimulate us to consider whether the current climate of political and social change may be one which in itself constitutes a challenge to our integrity as Christians. I would suggest that, while doctors will increasingly face a clinical challenge in the detection, diagnosis, treatment and rehabilitation of older people, and in managing their physical problems in accordance with the best practice of the present time, we may also be called upon, increasingly, to defend the Christian principles of disinterested service and compassion upon which our opportunity, motivation and ability to give such care are based, and upon which the medical and other caring professions were founded.

If we are to respond to this challenge, we require to look further than the immediate, to catch the vision of service beyond ourselves, and, by our own involvement and commitment, to ensure that standards of clinical care are not eroded. James reminds us that 'faith without deeds is dead' (Jas. 2:17). We require to maintain a concept of the intrinsic value of the old as people, and of the inherent value of their lives. Essentially, this is a spiritual issue. If we take our values from God, we must conceive of individuals at any age as being in the image of God. Contemporary society encourages a view of life which plays down God's sovereignty, diminishes the significance of human relationships, and would negate the need for life-affirming answers for people in need and in distress.

Challenge to the family

An increasing number of families have an elderly person living with them or dependent upon them. In many cases the older person is fit and well and plays an active role in the family, fulfilling and fulfilled. It is probably better, in most cases, if the older person lives near, rather than with the younger family, but both arrangements can work very well.

If and when the older person's dependency increases, however, the couple in middle life become sandwiched between the demands of the very young and of the old, and the wife in particular carries a considerable load which is often little appreciated or understood. In addition, in a Christian context, it is sometimes difficult for such a carer to express the problems, or even to ask for help, because it is so often perceived as an expression of failure of Christian responsibility to parents if we do not bear it gladly without complaint. To arrange hospital admission or residential care, no matter how necessary these may have become, generates a quite disproportionate sense of guilt and, let it be said, ill-informed and sometimes cruel criticism. Those who are involved in this kind of demanding care will readily recognize these feelings and opinions, and those who are not should be very careful before expressing an opinion, particularly a critical opinion.

Not infrequently, I find that one of the most helpful things the doctor can do for the carer is to accept full responsibility for the decision to pass the burden of care to someone else, saying, in essence, 'You are not "putting her away"; I am telling you that she must come into hospital, and that is my decision, not yours.' I sometimes even use the shortage of places as a reassurance: 'I wouldn't take her if it wasn't essential.'

Already, as I have suggested, the younger, fitter elderly are shouldering the burden of care for the older and more dependent, and as the population changes progress, they may be required to do so increasingly. With the increase in the very aged, even may retired couples are still looking after a parent at a time of life when they might have expected a diminution in their responsibility for others. Professionally, personally and as part of the church, we need to recognize the enormous personal cost of this and to see the relief of carers in such a situation as part of our responsibility, not only, perhaps, to shoulder part of the load ourselves, by personal involvement in care, but also by ensuring that the means of relief is properly organized, made available and delivered, whether by statutory or local authority bodies or on a voluntary basis.

The advances in child health and child care of the late 1920s and 1930s did not happen accidentally. Antenatal care did not simply get better because it was accepted as a vaguely 'good thing'. These services were planned, organized and delivered as part of an overall determination to find the problems and provide a solution, and we require to apply the same principle to age care, rather than letting it 'just happen'. A family with an older person increasingly dependent upon it is a family under pressure, and, indeed, a family at risk. As such, it ought to constitute a specific challenge to caring on the part of society, church and individuals.

Challenge to the church

The church, in the formal sense, tends to be a youth-orientated organization with a large number of old people in it. Outreach, evangelism, service and challenge are directed at the young, while support, caring and entertainment are seen as appropriate for the old. Pastors and ministers are often as discouraged by too elderly a congregation, just as they are excited at the challenge of a 'young church'. In the church, however (*i.e.* the Christian community, not the organization) are we meeting the real challenge? There are many old people about with just as great a spiritual need as any other, but still quite unreached by the message of God's forgiveness and grace.

In respect of the elderly in society, is the church (and are we) perceiving and meeting real needs? Or are we simply meeting *our* own perception of their needs, viewing 'the elderly' as a homogeneous group rather than seeing each one as an individual with personal life and value, as well as needs? One of the most fundamental of human needs is to be needed, wanted and significant, to have a place and a role in our own context, and this is something which even the church may be denying to the old. The old are so often perceived as the people for whom, rather than by whom or with whom, things should be done, and our approach is very often to seek to entertain rather than to challenge or in any sense to evangelize. In our day and age this may well be meeting the wrong challenge.

Comforting, pious ideas – the denial of death, bland universalism and empty reassurance – are of little help when an old person becomes aware that time is running out and eternity getting nearer. We so often offer patronizing help for which 'they' should be grateful. We may even be trying to satisfy our own consciences rather than others' needs. I would ask again: are we meeting real spiritual needs in terms of challenge to faith, presentation of the gospel, Christian compassion and involvement and expectation? Physical rehabilitation is about 'fulfilling and improving expectation'. So, also, is spiritual rehabilitation.

What are the spiritual expectations of older people today? Speaking to some of them I hear answers like these: 'I hope it will be all right in the end.' 'I hope I have been good enough.' 'I hope a loving God will be kind.' This is not Christian *hope*. This is not *hope* in Christ. In respect of the real spiritual needs of an ageing population, there is an almost deafening silence.

A patient in my own ward confided to me in the midst of counselling: 'It's too late, I can't be forgiven.' She had done something in her past for which she felt she could make no restitution, and which hung upon her as a deep depressive memory as she became aware of failing health and capacity. She could not conceive of forgiveness without restitution of her wrong. How often do we know what someone like that is trying to cover up as time slips away? How often do we stop long enough to find out?

God has personally involved himself with us in terms of body, mind and spirit in the person of Jesus Christ. He has met the challenge of human need in a very personal way. We find no age barrier here. 'God so loved the world . . .' (Jn. 3:16) is not an ageist statement. The oldest person in a neighbourhood, in an eventide home or geriatric ward, is entitled to say in the words of the old chorus: 'Hallelujah, whosoever – that means me'. Indeed, if we think of the person to whom the words of John 3:16 were first addressed, Nicodemus, we find him asking the question, 'Can a man be born when he is old?' (Jn. 3:4). Nicodemus had one particular man in mind, himself, and he was no young man. Nicodemus was asking on his own behalf, and behalf of all who realize that this life is passing, and that we need to look beyond it. God, in Christ, is reaching out to the elderly, as he does to all who will put their faith in him, finding forgiveness, peace and eternal life in his name.

Some years ago, in Dundee, I was preaching at a service in the geriatrics unit to a congregation of patients from the wards. I was speaking of the providence of God, and of his keeping faith with us, when an old lady, somewhat disinhibited and recognized as a bit of a character, interrupted with the loud comment, 'It's not true – he doesna do it.' While I was still gathering my thoughts to find a reply, an equally elderly man, just in front of her, turned round, looked her straight in the eye and said, 'What do you know about it? You never gave him a chance.'

If we will 'give him a chance', we will find his promises faithful at every age: 'Surely I am with you always, to the very end of the age' (Mt. 28:20).

Challenge to the individual

There is, of course, a personal challenge in the whole concept of ageing. Most of us will have been given a twenty-year bonus in terms of life expectancy over our grandparents and great-grandparents. What are we going to do with it? We are not really expected to do much with it by our current society. The role of the elderly is ill defined, and our expectation of an old person is small. 'What can you expect at your age?' 'What can I expect at my age?' I often hear these questions on the lips of younger and older people. 'Happy is he who expecteth little, for he shall not be disappointed' is a hollow and cynical pseudo-beatitude, but it does represent the expectations of many older people. Is this our own position as we grow older? God does not offer death without hope, but eternal life with him through faith in Christ. His expectation is of our response to his grace, and of our continued commitment to his service, whatever our age.

As Christians, we are told by the Lord Jesus: 'You are the salt of the earth' (Mt. 5:13). If we are salt, we will add this flavour and excitement to living for those who are around us, we will be a savour of Christ, and we will also act as a preservative agent, slowing down if not stopping the rot in society. Jesus also said of us, 'You are the light of the world' (Mt. 5:14). If we are light, we will bring vision and hope to those around us and we will show up what is dark, doubtful and dirty.

More of those around us today and for several decades to come will be older people who need that salt and light just as much and perhaps even more urgently than any other. Has our salt lost its savour? Is our light under a bushel?

ABOUT THE CONTRIBUTORS

Monty Barker MB FRCP FRCPsych. *Formerly Consultant Psychiatrist, Bristol United Hospitals, and Clinical Lecturer in Mental Health, University of Bristol.*

Dominic Beer MA MD MRCPsych. *Hon. Consultant Psychiatrist, Bexley Hospital, Kent, and Senior Lecturer, Department of Psychiatry, United Medical and Dental Schools, University of London.*

Woody Caan MA DPhil. *Research Psychologist and Head of Research and Development, Lifespan Healthcare, Cambridge.*

David Cahill MB MRCOG. *Senior Registrar, Obstetrics and Gynaecology, Royal United Hospital, Bath.*

George Chalmers MB FRCP. *Formerly Consultant in Geriatric Medicine, Glasgow Royal Infirmary; Clinical Director, Elderly Care Directorate, and Hon. Clinical Senior Lecturer in Geriatric Medicine, University of Glasgow.*

Susan Clarke MSc FRCP. *Consultant Physician in Nuclear Medicine and Senior Lecturer in Radiological Science, Guy's Hospital, London.*

David Cook PhD. *Director, The Whitefield Institute, Oxford; Fellow and Chaplain, Green College, Oxford.*

Paul Cosford MB MRCPsych. *Registrar in Public Health Medicine, North West Thames Regional Health Authority; formerly Lecturer in Psychiatry, St Mary's Hospital Medical School, London.*

Andrew Fergusson MB MRCGP. *General Secretary Christian Medical Fellowship, London.*

David Field BA. *Director of Professional Ministry, Church Pastoral Aid Society, Warwick; formerly Vice-Principal and Lecturer in Christian Ethics, Oak Hill College, London.*

Peter Green MB ChB. *Formerly Consultant in Accident and Emergency, Royal Free Hospital, London, and Secretary of the Medical Missionary Association.*

Anthony Jefferis MA MChir FRCS. *Consultant Otolaryngologist, Heatherwood and Wexham Hospital Trust, Berkshire.*

Alan G. Johnson MChir FRCS. *Professor of Surgery, University of Sheffield; Honorary Consultant Surgeon, Royal Hallamshire Hospital, Sheffield; chairman of the International Christian Medical and Dental Association.*

Alan W. Johnston MB MD FRCP. *Formerly Consultant Physician and Clinical Geneticist at the Aberdeen Teaching Hospitals (Aberdeen Royal Infirmary) and Clinical Senior Lecturer in Medicine and Genetics, University of Aberdeen.*

Michael Jones MB DipPC FRCP. *Director and Specialist Physician, Care for Mission; and Associate Specialist in Communicable Diseases, Regional Infectious Diseases Unit, Edinburgh.*

David Kerr CBE MB MSc FRCP. *Postrgraduate Advisor, North Thames Regional Health Authority; formerly Dean and Professor of Renal Medicine, Royal Postgraduate Medical School, London.*

Siân Kerslake MB FRCS MRCOG. *Senior Registrar Obstetrics and Gynaecology, St Thomas' Hospital, London, and Farnborough Hospital, Kent.*

Peter Lewis. *Senior Pastor, Cornerstone Evangelical Church, Nottingham.*

Dorothy Lowe MB BAO DPM. *Clinical Assistant in Psychogeriatrics, Bexley Community Health Service, Kent.*

Derek Macallan MA PhD MRCP. *Senior Registrar in Infectious Diseases, St. George's Hospital, London.*

Peter May MRCS LRCP MRCGP. *General Practitioner, Southampton.*

Roger Moss MRCS LRCP MRCPsych. *Senior Psychiatric Advisor, Centre for Mental Health Services Development, King's College, London; formerly Consultant Psychiatrist, South Devon Healthcare Trust.*

Dame Cicely Saunders OM OBE MA MD FRCS FRCP. *Chairman and former Medical Director, St Christopher's Hospice, London.*

Peter Saunders MB FRACS. *Student Secretary, Christian Medical Fellowship, London.*

Gordon Scorer MBE MD FRCS, deceased. *Formerly Consultant Surgeon, Hillingdon Hospital, Middlesex.*

David Short MD PhD FRCP. *Professor Emeritus of Clinical Medicine, University of Aberdeen.*

Trevor Stammers MB MRCGP. *General Practitioner, and Part-time Tutor in General Practice, St George's Hospital, London.*

Michael Webb-Peploe OBE MB FRCP. *Consultant Cardiologist, St Thomas' Hospital, London.*

Carl Whitehouse MA MB DObstRCOG DCH FRCGP. *General Practitioner, and Professor of Teaching Medicine in the Community, University of Manchester.*

John Wyatt MB DCH FRCP. *Senior Lecturer (Neonatology and Paediatrics) and Hon. Consultant Paediatrician, University College Hospital, London.*

ABBREVIATIONS

AGP	*Archives of General Psychiatry*
AJDC	*American Journal of Diseases in Children*
AJOG	*American Journal of Obstetrics and Gynaecology*
ASB	*Archive of Sexual Behaviour*
BJGP	*British Journal of General Practice* (formerly *JRCGP*)
BJOG	*British Journal of Obstetrics and Gynaecology*
BJP	*British Journal of Psychology*
BMB	*British Medical Bulletin*
BMJ	*British Medical Journal*
CFP	*Canadian Family Physician*
COG	*Clinical Obstetrics and Gynaecology*
ISM	*In the Service of Medicine*
JCMF	*Journal of the Christian Medical Fellowship*
JMF	*Journal of Marriage and the Family*
JRCGP	*Journal of the Royal College of General Practitioners* (now *BJGP*)
JRCP	*Journal of the Royal College of Physicians*
JRSM	*Journal of the Royal Society of Medicine*
JSI	*Journal of Social Issues*
KI	*Kidney International*
MI	*Medicine International*
NEJM	*New England Journal of Medicine*
QJM	*Quarterly Journal of Medicine*
RND	*Reproduction Nutrition Development*

NOTES

Preface

1. J. A. Vale (ed.), *Medicine and the Christian Mind* (Christian Medical Fellowship, 1975).

1. The doctor's character and lifestyle

The stressed doctor in a stressful society

1. T. B. Graboys, 'Stress and the aching heart, *NEJM* 1984/311, pp. 594–595.
2. J. E. Deanfield *et al.*, 'Silent myocardial ischaemia due to mental stress', *Lancet* 1984/2, pp. 1001–1004; J. P. Kahn *et al.*, 'Correlation of Type A behaviour with adrenergic receptor density: implications for coronary artery disease pathogenesis', *Lancet* 1987/2, p. 973; P. Martin, 'Psychology and the immune system', *New Scientist*, 9 April 1987, p. 46; L. O'Donnell *et al.*, 'Plasma catecholamines and lipoproteins in chronic psychological stress', *JRSM* 1987/80, pp. 339–342; W. Ruberman *et al.*, 'Psychosocial influences on mortality after myocardial infarction', *NEJM* 1984/311, pp. 552–559.
3. C. Patel *et al.*, 'Trial of relaxation in reducing coronary risk: four-year follow-up', *BMJ* 1985/290, pp. 1103–1106.
4. M. R. Gabrielczyk, 'Personal view', *BMJ* 1987/295, p. 209.
5. D. Watson, *You are my God* (Hodder and Stoughton, 1983), p. 70.
6. 'Living with and listening to stress', in *Christian Listeners' Course* (Acorn Christian Healing Trust, 1987).
7. M. Foyle, 'Caring for the evangelist', paper presented at the Scottish conference of the Christian Medical Fellowship, November 1986.
8. R. Mayou, 'Burnout', *BMJ* 1987/295, pp. 284–285.
9. A. H. Rimpela *et al.*, 'Mortality of doctors: do doctors benefit from their medical knowledge?', *Lancet* 1987/1, pp. 84–86; I. Sakinofsky, 'Suicide in doctors and wives of doctors', *CFP* 380/26, pp. 837–844.
10. I. C. McManus, 'Physician, heal thyself', *Lancet* 1987/1, pp. 1079–1080, reviewing G. Bennet, *The Wound and the Doctor* (Secker and Warburg, 1987).
11. A. J. M. Quayle, 'The houseman's trial – is it necessary?', *JCMF* 1987/33:1, pp. 14–15.
12. J. Firth-Cozens, 'Emotional distress in junior house officers', *BMJ* 1987/295, pp. 533–536.
13. G. Bennet, *The Wound and the Doctor*.
14. G. MacDonald, *Ordering your Private World* (Highland, 1987), p. 30.
15. J. D. McCue, 'The effects of stress on physicians and their medical practice', *NEJM* 1987/306, p. 458.
16. *Ibid.*
17. C. Colson, quoted by Edward England, 'God's priorities', *Renewal*, Sept 1987, no. 136, p. 3 .

18. G. MacDonald, *Ordering your Private World*, p. 42.
19. *Idem*, *Restoring your Spiritual Passion* (Highland, 1987), p. 32.
20. *Ibid.*, p. 34.
21 . Quoted in *ibid.*, p. 35.
22. J. D. Douglas *et al.* (eds.), *Illustrated Bible Dictionary* (IVP, 1980), vol. 3, p. 1371.

2. Medical careers

1. G. R. Dunstan, *The Artifice of Ethics* (the Moorhouse Lectures 1973) (SCM, 1974).
2. T. F. Davies, 'The NHS is dead, long live the NHS', *BMJ* 1976/2.
3. Sir Keith Joseph, Marsden Lecture delivered at the Royal Free Hospital, London, December 1973.
4. E. Durkeim, *Suicide* (1897; Eng. trans. Routledge and Kegan Paul, 1952).
5. Davies, 'The NHS is dead'.
6. *Ibid.*
7. *Ibid.*
8. I. Illich *et al.*, *Disabling Professions*.
9. Davies, 'The NHS is dead'.
10. R. E. Cooke, *AJDC* 1975/129, p. 1157.
11. G. Biorck, *JRCP* 1974/8, p. 107.
12. Dunstan, *The Artifice of Ethics*.

3. Communication

Sharing our faith with patients

1. John Stott, *Our Guilty Silence* (Hodder and Stoughton, 1967).
2. P. May, a series of fourteen articles under various titles, in *Nucleus* (Christian Medical Fellowship), between October 1987 and July 1991. See also Chapter 18.

Relationships with other professionals

1. J. Huntington, *Social Work and General Medical Practice* (George Allen and Unwin, 1981).

Confidentiality

1. I. Kennedy, 'The doctor, the pill and the fifteen-year-old girl', in M. Lockwood (ed.), *Moral Dilemmas in Modern Medicine* (Oxford University Press, 1985), p. 47.

4. The Christian doctor in a health service

The meaning of care

1. G. Biorck, *JRCP* 1974/8, p. 107; T. F. Davies, 'The NHS is dead, long live the NHS', *BMJ* 1976/2, p. 1376.
2. Davies, *ibid.*

3. B. Russell, *A History of Western Philosophy* (Simon and Schuster, 1945), p. 699.
4. I. Illich *et al.*, *Disabling Professions*.
5. The White Paper *Working for Patients* (Her Majesty's Stationery Office, 1989).
6. H. E. Hamilton King, 1927.
7. T. Sydenham, *Advice to Those Entering the Profession (ca.* 1670).
8. G. R. Dunstan, *The Artifice of Ethics* (the Moorhouse Lectures 1973) (SCM, 1974).
9. Folk-saying of fifteenth century or earlier inscribed on the statue of Dr Edward Livingstone Trudeau at Saramac Lake, New York.

5 . Women in medicine: a Christian perspective

1. The survey of Christian women doctors alluded to throughout this chapter is to be published by the Christian Medical Fellowship.
2. *Women Doctors and their Careers*: report of the Joint Working Party (Department of Health, 1991).

6. Medical missions in a changing world

1. Cited by Dr John Coleman in the Medical Missionary Association's 9th Maxwell Memorial Lecture, 1990.

7. The Christian and research

1. Francis Thompson, 'The Hound of Heaven', in *Poems* (1893).
2. D. C. Evered *et al.*, 'The correlates of research success', *BMJ* 1987/295, pp. 241–246.
3. M. K. Ward *et al.*, 'Osteomalacic dialysis osteodystrophy: evidence for a water-borne aetiological agent, probably aluminium', *Lancet* 1978/1, pp. 841–845.
4 . D. N. S. Kerr *et al.*, 'Aluminium-induced dialysis osteodystrophy: the demise of "Newcastle bone disease"?', *KI* 1986/29, suppl. 18, pp. S58–S64.
5. W. Elliott *et al.*, 'The in-vitro performance of the twin-coil artificial kidney. With suggested improvements', *Lancet* 1961/1, pp. 248–253.
6. A. O. Robson *et al.*, 'The diuretic response to frusemide', *Lancet* 1964/2, pp. 1085–1088.
7. L. Altman *et al.*, 'Fraud in science', *BMJ* 1983/286, pp. 2003–2006; T. J. Hamblin, 'Fake!' *BMJ* 1981/283, pp. 1671–1674; *idem*, 'Fraud in science', *BMJ* 1983/287, p. 355.
8. D. N. S. Kerr,. 'Fraud in science', *BMJ* 1983/287, pp. 355–356.
9. L. M. Koran, 'The reliability of clinical methods, data and judgments', *NEJM* 1975/293, pp. 642–646, 695–701.
10. G. A. von Montfrans *et al.*, 'Accuracy of auscultatory blood pressure measurement with a long cuff', *BMJ* 1987/295, pp. 354–355.
11. A. Taylor *et al.*, 'Measurement of aluminium – quality of analytical results', in A. Taylor (ed.), *Aluminium and other Trace Elements in Renal Disease* (Balliere Tindall, 1986), pp. 260–273.

12. Kerr, 'Fraud in science'.
13. M. H. Pappworth, *Human Guinea Pigs: Experimentation on Man* (Routledge and Kegan Paul, 1967).
14. D. Burke (ed.), *Creation and Evolution* (IVP, 1985).
15. See Hamblin, 'Fake!'.

8. Making ethical decisions in medicine

1. G. R. Dunstan, in A. S. Dunstan *et al.* (eds.), *Dictionary of Medical Ethics* (Darton Longman and Todd, 1981).
2. Declaration of Geneva adopted by the General Assembly of the World Medical Association, Geneva, 1948.
3. O. Wilde, *The Soul of Man under Socialism*.

9. Issues of early life

1. M. G. R. Hull, 'Indications for assisted reproduction', *BMJ* 1990/46, pp. 580–595.
2. D. J. Cahill *et al.*, 'Reversing vasectomy', *BMJ* 1992/305, p. 52.
3. Annual Report of the Human Fertilization and Embryology Authority, 1993 and 1994.
4. J. Haskey, 'Estimated numbers and demographic characteristics of one-parent families in Great Britain', *Population Trends* (Her Majesty's Stationery Office, 1991), vol. 65, p. 35.
5. J. Medina, *The Outer Limits of Life* (Oliver-Nelson, 1991).
6. H. Blocher, *In the Beginning* (IVP, 1984); D. G. Jones, *Brave New People* (IVP, 1984); *idem*, *Manufacturing Humans* (IVP, 1987).
7. J. Stott, *Issues Facing Christians Today* (Marshall, Morgan and Stott, 1984), pp. 258–279.
8. Jones, *Brave New People*, pp. 105–137.
9. I. Manifold, 'Artificial insemination by donor's semen – a Christian viewpoint', *ISM* 1982/28, pp. 21–27.
10. G. M. Stirrat, 'Artificial insemination by donor –a Christian viewpoint', *ISM* 1983/29, pp. 13–15.
11. R. Snowden *et al.*, *The Gift of a Child* (University of Exeter Press, 2nd edn., 1993).
12. Surrogacy Report. Appendix V to Annual Report of Council, British Medical Association, 1989–90, pp. 39–48. In *BMJ* 1990/300, after p. 854.
13. British Medical Association, 'Medicopolitical digest', *BMJ* 1994/308, p. 1375.
14. Second and third Annual Reports of the Human Fertilization and Embryology Authority, 1993 and 1994.

10. Abortion

1. R. Whelan, *Legal Abortion Examined* (Society for the Protection of the Unborn Child Education Resource Trust, 1992), pp. 3–9.
2. R. Shain, 'A cross-cultural history of abortion', *COG* 1986/13, pp. 1–17.
3. Whelan, *Legal Abortion Examined*.
4. UK multi-centre trial, 'The efficacy and tolerance of mifepristone and prostaglandin in first-trimester termination of pregnancy', *BJOG*

1990/97, pp. 480–486.

5. R. G. Castadot, 'Pregnancy termination techniques, risks and complications and their management', *Fertility and Sterility* 1986/45, pp. 5–17.

6. The Declaration of Geneva, adopted by the General Assembly of the World Medical Association, Geneva, 1948.

7. International Code of Medical Ethics, adopted by the 3rd World Medical Assembly, London, October 1949.

8. UN Declaration of Human Rights and Freedoms, 1948.

9. UN Declaration of the Rights of the Child, 1959.

10. Declaration of Oslo, adopted by the 24th World Medical Assembly, Oslo, 1970.

11. Whelan, *Legal Abortion Examined*, pp. 31–32.

12. Office of Population Censuses and Surveys abortion statistics. Series AB, no. 14 (Her Majesty's Stationery Office, 1987).

13. P. Frank *et al.*, 'The effect of induced abortion on subsequent fertility', *BJOG* 1993/100, pp. 575–580.

14. L. Heisterberg *et al.*, 'Sequelae of induced first trimester abortion', *AJOG* 1986/155, pp. 76–80.

15. M. Jarmulowicz, *Physical and Psychological Effects of Abortion: A Review of the Medical Literature*. A written submission to the Commission of Inquiry into the Operation and Consequences of the Abortion Act (June 1994).

16. P. Frank *et al.*, 'Induced abortion operations and their early sequelae', *JRCGP* 1985/35, pp. 175–180.

17. P. Frank *et al.*, 'Outcome of pregnancy following induced abortion', *BJOG* 1985/92, pp. 308–316.

18. *The Physical and Psycho-Social Effect of Abortion on Women*. A Report by the Committee of Inquiry into the Operation and Consequences of the Abortion Act (June 1994).

19. H. P. David, 'Post-abortion and post-partum psychiatric hospitalization', in *Abortion: Medical Progress; and Social Implications*, a Ciba Foundation symposium (Pitman, 1985), 115, pp. 150–164, cited in the Rawlinson Report (see n. 18 above).

20. G. Zolese *et al.*, 'The psychological complications of therapeutic abortion', *BJP* 1992/160, pp. 742–749.

21. P. Saunders, 'Abortion – time to reconsider', *JCMF* 1994/40:4 160:12–17.

22. Linda Beecham, 'Conscientious objection to abortion', *BMJ* 1992/304, p. 321.

23. Janaway *vs* Salford Health Authority [1989] AC, [1988] A11 ER 1079 (HL).

24. LIFE and Christians Caring for Life (CCFL).

11. Human genetics

1. A. E. Garrod, *Inborn Errors of Metabolism* (Frowde, Hodder and Stoughton, 1909).

2. *Idem*, *The Inborn Factors in Disease* (Oxford University Press, 1931).

3. C. B. Bridges, 'Non-disjunction as proof of the chromosome theory of heredity', *Genetics* 1916/1, pp. 1 and 107.

4. J. H. Tjio and A Levan, 'The chromosome number of man', *Hereditas*

1956/42, p. 1.

5. R. Harris, 'Counselling for the new genetics', *MI* 1994/22, pp. 4–5.
6. P. A. Jacobs and T. J. Hassold, 'Chromosome abnormalities: origin and etiology in abortions and live births', in F. Vogel and K. Sperling (eds.), *Proceedings of the 7th Congress on Human Genetics, Berlin, 1986* (Springer, Berlin, 1987), pp. 233–244.
7. P. A. Jacobs, 'The role of chromosome abnormalities in reproductive failure', *RND* 1990, suppl. 1, 63S–74S.
8. P. A. Baird *et al.*, 'Population-based study of long-term outcomes after amniocentesis', *Lancet* 1994/34, pp. 1134–1136.
9. Nuffield Council on Bioethics, Genetic Screening: Ethical Issues (Nuffield Council on Bioethics, 1993).
10. *Report of the Committee on the Ethics of Gene Therapy* (Clothier Report) (Her Majesty's Stationery Office, 1992).
11. D. MacKay, 'The beginnings of personal life', *ISM* 1984/30, pp. 9–13.
12. D. G. Jones, *Manufacturing Humans* (IVP, 1987).
13. O. O'Donovan, *Begotten or Made?* (Oxford University Press, 1984).
14. J. R. W. Stott, *Issues Facing Christians Today* (Marshall, Morgan and Scott, 1984).
15. J. Wilkinson, *Christian Ethics in Healthcare* (Handsel, 1988), p. 243.
16. Jacobs and Hassold, 'Chromosome abnormalities'.
17. T. Chard, 'Frequency of implantation and early pregnancy loss in natural cycles', *Baillieres Clinical Obstetrics and Gynaecology* 1991/5, pp. 179–189.
18. P. G. Whitaker *et al.*, 'Unsuspected pregnancy loss in healthy women', *Lancet* 1983/1, pp. 1126–1127.
19. A. C. Berry, *Beginnings* (Christian Medical Fellowship, 1993).
20. Human Fertilization and Embryology Authority, 'Sex selection', in its third Annual Report, 1994.
21. *Idem*, *Donated Ovarian Tissue in Embryo Resarch and Assisted Conception* (1994).
22. J. Hall and R. Stillman cited in P. Elmer-Dewitt, 'Cloning: where do we draw the line?' *Time*, 8 November 1993, pp. 63–68.

12. Sexuality

Virginity

1. 'The sexual renaissance', *JSI* 1966/22, pp. 123–137.
2. J. McDowell, *Why Wait? What You Need to Know about the Teenage Sexuality Crisis* (Here's Life, 1987).
3. D. F. Shope *et al.*, 'Level of sexual experience and predicted adjustment in marriage', *JMF* 1967/29, pp. 424–427; R. Athanasiou *et al.*, 'Premarital sexual behaviour and postmarital adjustment', *ASB* 1974/3 pp. 207–225.
4. L. M. Terman, *Psychological Factors in Marital Happiness* (McGraw Hill, 1938).
5. J. Bancroft, *Human Sexuality and its Problems* (Churchill Livingstone, 1983).
6. L. Smedes, *Sex in the Real World* (Lion, 1979), p. 122.
7. L. Morris, *1 Corinthians: An Introduction and Commentary* (Tyndale, 1971), pp. 102–103.

8. McDowell, *Why Wait?*, p. 422.

Homosexuality

1. W. Byne *et al.*, 'Human sexual orientation: the biological theories reappraised', *AGP* 1993/50, cited in True Freedom Trust Seminar Notes (unpublished).
2. S. LeVay, 'A difference in hypothalamic structure between heterosexual and homosexual men', *Science* 1991/258, pp. 1034–1037.
3. D. Hamer *et al.*, 'A linkage between the DNA markers on the X chromosome and male sexual orientation', *Science* 1993/261, pp. 321–327.
4. M. Baron, 'Genetic linkage and male homosexual orientation: reasons to be cautious', *BMJ* 1993/307, pp. 337–338.
5. E. Moberly, 'Homosexuality: structure and evaluation', *Theology* 1980/83, cited in R. Winter, 'Homosexuality', in B. Palmer (ed.), *Medicine and the Bible* (Paternoster, 1986), p. 158.
6. T. Landess, 'Gay rights in America: the ultimate PR campaign', *Rutherford* 1994/3(7), pp. 3–11.
7. A. Kinsey *et al.*, *Sexual Behaviour in the Human Male* (W. B. Saunders, 1948).
8. A. Johnson *et al.*, *Sexual Attitudes and Lifestyles* (Blackwell Scientific, 1994), cited by A. Tonks, 'British sex survey shows popularity of monogamy', *BMJ* 1994/308, p. 289.
9. P. Bell *et al.*, *Homosexualities: A Study of Diversity Among Men and Women* (Simon and Schuster, 1978).
10. T. Schmidt, *Straight and Narrow? Compassion and Clarity in the Homosexuality Debate* (IVP, 1995), ch. 6.
11. *Ibid.*
12. From the literature of the Gay Christian Movement.
13. Schmidt, *Straight and Narrow?* ch. 6.
14. *Ibid.*
15. From the literature of the Gay Christian Movement, cited in Winter, 'Homosexuality'.
16. Schmidt, *Straight and Narrow?* ch. 6; Winter, 'Homosexuality', pp. 145–163.
17. R. Lovelace, *Homosexuality and the Church* (Lamp, 1978), pp. 65–86, cited in Winter, 'Homosexuality', p. 163.
18. W. H. Masters and V. E. Johnson, *Homosexuality in Perspective* (Little, Brown and Co., 1979).

13. AIDS, morality and God

1. *Sunday Telegraph*, 23 November 1986.
2. See also V. Moss, 'AIDS – a challenge to Christian involvement', *JCMF* 1987/33:3, pp. 16–20.

15. Hope, healing and the charismatic movement

1. D. A. Carson, *The Sermon on the Mount* (Baker, 1978), pp. 87–90.

2. D. Bridge, *Signs and Wonders Today* (IVP, 1985), p. 61.
3. G. H. C. MacGregor, quoted in L. Morris, *The Gospel of John*, New International Commentary (Hodder & Stoughton, 1971); p. 362.
4. D. McBain, *Eyes That See* (Marshall Pickering, 1986), p. 37.
5. Bridge, *Signs and Wonders Today*.
6. R. Gardner, *Healing Miracles* (Darton, Longman and Todd, 1986), p. 31.
7. H. Muhlen, *A Charismatic Theology* (Burns and Oates, 1978), pp. 162–163.

17. Psychiatry

Demons

1. H. A. Virkler, art. 'Demonic influence and psychopathology', in D. G. Benner (ed.), *The Baker Encyclopedia of Psychology* (Baker, 1985).
2. H. Küng, *On Being a Christian* (Collins, 1977), p. 321.
3. K. McAll, *Healing the Family Tree* (Sheldon, 1982).
4. K. E. Koch, *Christian Counselling and Occultism* (Kregel, 1972).
5. Virkler, 'Demonic influence'.
6. R. F. Lovelace, *Dynamics of Spiritual Life* (Paternoster, 1979), p. 143.
7. *Ibid.*, p. 143.

19. Euthanasia

1. For example, Barbara Smoker, a former chairman of the Voluntary Euthanasia Society, writes: 'As for the voluntary element, this is, of course, fundamental in the case of adult patients who are capable of communication, but in many other cases it cannot apply – though, admittedly, it may be tactically right for the VES to ignore such cases. These include not only infant euthanasia (which has always been kept outside the terms of the Society's objects), but cases where adults who would otherwise be proper candidates for euthanasia have failed to provide an advance declaration.' *Voluntary Euthanasia Society Newsletter*, September 1991, p. 10.
2. P. J. van der Maas et al., 'Euthanasia and other medical decisions concerning the end of life', *Lancet* 1991/338, pp. 669–674.

20. Other issues at the end of life

Christian care in the hospice

1. G. Hughes, *Peace at the Last: A Study of Terminal Care in the United Kingdom* (The Calouste Gulbenkian Foundation, 1960).
2. *Report on a National Survey Concerning Patients Nursed at Home* (Marie Curie Memorial Foundation, 1952); J. Hinton, 'The mental and physical distress of the dying', *QJM* 1963/32, pp. 1–21.
3. V. Henderson and G. Nite, *Principles and Practice of Nursing* (Macmillan, 1978).
4. J. V. Taylor, 'Growth through loss', paper presented at St Christopher's Hospice International Conference, London 1982.